Introductio

M000216807

One of the greatest responsibilities for any poultry keeper is to ensure the good health of the birds in their care. Chickens, while more resilient than many people give them credit for are, nevertheless, totally dependent for their overall welfare on those who look after them.

Good standards of husbandry are absolutely essential if health is to be maintained, and certain basic requirements must be met. At the most fundamental level, all poultry require a supply of good quality feed, constant access to fresh, clean drinking water and a secure, weather-proofed house

in which to shelter and roost a The hen house must also be kep clean and fresh, and provide draught-free accommodation for the birds that use it.

However, there's more to it than this. Chickens are very prone to stress, which can be promoted by all sorts of practical yet preventable reasons. Avoiding this is important because stressed birds are far more susceptible to illness and disease. Key aspects such as over-crowding, bullying, feather pecking, poor housing conditions, bad hygiene, and inappropriate diet can all be contributory factors.

All of these important issues are

represents a compilation of the most down-to-earth and informative features published in Practical Poultry over the past few years. It provides a wealth of helpful and authoritative information for those new to the poultry-keeping hobby, and plenty to interest the more experienced Fancier too. Ensuring that your birds remain healthy is not only great for them, but it'll make your life as a responsible keeper so much easier as well!

Chris Graham
Editor,
Practical Poultry magazine

Published by **KELSEY PUBLISHING LTD**

Printed by William Gibbons Ltd. on behalf of Kelsey Publishing Ltd,
Cudham Tithe Barn, Berry's Hill, Cudham, Kent TN16 3AG
Tel: 01959 541444   *Fax:* 01959 541400 *E-mail:* kelseybooks@kelsey.co.uk *Website:* www.kelsey.co.uk
©2008 **ISBN: 9781873098882**

Contents

40

92

6

146

TENTATIVE STEPS

Robin Creighton advises on the fundamentals of getting started with poultry, and explains how to assess a bird's general health when buying.

Once you've made the decision to start keeping poultry, your first job is to get down to some serious planning! This really is vital if future disasters are to be avoided; I hear all too often about people who rush into the hobby, buy or make unsuitable housing and then wonder why their birds become ill.

Another common mistake made by beginners is to buy unsuitable breeds of chicken on impulse.

HOUSING

The key aspect to be considered is the space you have available. In essence, the more you have the better, and the happier the birds you keep will be. But, whatever you have, it's important to match the birds to it. So, for example, if you've only got room for a 6x4' house and similar sized run, then you need to look at buying bantams rather than large fowl. Obviously, the latter need more space.

As well as being vermin-proof, the housing needs to be well constructed to prevent predators such as foxes, stoats or mink getting inside. Rats and mice will transmit diseases such as salmonella, and will also spoil any food they can get at. I'll not go into the details of poultry house construction here, but a couple of fundamental requirements are that the structure must be damp-free and well ventilated; the latter being vital for preventing respiratory disease.

Also, there needs to be enough perching space for all the birds using the house, so there's no fighting for space. Perch positioning is important too – they must be sited out of drafts, and be at the correct height for the birds using them. Much of managing livestock correctly comes down to common sense. Often I'll put myself in the birds' position, especially where housing is concerned. If the conclusion is that I'd be happy to spend time in their house, then so will they. If not, then something's wrong.

A poultry house needs to be large enough so that, on a wet day, all the birds can comfortably shelter inside it. If the accommodation is too small for the

A quick look inside the beak, at the condition of the mucus membranes within, provides another very useful indicator of a bird's general health.

number of birds you have, those at the bottom of the pecking order will end up being forced to stand outside in the rain. Always bear in mind that overcrowding is one of the commonest causes of problems, including respiratory diseases and coccidiosis. Too many birds will increase the concentration of these agents in the environment, making infection more likely.

Overcrowding will also lead to bullying, and bullied birds can suffer terribly. Typically they go short of food and suffer badly with debilitating stress which increases their susceptibility to disease. The situation will be made worse if different age groups, and birds of different sizes, are mixed together.

FOOD & WATER

As a general rule I prefer to locate feeders and drinkers inside the hen house. This prevents the feed being 'spoilt' by rain, and also reduces the risk of contamination from wild bird faeces – a vital aspect nowadays with the threat of Avian Influenza constantly in the background. Obviously,

Mixed flocks need careful management, in terms of breed choice and supervision, if problems are to be avoided. Beginners are perhaps best advised to keep different breeds segregated until their husbandry experience develops.

Handling is vital when assessing a bird you're about to buy. A pronounced, sharp breast bone should be a concern, indicating a bird that's under weight for some reason.

adult hen. So you must do your research and be definite about what you want before going to buy. The impulse buying of unsuitable birds is just about the worst thing you can do, and is almost certain to lead to problems.

Take time to pick a suitable source for the birds as well. Personally, I never buy from markets; they can be a hotbed of disease and infection. In my opinion it's far better to buy direct from a respected breeder. Most breed clubs and local poultry societies will be happy to put you in touch with recommended suppliers offering good quality, well-▶

feeders and drinkers should never be positioned beneath the perches otherwise they'll be contaminated with faeces, greatly increasing the risk of disease. Also, drinkers and feeders should be such that the birds cannot perch on them – putting lids on the feeders will prevent this.

It's also wise not to place feeders and drinkers directly next to each other. Diseases like coccidiosis thrive in damp conditions, as might occur in the litter next to a drinker, for example. Then, if pellets get scattered over these areas because the feeder is placed close by, the birds' intake of coccidial oocytes will be increased. However, this is really only of concern in young birds. Raising the drinkers and feeders off the ground on bricks will reduce the faecal contamination of the food and water.

SELECTING BIRDS

Having completed all your planning, sited your house and built a run, the next step is to choose your birds. There are pitfalls to be avoided here, so considerable thought is needed about which breed is most suitable for your situation. For example, it wouldn't be suitable to put large Old English Game together with Sebrights. The golden rule is to make sure that the birds are roughly the same size – can you imagine living with someone four times bigger than you, who keeps pecking your head?

Some breeds can be aggressive,

making them unsuitable for a mixed-flock environment. You also need to get birds of a similar age. A young pullet could easily be badly bullied by an

Check the vent area carefully for signs of parasite infestation and faecal soiling.

Birds which fight can show pockmarked combs. While this isn't necessarily a problem in itself, it should raise question marks about the standard of husbandry being provided.

bred stock.

However, before buying any bird, have a good look at all those available and the conditions in which they are kept. This will give you a good indicator of the breeder's standards of welfare and, thus, a valuable pointer towards the quality of birds being offered. Never be afraid to simply walk away if you find birds in dirty conditions, or they are obviously sneezing or looking unhealthy. Remember, also, that even if you buy outwardly healthy-looking stock, they may actually be carrying diseases. As such, they could pose a serious threat to any existing birds you already have, so isolation for a few weeks after purchase is always important.

I know that some people deliberately buy unhealthy birds from substandard suppliers simply because they feel sorry for them. I can understand this because they want to do the best for the bird. However, I feel it would be better if nobody brought from these outlets so they are forced out of business; there are no excuses for poor welfare.

INSPECTION TIME

So, what should you actually be looking for when assessing a potential purchase? Well, the aspects I always consider when buying are as follows.

Comb: In most breeds this should be red, indicating good health. But, some breeds – like the Silkie – have a mulberry-coloured comb, which is a standard feature. Young birds can naturally be quite pale in the face sometimes, but their combs should at least be pink, if not red. However, a very pale comb on an adult bird is a bad sign which can indicate anaemia. The commonest cause of this is red mite (a tiny, blood-sucking creature that lives off the birds in the hen house, and 'attacks' the birds at night, as they are roosting).

A bluish/purplish comb indicates cyanosis (a lack of oxygen in the blood stream). This can be caused by heart failure, but the commonest cause is chronic respiratory disease, leading to lung damage.

Eyes: These should be bright and alert. Sunken eyes indicate dehydration, which only occurs if the bird is seriously ill. Also look for any discharge from eyes, or crusting on the face indicating that this has happened recently. Eye discharge can be thick – resembling pus – or very bubbly and watery. The latter can be an indicator of mycoplasma. However, this isn't a straightforward issue as Indian Game, for example, will often show frothy bubbles at the corners of their eyes when they are perfectly healthy.

If the discharge is only in one eye, this points towards a localised problem or disease, rather than a systemic one affecting both. The most common cause of single-eye discharge is a corneal ulcer, resulting from a scratch to the surface of the eye, or a foreign body lodged under the eyelid. This may heal on its own, or might require antibiotics to clear it up. Also look for any sinus swelling below the eyes – another indicator of mycoplasma.

Beak: Inspect the beak to make sure it's not twisted or malaligned. These defects may cause eating difficulties for the bird, and will require regular clipping.

Nostrils: Check for signs of discharge here too – nasal discharge could indicate an upper respiratory tract infection. Sometimes there's no actual discharge because the nostrils have already become blocked with it. To inspect further, gently open the beak and make sure that the mucus membranes

Scaly leg mite is another important problem to watch for when buying. Feathered-leg breeds tend to be at greater risk from this uncomfortable condition.

inside are pink, and that the back of the mouth (pharynx) is free from discharge. Large amounts of discharge here indicate an infection.

CROP & VENT

Crop: Feel the crop at the base of the neck; it should be the size of a golf ball on an average bird. If the bird isn't eating, the crop maybe completely empty. Alternatively, if it's large and pendulous, this can be a sign of sour crop (a fungal infection caused by candida albicans).

A very large and hard crop can indicate a condition known as crop impaction, caused by the consumption of indigestible, fibrous material.

Plumage: Always take time to examine a bird's feathers. Ideally they should be smooth and shiny. Gently part them to check for any evidence of lice. These parasites are generally 2-3mm long and quite fast-moving. Some live in the feathers of the body, while others congregate around the vent.

Vent: Always inspect the vent area carefully; it's a favourite site for lice infestations. If they're there, you'll be able to see them quite clearly running around on the bird's skin. If you spot white deposits on the feather shafts around the vent, these are lice eggs.

Northern Mite is another parasite commonly found in the vent area. These appear as small dark specs, and can be seen crawling around, albeit much more slowly than lice. Northern Mite can also be found in small clusters around the comb, so check here too.

Check the vent itself, too. It should be clean, pink and smooth. There is a condition called 'vent gleet'; the vent becomes covered in crusts. This is thought to be caused by a bacterial infection, and is difficult to cure. So it's best avoided.

Finally, assess the condition of the feathers below the vent – they should be clean and fluffy. If they're covered in faeces, this could indicate diarrhoea. In young birds, blood around the vent can be an indicator of coccidiosis.

Body condition: Feel the breast bone and breast muscles, to give you an idea about the general condition of the bird. Unfortunately, it takes practice to learn to appreciate the good and bad points in this area. However, some young birds – and birds in lay – can be naturally a bit thin here. If the breast bone (keel) is very prominent and sharp, this indicates the bird is thin, and might have some underlying disease problem.

Legs: A healthy hen should have smooth legs with no raised scales. Scaly leg is a common and uncomfortable problem caused by mites which burrow into the legs, lifting the scales as they do so. This condition can appear quite minor initially, but will quickly worsen if allowed to do so.

AND FINALLY...

Of course, if you pick your breeder carefully then, hopefully, you're unlikely to run into any of the aforementioned problems. Nevertheless, it's always sensible to make a careful check of prospective purchases anyway. If nothing else, it'll provide good handling practice!

If you do make a purchase then don't overlook the transportation needs of the birds you're buying. Make sure you use suitable, sturdy and well-ventilated boxes to take them home in. It's also wise not to put birds which have not been together previously in the same box on the way home. As a rule, chickens should only ever be mixed together under close supervision. Always remember that a dominant cock or hen can do serious damage to other birds, given the chance.

Buying good, healthy birds in the first place really is the name of the game. Get it right and you'll be rewarded with hours of pleasure from your new feathered friends. Make a mistake, though, and all you'll get is stress and vets bills! ❧

Eye, comb and nostril condition can tell you a great deal about the overall health of a prospective purchase.

GETTING A
GOOD'UN

If you're in the market for some birds then there's plenty to think about before you hand over the cash. Chris Graham talks with Andy Marshall about how, when and where to buy.

I doubt that Frank Sinatra was much of a poultry enthusiast although, having said that, you could argue that a number of his recordings suggest otherwise. Perhaps *The Girl from Ipanema* represented a heartfelt tribute to a favourite Araucana hen, while *C'est Magnifique* could well have celebrated a prize-winning French Maran.

The haunting *Stranger in the Night* may have alluded to the foxes in the Hollywood hills while, the troubled *Damn That Dream*, to the singer's frustration about never getting a bird to the National, at Stoneleigh! Finally there's the classic *Fools Rush In*, with its warning to all poultry buyers and breeders alike. Verse two laments: *Though I see the danger there, if there's a chance for me then I don't care.* Poignant words indeed.

TAKE YOUR TIME

But there's a serious point to all this, and it's that everyone – especially beginners – should take their time when buying birds. To do the job properly you need to set aside anything up to a year for researching the market, as well as sorting out the environment in which the birds are to be kept. Pick your breed or breeds carefully and try to match their characteristics to the facilities you have available; size, temperament, hardiness are the sort of factors you must consider.

Then, once you've decided on a type you like, put in some leg work and get around a few shows. The major events are a must, with the best two being the national shows in December at Stoneleigh and Stafford. Use these to identify the birds that are winning from your chosen breed, and get details of their breeders. If you can, make an effort to speak to them. Often you'll be able to do this at the show but, if not,

arrange a visit instead. All genuine breeders should be very approachable, and will be happy to talk about how they operate. Those who are reluctant are best avoided.

Dealing directly with a breeder is usually the best approach when sourcing birds, for a number of reason which I'll deal with later. However, there are other buying options available which we should look at first. The big three, in no particular order are: buying at a show; buying at an auction; buying at an agricultural market.

Auctions probably represent the least favourite, particularly the general livestock market-type affairs. There are exceptions though, which are held at specialist events during the year and can be a good source of quality birds; the relevant breed clubs will have all the details.

AUCTION AVOIDANCE

The more common type of auction – the ones associated with agricultural and livestock markets – are the events to avoid if you can. These are very often used by the less scrupulous breeders as a sort of 'clearing house' for their sub-standard birds (and that's putting it politely!). So buying this way really is a lottery; a point that can't be emphasised enough. You need to be experienced, or very lucky, to stand any chance of a

good result. The descriptions offered can be wildly inaccurate, with individual birds classed as pure-breds when they're not, given the wrong age or even the incorrect sex!

The other big danger is that birds bought from auctions like this will be extremely stressed. Often they will have been through several such sales in a matter of days, as successive owners move them on in search of a quick profit. And, as we all know, stress is a major contributor to poultry disease. Birds made anxious by frequent transportation, poor conditions and rough handling will quickly deteriorate, and are certainly much more likely to catch any diseases on offer. ▶

> *"The major events are a must, with the best two being the national shows in December."*

One big advantage of buying from a breeder is that you get the chance to handle the birds before you're committed.

Multi-breed flocks are all the rage now, providing an interesting selection of egg colours. But don't over-stretch yourself with too many.

Take care to match the breed you buy to your environment. These feather-legged Cochins are not suited to muddy, wet conditions.

WHEN TO BUY

By and large standard-bred birds are best bought in the autumn and winter months, when they are in peak condition. This is unfortunate in a way because most newcomers to the hobby tend to start thinking about buying birds in the spring, which is the wrong season completely.

Spring purchases can catch the unwary. Birds being sold at this time are unlikely to be in their first flush, and will probably be examples which the breeder has rejected from his or her breeding program; the 'throw outs'. Unfortunately, there are a good number of less than scrupulous breeders who prefer to sell-on their substandard birds to make a bit of extra cash. Good breeders, on the other hand, take the decision to cull poor examples, and only sell their surplus quality stock.

It really is a vicious circle for the birds pushed through this system. These events, by their very nature, provide a bubbling cauldron of infection because so many already poorly or stressed birds are gathered together in one place. Cross-infection between adjacent pens is common, and the risk of disease being spread by the handlers who load the auction pens is high.

"It really is a vicious circle for the birds pushed through this system."

BETTER OPTIONS

Buying at shows or other specialist poultry events tends to be a better bet, and can yield good results. However, always remember that the quality of the birds being sold will vary enormously, so you'll still need your wits about you, or a knowledgeable guide at your side. These events tend not to operate like a conventional auction; the birds are marked-up with a non-negotiable price on the pen. Birds are sold for that price, a percentage of which is taken by the organisers and the rest ends up with the seller. It's a simple, no-fuss, no-haggle way of buying that can be attractive to the nervous newcomer. You don't have to deal with the seller at all; money is handed over at the organiser's table and that's that. If you wish, though, the organiser will normally be happy to point out the seller – they're invariably at the event – so you can have a chat.

Another interesting option for buying is through your local animal feed supplier. A good many of these nowadays will offer point-of-lay (POL) pullets for sale which have been bought in batches from commercial rearers. These will be hybrid birds which will offer great value for money for first-time buyers, fantastic laying performance and usually impressive resistance to most sorts of disease.

But do bear in mind that 'point-of-lay' can be a bit of a misleading term. Don't always assume that just because birds are classified as being 'POL', they are about to start producing eggs immediately; in most cases they're not!

Don't be surprised to find that the POL hens you buy don't actually start laying for anything up to eight weeks after purchase. Quite apart from everything else, the physical disruption of the sale process delays the onset of laying as well. Chickens are habitual creatures and love routine. Upsetting this by changing their environment – new housing, feed type and times etc. – always has a negative effect and introduces stress, however smooth you make the process.

Buying poultry at a show can be a good way of sourcing quality stock from established breeders, but you need to pick the event, and the breeder, carefully!

PICK A BREEDER

By and large, though, the safest and most reliable way to buy birds is from an established breeder, following a personal recommendation or consistent prize-winning performance. This way you should at least be guaranteed a basic level of stock quality. Also, you'll stand the best chance of securing disease-free poultry, which is a vital factor. Of course, buying this way won't necessarily offer the cheapest deal, but it will certainly provide value for money. Always remember that with poultry, like everything else, you get what you pay for. In most cases expensive birds are priced that way for a reason.

Another big advantage of going directly to a breeder is that you'll be able to handle the birds before you

If you're after rare breeds like this fine Hamburgh, then you must seek out a specialist breeder to find good examples.

buy, and decide what to do based on that inspection. This is very different from buying at an auction or show, where you'll be limited to a visual assessment. Often the first opportunity you'll get to look at your purchases

County shows often have a poultry exhibit where you can talk to owners. Never be afraid to ask questions!

closely will be when you get them back to the car, by which time it's too late should there be a problem.

Another bit of good advice is, if possible, to buy all your birds at the same time. Every time you introduce new birds to an existing flock, stress levels are raised. Sometimes this can't be avoided, of course, in which case you should take all precautions possible to minimise the upset. Always ensure a lengthy period of acclimatisation (up to two weeks) during which the old and the new birds can see each other, but can't actually mix. Then, when you finally put them together, do so at night when

WHAT TO PAY?

Prices vary enormously, depending on what you buy and where you buy it. At market auctions birds can sell for anything from 50p to £100. Good quality commercial POL pullets (four to six months old) will be priced at between £5 and £10 each.

The minimum you should expect to pay for a good pure breed is £20; they're more expensive because they eat more food and are more time-consuming to rear plus, often, there's a rarity value attached as well.

Entry levels for bantams should be around £10-15. Ducks normally start at about £20 each, while pure-bred geese will often cost over £100 each (they live for 20 years). Heavier breeds, like Toulouse, Embdens and Africans, will generally cost more than less popular breeds such as the Chinese, Pilgrims or Romans. Turkeys will cost £50+ for good quality, well-bred examples.

everything's calm and quiet. Having them all wake up together can make a big difference, although it's no guarantee of a trouble-free introduction. The pecking order among chickens is very important, and anything which upsets it will cause problems; aggressive, dominant birds may need to be removed during the early stages if things get too hostile. Never forget that, however cuddly and cute your chickens may look, under the surface lurks an extremely vindictive creature. So whenever you add new birds to an existing flock, make sure you're around more than usual to keep a wary eye out for trouble. Adding a male to the flock will normally stop any bullying in an instant but, obviously, this isn't always possible in the urban environment.

FASHIONABLE CHOICES
In today's image-conscious society,

"Adding a male to the flock will normally stop any bullying in an instant."

poultry doesn't escape the trend-setter's eye. Breeds fall in and out of fashion and, at the moment owning half a dozen birds, each of a different breed to ensure multi-coloured egg production, is all the rage. To achieve this, enthusiasts will typically buy an Araucana for blue eggs, a Maran for a dark brown egg, a Spanish or Leghorn for a pure white egg, and a Wyandotte or Sussex for a tinted egg.

This 'Heinz 57' approach to poultry keeping is perfectly feasible; most breeds will live quite happily together assuming the environment is right. Nevertheless, the more experienced keepers and breeders frown on this sort of mix 'n' match policy, preferring instead to concentrate on one or maybe two only. The danger is that people get carried away and buy too many different types, without having the necessary facilities to look after them all adequately.

The old favourites, like the Rhode Island Red, Light Sussex and Maran are consistently in demand, while rarer options, such as the Scots Grey or Spanish, come and go in the popularity stakes. Quieter, more docile breeds like the large Cochin or small Pekin bantam, remain favourites among many urban keepers.

The same sort of rules apply to the bantam market. Breeds like the Sussex, Plymouth Rock and Ancona, which are all popular good layers, are always sought after. The slightly more decorative breeds, such as the Belgian or Old English Game, which will happily roost in the rafters of your barn, drift in and out of favour as the market swings. ❧

Buying birds at shows is quick and easy.

Buying Healthy Birds

Chris Graham and Andy Marshall provide some practical advice about how to recognise the good from the bad when buying a chicken.

Buying birds is fraught with potential problems, particularly for the inexperienced poultry keeper.

But, of course, it's not all doom and gloom. There's a lot of commonsense involved in buying good poultry and just about anyone, with a bit of patience, a good eye for detail and the right advice, should be able to make a reasonable purchase.

LOOK AND LEARN

Although it's always best to be able to handle a bird before you buy it (for reasons we'll cover later), this isn't always possible. Buying at a sale tends to restrict you to a visual inspection only, although this isn't the end of the world as there's plenty of useful information to be gathered from some careful observation. Your primary objective must always be to buy birds that are healthy and, as a general rule, we'd advise that you reject any that present the slightest cause for concern based on the information detailed here. Unfortunately, many of the points to be considered when visually assessing a bird are subjective, which is why having an experienced keeper's eye alongside you when you buy can be such an advantage.

First impressions are important. A good prospect – whether it's a pure breed or a hybrid – will look happy and alert. A bird found sitting huddled in the corner of the pen, with its feathers fluffed-up and head drawn in close to its body, is not a happy creature; it could

> *"There can be many pitfalls awaiting the unwary buyer at these events."*

TAIL SHOULD BE HELD STRAIGHT AND TRUE. IT'S IMPORTANT THAT IT POINTS IN THE RIGHT DIRECTION; THERE ARE A NUMBER OF FAULTS TO WATCH OUT FOR

INSPECT EYE FOR BRIGHTNESS, CLARITY AND THAT ALL-IMPORTANT SPARK OF LIFE

COMB SHOULD BE BRIGHT RED AND FREE FROM SCABS AND DISCOLOURATION

DAMAGE TO THE WATTLES CAN MEAN THE BIRD HAS BEEN FIGHTING

CHECK NOSTRILS FOR LIQUID DISCHARGE DENOTING RESPIRATORY DISEASE, AND WATCH FOR BEAK DEFORMITIES

PLUMAGE CONDITION SHOULD BE GOOD, WITH CLEAN, SLEEK FEATHERS. BIRD SHOULD APPEAR ACTIVE AND ALERT

ANOTHER FAVOURITE PLACE FOR PARASITES TO GATHER UNDER THE WING. CHECK SHAPE AND CONDITION OF FLIGHT FEATHERS TOO.

CHECK AROUND THE VENT FOR PARASITE INFESTATION AND GENERAL DIRT

CHECK FOR BREAST BONE STRAIGHTNESS AND THE PRESENCE OF ABSCESSES

QUICK REFERENCE BUYER'S GUIDE

SPUR LENGTH IS A GOOD INDICATOR OF A MALE'S AGE

CONDITION OF LEGS IS IMPORTANT. SCALY LEG MITE IS AN INFECTIOUS NUISANCE. WATCH FOR 'KNOCK KNEES' AND ROUGH SCALES

well be ill and is best avoided. Also, birds that appear generally scruffy or dirty (a mucky backside can spell trouble) are best left too. Pay particular attention to a bird's eyes. They should be bright, with that all-important spark of life. Eyes that appear small or sunken can be a sign of dehydration, or that there's something more serious wrong. Check closely around the eye and nostrils for signs of watery discharge. If you see any then keep walking – the bird could well have a respiratory problem such as Mycoplasma.

Combs are an important indicator too. Always look for a good, rich red colouring – anything faded is off-colour, literally. Steer well clear of any bird you see with scabs or lumps on its face, comb or wattles because these are signs that, for whatever reason, it's been fighting. Chickens that fight, or get picked on, are potentially bad news when brought into an established flock. Sometimes you may find a bird that has a bit of scabbing or discolouration on the top of its comb serrations, but this isn't necessarily a problem. This sort of effect can be caused by the comb rubbing on the top of the box or crate during transportation.

Finally, with regard to the comb, make sure that you're aware of the type that's expected on the breed you are buying. Combs come in a variety of different types – single, triple, rose, pea, walnut – and it's important that you buy a bird that is genuinely representative of the breed.

PHYSICAL DEFECTS

Sticking with the head, switch your

While moulting is a completely natural process, buying a bird in this condition can lead to problems as its resistance will be low.

attention to the bird's beak. There are a number of deformities which it's best to avoid. One such is called 'twisted beak' and this can give the bird serious eating difficulties. The upper and lower parts of the beak don't align correctly, making it difficult to use as nature intended. This tends to be an inherited problem and so breeding from birds with the condition is a bad idea.

The legs and feet provide another helpful indicator as far as overall condition is concerned.

Two problems that are easy to spot are 'knock knees' and 'pigeon toe'. Birds showing the knock-knee condition will have legs that bend inwards at the knee joint, when viewed from the front. This can be a key pointer to the bird having a poor 'confirmation' (body structure), and it's likely that such birds will be poor specimens that won't lay well or develop satisfactorily. The 'pigeon toe' condition is recognised by inwardly-facing feet. Both problems can represent a genetic weakness. Twisted toes, where one or more toes grows at a strange angle, can be inherited too, but it can also be promoted in birds that are reared on wire mesh.

General feather condition offers another major clue about a bird's overall health. Plumage that appears sleek, tight-fitting and clean usually indicates that the bird is in good health. If, on the other hand,

"Eyes that appear small or sunken can be a sign of dehydration."

it looks rough, fretted and dull – or there are actually feathers missing – then be more wary.

There's an undesirable condition known as 'squirrel tail', where the bird's tail feathers curve forward towards its head, instead of being more vertical or facing to the rear. Another defect, known as 'wry tail', is characterised by a tail that's carried off centre, when viewed from above. While these faults won't usually affect a bird's ability to lay, they are both caused by a genetic disorder and, as such, should not be perpetuated.

Finally, with regard to feathers, it's generally best not to buy birds that are moulting. While this, of course, is a perfectly natural process, bear in mind that moulting birds tend to be stressed birds, and stressed birds are much more susceptible to picking up disease and infection. So the general upheaval of the sale process makes a moulting bird considerably more vulnerable to problems, particularly under typical livestock auction conditions.

GOOD HANDLING

Parasite infestation is one of the most common problems affecting birds put through the sale process. The trouble is, actually confirming this is nigh-on impossible without a careful, hands-on inspection. The top three offenders are usually Scaly Leg Mite, Lice and Northern Mite.

This is how a 'wry tail' might look.

Scaly Leg is the easiest to spot, and is a condition caused by mites that live and burrow around under the scales on a bird's legs. This, as you might imagine, sets up an intense and uncomfortable irritation for the bird, and can be recognised by the outwardly rough appearance of the scales, which will often show white, crusty deposits too. It's a very infectious problem and is not something you want to bring home to your flock.

Lice are impossible to detect from any distance, and will only be apparent after a thorough inspection. They move about on the skin under the feathers and can be quite tricky to track down. Typically they will congregate around the bird's vent, and their white eggs (like nits in

Foot and leg condition is another important aspect. Rough scales, particularly around the joints, indicate an older bird; younger birds will be much smoother, as above. Crusty, white deposits are a sign of scaly leg mite.

hair) can be found stuck in clusters on to the base of feather shafts.

Northern Mite is a tiny creature that's too small to be seen with the naked eye, however carefully you check a bird. They have their favourite areas too, including around the vent, under the

wings and on the head. They cause a great deal of irritation for the bird, but are only really apparent to onlookers if there's a serious infestation, when it can be so bad that you'll see the feathers moving.

Something else which can come to light during a hands-on inspection are problems with the bird's breast. Two things you might be able to detect with your fingers are a crooked or twisted breast bone, and the presence of abscesses. Holding the bird correctly, with one hand supporting the body from underneath so that it's relaxed and balanced, will allow you to feel along the length of the breast bone. Any deformities you feel may be an inherent fault, or they may result from it having been allowed to start using a perch too early.

Abscesses or other swellings on the breast are also a factor to watch for. Often they will have been caused by the bird living in poor housing conditions where the perches are either too narrow or too rough, and damaging its breast as a result. While not a serious defect, the presence of this sort of problem can speak volumes about where the birds have come from, and the levels of husbandry involved.

AGE CONCERN

Being able to assess a bird's age is another valuable skill because the unscrupulous seller will think nothing of

Eye and beak condition are both important factors when buying a bird. Discharge from the nostrils signifies problems.

attempting to pass off an ageing hen as a young layer, in the hope of fetching a better price. With male birds the length of the spur, which grows out of the leg above the foot, is a good indicator of age. Actual lengths vary from breed to breed so it's hard to be specific. However, in most cases the spur doesn't start to grow until the bird reaches sexual maturity, which normally takes at least four months. So you should expect a six-month-old male to show a spur that's less than a centimetre long. On more mature birds it can have grown to anything up to 3-4cm in length.

Overall size of the foot is a useful tell-tale sign as far as hens are concerned. A pullet will have much smaller feet, with much tighter scales, than an older hen. Also, the scales on older birds will

A hands-on inspection is essential if you want to be sure about a bird. Most generally you can gauge its weight. If it feels like a bag of skin and feathers then there are problems. Note the large, thickened feet on this older bird.

PEST CONTROL

As a rule you should always treat new birds with a recommended and approved anti-parasite powder or spray as soon as you get them home. Also, assuming you have the space to do so, new birds should remain isolated from the existing flock to avoid any risk of spreading the problem. Both Northern Mite and lice will usually require several treatment applications before the birds can be considered completely clear, so the whole process is going to take several weeks.

...end to look rougher, particularly at the joints between the toes and the foot. A new set grows every year and, if the previous set isn't completely shed, the build-up leads to roughness.

Droppings can provide useful clues about a bird's health. This is how it should look.

Spreading the wing is another useful thing to do when judging age. Most young POL pullets, aged between four and six months, won't have grown a complete set of wing feathers. Pointed wing feather tips on a chicken indicate a young bird. Mature feathers have rounded ends.

Finally, if you get a chance to inspect the droppings, do so. Faecal condition can be extremely revealing as far as the bird's general health is concerned. Any blood visible in the droppings is a bad sign and can indicate the presence of coccidiosis, as can a runny consistency or an unnaturally green colour. Diarrhoea can also be caused by worms What you're after is a predominantly dark-coloured dropping that has a white cap and a generally firm consistency. This appearance will indicate that the bird is more than likely clear of internal parasites and generally fit. 🐦

Pointed-tip wing feathers are a sign of a young bird. Final flight feathers have rounded ends.

Don't get stressed

Some practical hints and tips on keeping your birds in the best of health by Lindsay Sissons

The vet's role in the world of poultry keeping is often misinterpreted as a case of dispensing drugs to the poultry keeper when the birds become ill – merely treating infections as they arise. But some of us prefer to think of our role as preventative, only providing medication when all else fails. After all, remember that good husbandry – housing, management, feeding, and breeding – will keep the birds in the best natural condition, making them fit enough to fight off most health challenges that arise, or avoiding or reducing the risk of infection in the first place. Once implemented, these measures can greatly reduce the need for veterinary intervention – which after all, only treats the condition rather than dealing with the original cause. Any sort of stress will reduce the bird's ability to fight infection, so making it less resistant to disease and also lengthening the time taken to recover, assuming it recovers at all.

Stresses can be environmental, nutritional or climatic. Housing can be the cause of many problems. The right amount of ventilation is vital. Too little can mean that dust and ammonia in the air will increase the risk of respiratory infection. But, at the other extreme, too many drafts can be bad too. Also, bedding can be dusty, or have mould spores, both of which might promote respiratory infection.

Birds that are too tightly housed can begin feather pecking, or some may lose weight when not allowed to feed by the others. Inadequate cleaning out of roosting areas and nest boxes will increase the amount of ammonia in the air, while increasing the infectious challenge (bacteria, mite etc) in the house. These can all be altered simply, with little cost to the keeper and with good rewards in productivity.

The birds' nutritional needs vary according to age and what production is expected of them. Commercial feeds are finely tuned with all of the basic requirements supplying the daily recommended amounts of protein, oil, vitamins and minerals for the specific production required. Organic feeds are now also widely available. If the bird is fed for growing, laying or breeding specifically, a balanced diet will ensure that all its needs are met, giving a healthier, more productive bird.

Parasites take their nutrition directly from the bird, resulting in weight loss, anaemia and weakness, all of which make the bird more susceptible to disease. Many parasites can be avoided/prevented by using the knowledge of their life cycles to modify husbandry, or keep treatments to a minimum level.

Chick losses are often high, again due to poor management. Survival numbers can be greatly increased by following a set of basic and simple rules, such as not putting new hatched chicks where other birds have been, and keeping hatching batches together to avoid mixing ages of chicks. Basic hygiene measures, such as handling/feeding chicks and birds starting with the youngest first, also help greatly and just require a little forethought.

It's often easier than you might imagine to keep birds healthy and in good condition. What's more, the resultant increase in production, be it in eggs, meat or show fitness, easily outweighs any expense incurred in changes to ventilation or buying a more expensive but better feed, for example. The advisory role of the vet can always be called upon when necessary, with medication only if essential. But the essence of poultry keeping is that good husbandry is the key to happy, healthy birds. ❦

"Any sort of stress will reduce the bird's ability to fight infection."

Happy birds tend to be healthy birds. A relaxed and peaceful environment plays a big part in general well being

Poultry Point

Geoff Silcock rails against the use of toxic chemicals in the fight against common poultry parasites, preferring instead, a more natural approach

Years ago I remember an old-timer asking me: "What's the first thing that a chicken does after scratching in the dirt?" The question had been for his amusement and, my answer, "It eats what it's found", was wrong. What actually happens is that the chicken steps back to have a good look at what it's unearthed. That got me thinking that perhaps this idea should prompt us chicken folk to do the same thing.

I was alarmed by reading Ivermectin described as an 'unlicensed veterinary special according to the manufacturer'. But, even more so by the suggested seven-day egg withdrawal period. It seemed to imply a casual approach to using what is a powerful, unlicensed, toxic neuro-insecticide and pollutant, when non-toxic treatments are freely available and less expensive. I beg anyone thinking of using Ivermectin, to step back and take a look first. Check the internet and see what can be unearthed.

This seemingly carefree attitude can be all too easily contagious, with harmful results. For many it runs counter to why we are keeping chickens in the first place. I'm not saying that Ivermectin is no use to the chicken keeper but, I for one, don't plan to trundle up and down the yard with a barrowful of toxic chemicals. So here are a few practical, non-toxic pest solutions.

This is a purpose-made peat dust bath. The birds love to use it.

RED MITE

This pest must be tackled, in the first instance, in the housing. Proprietary products such as Poultry Shield are widely available. It is food-safe and non-toxic, and works by breaking down the mite's wax coating to produce a 96% kill rate in 48 hours (including eggs). What's more, there's a 'buy one, get one free here' aspect here as well. At the right mix strength, this product can be used directly on the birds, thus controlling most other external parasites to some degree. A pre-emptive approach as part of a 'good-keeping' routine has much to recommend it.

Depluming mite can be difficult to deal with; bathing the birds as you would a pet dog, in a medicated dog shampoo bath, is as good a treatment as I've found. The medication is pyrethrum; a fairly safe, plant extract-based pesticide. It has a reputation for being relatively non-toxic for humans, but bad news for insects. This dunking of the chicken is done after they have laid, and provision must be made for drying them and keeping them warm afterwards. There's an added benefit with this approach too; handling. There's no better way of getting to know your chickens.

BEATING THE WORMS

There are good, licensed poultry worming products available – Flubenvet, for instance. But there are also alternatives. One experienced and very knowledgeable old hand once told me, that he's kept birds on the same ground for 30 years and never wormed them once. Of course, his first class exhibition stock has a mild population of worms, but that was all. Levels were kept in check by old-fashioned, good husbandry – the birds achieved a natural balance. But this important status quo can be disrupted by adverse environmental factors. It's our job as keepers to control these as best we can.

Recent unsavoury research is indicating that a mild population of worms in humans is indeed beneficial to our health; it appears to boost the immune system. So it makes me wonder, as far as common worm problems in our chickens are concerned, what we're actually achieving by worming every six weeks, when birds on the ground, are picking up the infestation continually? Some would argue that, under good management, the birds are generally better left to find an equilibrium.

Finally, I find that one of the most useful tools that can be used against external pests is the traditional dry dust bath. Bonfire ashes or dry earth are perfect and, to enhance the effect, you can add a little louse powder that contains Permethrin (low mammalian toxicity). It's a 'nature's way' type of solution which birds are happy and keen to use. What could be better? 🐦

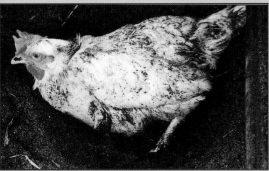

A White Leghorn enjoys a peat bath, just as nature intended

INTRODUCTION AGENCY

Introducing new birds to an existing flock can be fraught with problems.
Andy Marshall advises on how best to avoid trouble.

Birds which have grown up in mixed
flock situations are likely to be far
more tolerant of new arrivals.

Most people, once they've started keeping poultry, soon begin hankering after a few more birds; the hobby is that addictive! The trouble is that few newcomers realise that bringing in new stock can generate all sorts of aggravation between the new and the established birds – beaks can seriously be put out of joint!

I suppose the first thing to be emphasised is that if you don't absolutely have to introduce strange birds to each other, then don't do so. If you've got the space to keep them separate, in individual pens, then this is the best option. Remember that, in the wild, chickens live in small groups – one male with a few females. Jungle fowl do this, with the annual brood normally being driven-off to start new flocks of their own once they've been safely reared. Birds don't normally stay with their parents. So, with this in mind, you shouldn't be surprised if mayhem erupts in your normally calm poultry pen the moment a handful of new arrivals are added.

However, as with so much else in poultry, if you take the time and trouble to follow a few simple rules, introductions can be made smoothly and with minimal trauma for you and, more importantly, the birds.

I've heard plenty of horror stories of what can happen when owners get it wrong. For example, I had a distraught keeper on the 'phone recently. He'd introduced his new Spanish and Noir Cuivree Marans to his existing birds and, within the first few hours, the Spanish had been scalped by his Araucana. Fortunately, following several reassuring telephone calls and some TLC from the owner, the Spanish was saved, and has now thankfully been accepted as part of the flock.

This was a shocking, but typical, illustration of the sort of thing which can happen. So why did the Araucana get so aggressive, and why did the Spanish act to timidly, standing in a submissive posture and allowing the attack to continue? Learn to appreciate the answers to these questions and you'll be a long way towards avoiding trouble in the future.

BACK TO BASICS
To understand these potentially violent reactions we need to take a step back, and consider young birds first of all. Most hybrids are flock-reared in their thousands, so the pullets (all males are disposed of at hatching) only ever see the same type and colour as themselves. So, if you started with some hybrids and

then decide, a year later, to buy some pure breeds, your original birds will be completely shocked, never having seen anything so different. Understandably, they'll adopt an aggressive attitude towards the newcomers. Right from the off they're likely to chase and peck the strange 'impostors'.

The situation will be compounded by the fact that the new birds will already be suffering from the general trauma of their move (being caught, confined in a box, gawped at and poked by humans and then transported, is disturbing for a chicken). Following all this, they are released into a strange pen containing an unfriendly group of other hens that are intent on beating them up.

If birds have been reared in mixed groups, then the growers will have become familiar with black, brown and white birds, and any new arrivals won't be seen as such a threat. Growers and pullets are naturally unsure of themselves, so if they are suddenly confronted by fully-grown, confident hens they will immediately adopt a submissive posture, and normally suffer some quite serious pecking.

Reputable suppliers of pure breeds will always ask the purchaser what they ▶

"In the wild, chickens live in small groups – one male with a few females."

Keeping unfamiliar birds separated, but in sight of each other in the early stages makes a lot of sense. They can get used to each other without coming to any harm.

Watch for size mis-matches as well. New birds that are appreciably smaller will tend to get a hard time from larger, more established stock

growers subjected to this sort of bullying will often be hounded to death. Older, larger birds are not killed as frequently like this, but will often be found very bloodied and featherless around the head or back. Birds in this condition must be isolated immediately, treated appropriately, and only reintroduced to the others once fully recovered. This should be done under careful supervision to ensure that all is well.

intend to do with the new birds, and advise on how best to introduce any new arrivals so that the risk of problems is minimised.

First, always try to ensure that, when introducing birds, the new ones are of a similar size to the current residents. If those being added are small, or not yet fully mature, they will tend to get bullied much more than if they'd been full-grown and the same size as the birds they are joining.

TERRITORY MATTERS

Chickens are very territorial creatures, and a strict pecking order is established in every group. Consequently, any new bird will be regarded as a threat. This problem is particularly apparent among birds aged between two weeks and 12 months. However, as mentioned earlier, birds that have been reared in mixed batches are usually more tolerant of new colours than those that have grown up in a monoculture.

Different breeds will also have very different attitudes to new arrivals. I've seen young White Wyandottes gut a grower in one night, quite literally. Normally, though, they will only do this to a fellow White Wyandotte; they tend to leave other breeds alone. Dealing with this problem is all about providing a distraction. In my experience, hanging old CDs at grower height, so that they can peck these all day and leave their fellows alone, works really well. I've also

overcome grower bullying by separating the sexes, at as early as eight weeks old. Keeping the birds in large airy sheds, so that overcrowding is avoided completely, is another great way of preventing this sort of trouble. Obviously, though, this depends on individual circumstances.

These sorts of problem can be particularly bad with white birds because the bloody consequences of any feather pecking show up so obviously, and act as a stimulant to the other birds. Young

"Right from the off they're likely to chase and peck the strange 'impostors'."

It's for these reasons that experienced breeders will usually separate the sexes as soon as they are able to identify them, and often place an experienced adult male in with the young males to act as a minder. Such males won't tolerate any dissent; one, well-placed peck from them sorts out most problems! However, take care with the breed of adult male you appoint as the minder. A strong, aggressive cockerel is perfectly capable of killing a young grower with a single,

Don't put new young birds in with older stock; it can promote bullying. Pointed tips to the wing feathers denote an immature bird.

Perches that are set at different heights and angles in adjacent pens will reduce tension too. Birds that aren't able to face each other will be less inclined to become aggressive.

well-delivered peck. I've seen it happen when the minder being used has been a large Rhode Island Red or Sussex. These are big, strong birds, and can be a bit heavy-handed when it comes to controlling the minors.

OLDER INTRODUCTIONS
Moving on to the introduction of older birds, the following suggestions represent my top six tips for the steps that must be taken to avoid problems.

1. Make sure that the pullets you've bought are fully mature and well developed before any introduction is made. If the new birds are still showing their chicken feathers (wing feathers with pointed instead of rounded tips), then they have yet to moult into their adult plumage. Birds that are still at this stage are likely to behave in a submissive manner when confronted with existing stock, and this attitude is likely to promote bullying.

2. Assuming the birds are fully-feathered, only ever introduce them into the hen house at night, when it's dark. Never attempt this during daylight hours. Also, make sure that the pullets have had a good feed and drink somewhere else before placing them into their new home.

3. Stand and observe what happens when you first let the birds out the morning after the introduction. You may notice the odd peck here and there but, if you're lucky, that'll be about it. But if one of your original birds persistently goes for the new arrivals, then remove it but leave all the new ones in place. Then, hopefully after a few days, everything will have settled down and you'll be able to re-introduce the bully without any further problems.

4. If you have the space and accommodation available, the alternative is to split the original pen and allow the birds to meet through a wire fence for a week or so. After this period you can then let them mix during the day, each sleeping in a separate house and then allowing them to run together. This method is ideal if you have purchased fairly young birds as they have the chance of seeing the originals without being bullied.

5. If you've got the facilities to do so, keep the two groups of birds totally separate, in different units for a week or so. Then, if the new arrivals are carrying

> *"Only ever introduce them into the hen house at night, when it's dark."*

any disease, you will have a chance to spot and deal with it before it gets a chance to infect your existing flock. Conversely, if your own birds have some problem, then there will be time to sort this out and avoid infecting the new arrivals.

6. Finally, the one sure way to avoid any introductory trouble at all is to simply replace the original birds with new pullets each year!

To sum up then, introducing new arrivals will work providing some care and thought has gone into the process, and you've avoided impulse buying. If your original birds have a large run, and/or live a free-range lifestyle, plus they enjoy the benefits of a hen house offering plenty of room (more than five square feet of floor space per bird), the risks of problems will be significantly reduced. But not all birds are able to revel in such luxury and, in many cases, space is tight. Under these conditions, owners should think very carefully about whether adding to the flock at all is a sensible thing to do. Overcrowding your poultry will not only make the introduction of new birds much more problematic, but it'll also compromise the quality of life for all of them thereafter. ☙

FEATHER FEARS?

Terry Beebe explodes some of the myths surrounding the annual moult, emphasising that it should be nothing to panic about.

The term 'moulting' is very commonly used with regard to all types of animals and birds but, if you're a newcomer to the hobby of keeping poultry, this natural process can be one of the most upsetting and worrying of them all. Defined, in relation to birds, as the routine shedding of old feathers, moulting is a completely natural and functional event, but the visual shock-factor involved frequently takes newcomers by surprise.

I get so many inquiries from worried keepers whose birds are losing their feathers during the summer months. The apparent descent towards baldness often induces a state of panic among owners who've not experienced this annual event before. They automatically start to think there's something seriously wrong,

and that they have somehow caused the problem. One of the first conclusions that a lot of keepers jump to is that feather mite is at the root of the problem, while others put it down to feather pecking or shortfalls in their husbandry techniques.

DON'T BE FOOLED

The truth is, of course, that in the majority of cases it's the annual moult that's causing the apparent 'problem'. It happens to all birds every year – sometimes more than once. It's not a completely predictable event either, and seems to be becoming even less so as the years pass; I've heard global warming being blamed for this. Anyway, whatever the trigger may be, this transformation is nature's way of replacing old, worn out feathers with perfect new ones. It's a process which can't be rushed and the time it takes varies from bird to bird. But it's important to realise that the effects of the moult are much more than simply visual. The whole process represents a major ordeal for the bird, and consumes a great deal of its energy. The effort involved in growing a new set of feathers erodes stamina levels, which can make moulting birds appear lethargic and quite ill.

Feathers are, in

This is typical of the sort feather damage you'd expect to see caused by a male bird in the mating pen.

fact, 85% protein which is why replacing them represents such a tough job. This is also why egg laying usually stops during the whole period; hens simply can't produce eggs and feathers at the same time, and it's the feathers which take priority.

Consequently, the moult represents a critical time for a bird's general health, and it's sensible to offer a little assistance to help them through it. I always like to provide extra vitamins and calcium to the feed ration, plus some sort of extra protein source. Mashed hard-boiled, or scrambled, egg is a good way of using any surplus eggs while providing a valuable additional source of feather-building protein.

Reading an old poultry book recently it was suggested that rape seed – containing sulphur – and sunflower seed were good things to feed as supplements. These are good ideas, I think; extra sources of important nutrients are never a bad thing during this important period. What must not happen, though, is that you allow the birds to get either too fat or too thin; either of these conditions will hinder the bird's ability to progress through the moult smoothly. I also recommend the use of cod liver oil, which is another great way to help replace many of the lost vitamins and additives which seem to disappear during this testing time.

A healthy, young chicken will get through the whole transformation more

The annual moult can be a shocking time for keepers as well as birds! If you've not experienced it before, then feather loss like this can trigger all sorts of panic.

It's important to be able to assess the reasons for feather loss; is it being caused by the moult, feather pecking by other birds or mating damage?

unpleasant vices like feather pecking. Any signs of this should prompt you to separate the birds until the feathers are fully grown and back to normal. Foul-smelling, anti-peck sprays are available and provide a useful deterrent; always wear gloves when using these products. Stockholm Tar is an old favourite that works well in my experience. Such treatments are usually messy, although aerosols make life easier (always keep such treatments well away from the bird's eyes, beak and face).

With the unpredictability of the weather in the UK these days, there is no hard and fast rule about when the moult will take place. As a general guide, though, it's most likely to occur towards the end of the summer. This is logical really, as birds don't want to be losing their feathers just as the weather starts turning colder.

When you are hatching late in the season, remember that these hatches will more than likely bring the birds into a late moult, and that this isn't generally a good idea; it can take much longer to complete and, if it's egg production you're after, this will effect the profit from sales. I always find that the late-hatch birds tend to be weaker and more prone to health problems, although fertility rates do seem to increase for these birds. One other point to note is that late-hatched birds are often produced for the exhibition scene; the bantams are always smaller, which generally makes them better suited to the all-important breed

quickly than an older one, or one that has some other health issue. If the feathers fall out rapidly, then tend to grow back very slowly, this can indicate a health deficiency that needs to be addressed. Another sign of trouble is if the new feathers are brittle. Typically this will be caused by disease (either past or present), and is very unlikely to be related to a dietary problem. The main objective must always be to keep the birds as well fed and healthy as possible so that their passage through this potentially traumatic time is made as smooth as possible.

HOW LONG?
The moulting process can take quite a long time but, under normal circumstances, it should ideally be completed in just a few weeks. The way it happens can vary too. Feathers can drop out gradually, or they may be lost in larger amounts all of a sudden. Birds can end up

almost bald, but don't worry because the replacements will grow back pretty quickly and everything will return to normal. However, it's important to appreciate that not all your birds will moult at the same time. For this reason you must keep a careful eye on how each bird is reacting, and take various precautionary measures as needed. Remember that those in moult are more vulnerable to

standard.
Of course, this aspect isn't of much relevance to the hobby keeper, or breeder of utility fowl. I always try to hatch early for the large fowl but, on the downside, this approach definitely results in lower fertility levels. Ultimately, anyone

Moult-related feather loss from the side of the neck. Male birds can pull feathers from the back of the hen's head/neck during mating, but not from the side like this.

The replacement of feathers takes its toll on a bird's energy levels, so extra TLC is required during the moulting period.

governs the times of year when it's possible to breed and show, as well as egg production rates.

WHAT'S THE CAUSE?

When you find birds that are losing their feathers you must always check to make sure that this is in fact due to the natural moult, rather than some other pecking-related problem. Feather pecking can usually be identified by the presence of dull, broken feathers, plus bare patches of skin on the neck, back, breast and around the vent. Plucking feathers from the tail is a very bad habit, but it's quite common among growing stock. However, any form of feather pecking is usually down to something relatively simple, such as overcrowding, mite infestation or lack of exercise. Always check the basics first. However, don't overlook the fact that there are bound to be feather losses anyway in a breeding pen; male birds inevitably pull feathers from the hens during mating.

Of perhaps even greater concern is vent pecking, which is something that demands a swift reaction from the keeper. There's always a good chance that unless it's nipped in the bud, the aggressors will keep going until the victim is pecked to death. Younger birds tend to be more prone to this unwelcome vice. Finally, there's head pecking to consider. This is another relatively common problem, but is more likely to occur when birds are kept in adjacent pens, and are able to see and reach each other. Given the opportunity they'll peck through to damage heads and combs of neighbouring birds, so it's always best to use solid dividers and prevent the problem completely.

Hopefully, then, all this information will

Feathers are 85% protein, which is why replacing them represents such a challenge for the average chicken.

breeding birds must be responsible for their health and well-being, and part of this involves allowing adequate time for the breeding process. It's good to keep the birds you breed to the standard size, and to know that you've bred them correctly. The reason I've mentioned poultry breeding here is because often it's very closely linked with the moult. In many respects it is a key factor that

have helped put a few minds at rest. The annual moult is a completely natural, albeit visually alarming, process which, if correctly managed, shouldn't pose any serious problems at all. As with so many other aspects of poultry keeping, good husbandry is a key factor in minimising the potential effects of the moult, as is a thorough knowledge of your birds and their characteristic behaviour. ❧

It's easy to jump to the wrong conclusion when presented with this sort of condition.

Breeding season; cockerels are at their peak and can do a tremendous amount of damage to the hens during mating. The male bird mounts the female by standing on her back (called 'treading'), grabs the feathers on the back of her head with his beak and steadies himself by gripping her lower back with his feet and spurs. Normally the result of this is a hen with missing feathers from her head, neck and back.

However, in bad cases, the hen can get so badly cut by over-enthusiastic or excessive 'treading' that she actually dies from her wounds. Chickens become very aggressive at the sight of blood, so treading damage can throw up real problems if it's not noticed by the keeper. Other hens will pick on an injured, bleeding bird, sometimes with merciless brutality.

The loss of feathers can also trigger feather pecking – another undesirable and destructive poultry vice. Things can rapidly turn from bad to worse as other

A hen fitted with a correctly-sized saddle should be safe from the over-enthusiastic and potentially dangerous activities of male birds.

hens in the flock peck at an individual hen's bald patches and/or bloody quills. Not only is this potentially deadly for the hen in question, it becomes a habit for

If you care about your chickens, protecting them from damage should be a prime concern, especially during the breeding season, says Terry Beebe.

the 'peckers' too, so it must always be nipped in the bud.

One practical way to help minimise the effects of male treading is to fit the hens with a poultry saddle. This effectively covers and protects the bird's back, while allowing mating to continue as normal. Also, because it also allows the male bird to grip better with his feet, fitting a saddle usually minimises the number neck/head feathers that are pulled out too.

Most poultry saddles are made from canvas, which is easy to clean and can be re-used year after year. You can also buy leather versions, but the danger with these is that, without the necessary care and attention, they become very hard and uncomfortable for the bird to wear. Saddles come in three sizes; small, medium and large, and the simple fitting procedure is the same for each. Once on, saddles can remain in place for as long as necessary. As far as sizing goes, soft-feather bantams will need a small saddle, medium-sized, soft-feather, heavy and several hard-feather breeds will be fine in a medium, while Orpingtons, Large Sussex and turkeys will need the large size.

Fitting is always easier with two people, especially if you're inexperienced. There isn't much to it

really, although I have heard of people getting in terrible muddles. Essentially, the saddle is held on by the bird's wings, which have to be passed carefully through adjustable strap loops, one at a time. It's obviously important not to twist the wing as you do this, or to catch/break any feathers. When both wings are through, level off the holding cord to make the saddle fit evenly over the back. Check that it's not too tight but that, at the same, it's not too loose either.

Once fitted, there shouldn't be any need for attention until the time comes to remove and clean the saddle ready for the next season. Just about all you need concern yourself with is that parasites like mites don't start to infest the area beneath the saddle. Take care to dust the bird's back with a good anti-lice powder before fitting the saddle, and make checks once every 10 days while it's fitted.

Saddle sense

CLIP & PLUCK!

Terry Beebe explains why every poultry keeper should have sharp clippers, and a good pair of scissors, in their poultry 'toolkit'

While much about keeping poultry is little more than common sense, there are still certain things which demand a bit of specialist knowledge if you're to maximise the welfare of your birds. An effective program of routine 'management' is vital to ensure that chickens live the happiest and healthiest lives possible, and that they grow and perform just as they should. Caring for their beaks, claws and spurs – providing a poultry manicure, if you like – is typical of the sort of important regular work, that I'll be focussing on in this feature. Failure to attend properly to these important issues will, in the worst instances, result in needless suffering.

Of course, the reality nowadays for many backyard keepers is that space is limited, and birds don't have the luxury of being able to free-range over a wide area. This is particularly true in these days of anti-AI precautions, when plenty of owners have already decided to restrict their birds to life inside covered runs. The upshot of this relative inactivity is that claws and beaks don't

Partially-healed comb damage, probably caused by fighting.

get worn down as much as they would under more natural, free-range scratching conditions.

Consequently, the responsibility for keeping the excess growth in check rest with us, the keepers. Beaks and claws left unattended can create different problems. Over-long beaks can actually make it very difficult or, in really bad cases, actually impossible for birds to eat. Likewise, claws which are allowed to grow too long can cause uncomfortable problems for the birds as they walk and perch.

Spurs like this should have their pointed tips clipped off.

NAIL CLIPPING

The most essential requirement for doing an effective and neat job on a chicken's claws is a really good pair of sharp cutters/clippers. There are some very good ones on the market that are designed specifically for the job. But it's also worth noting that a top quality pair of wire cutters can be used to equally good effect.

The golden rule when trimming claws is not to cut too much off; make this mistake and you're likely to create a painful, bloody mess. The thing to look for is the change in colour of the claw itself. In the same way that the excessive growth on our own finger and toe nails is marked by a lightening of colour, so it is with a chicken's claw. Take care to only ever remove the lighter-coloured material at the tip of the claw. Nick the darker material and you're likely to start a bleed.

BEAK CLIPPING

To clip the beak is more or less the same process as clipping the claws, although I

always find that it makes life easier if you wrap the bird in a towel when doing it. This makes the job simpler because the bird is easier to control and less stressed; it prevents any disturbing flapping and struggling.

Before you start, always check

A beak like this needs to be clipped back.

carefully for the white/paler tip of the beak, and use this as a cutting guide (as with the claws). Never rush the job and be sure not to over-cut. Once I've finished the trimming, I always like to use a small manicure file to smooth-off any rough edges, and to finally shape the tip into an attractive, rounded point. This is purely cosmetic though, and will get worn back to its original shape fairly quickly as the bird pecks.

WING CLIPPING

This is done primarily to ensure that the

Wing clipping: take care not to cut off too much.

birds stay where they are meant to be, by preventing them from flying. Whether or not it's necessary depends totally on your situation, and how the birds are being kept. Those in an urban environment might find this measure useful as a way of keeping their chickens out of next door's garden. Stray birds scratching around in a well-tended herbaceous border will irritate non-poultry keepers beyond measure, so make life easy on yourself and clip if necessary.

However, before doing any clipping it's worth remembering a couple of important points. For a start, no bird under the age of six months should have its wings clipped – the feathers are still growing up to this point. Also, adult birds with clipped wings will not be accepted at a poultry show. So if you've earmarked a particular bird for an exhibition later in the season, leave its wings intact.

You can clip one or both wings but, generally, just doing one will have the desired effect. As with the other trimming techniques mentioned here, it's vital when clipping wings to cut at the right point. Spread the feathers and look along the feather shafts until you see the colour change from dark to light. Always cut in the light section to avoid bleeding, using a good, sharp pair of

scissors. The part you cut off has no blood supply so, therefore, causes no discomfort to the bird.

Sometimes it can be easier with two people; one holds the bird, the other clips.

Remember, though, that a clipped wing will mean the bird is effectively grounded, and so will have no means of ▶

CAREFUL CLIPPING

If you make a mistake with any clipping operation, and draw blood, then it's best to separate the bird from the rest of the flock. A bleeding bird is sure to be picked on by the others and, once such an attack starts, it can get very bad, very quickly. So don't take risks and keep injured birds safely isolated until things have healed completely.

Do your best to avoid 'clipping nicks' as they cause needless pain and distress. However, if the bird is in good general health, then the healing process should be rapid.

FEATHER PECKING

While not strictly a manicure-related topic, feather pecking is a very important issue which needs to be watched for as part of your routine husbandry. It's a very destructive poultry vice, and one which needs to be stamped-out as soon as possible. If left unchecked it will quickly turn into a major issue, and is likely to result in a painful death for the birds involved.

The fact that poultry keepers are being encouraged to keep their birds in covered enclosures as a precaution against Avian Influenza simply serves to increase the risk of feather pecking, so anyone who has taken this 'security' measure needs to be doubly watchful.

Fortunately, there are a number of ways to minimise the risk of this unpleasant problem. The first is to avoid overcrowding your birds. Keeping stress levels at a minimum is important, as is preventing boredom. Suspending distractions (old CDs, cabbages, greens etc.) in the run will help keep the birds occupied. Also, throwing in treats like apples, weeds from the garden or even pieces of fresh turf will have the same effect. Feeding mash can also help; it keeps the birds busier and more active than they are with the pellet alternative.

If you discover a bird that's been feather-pecked then, ideally, it should be separated from the rest of the flock immediately (certainly if there's blood involved). But much depends on the severity of the problem. If the damage is fairly minor, and there's no open wound or blood, then another option is to use an 'anti-peck' treatment. These are available from specialist outlets in spray or cream form, and they smell absolutely awful! One I've found to be very good is called Stockholm Tar; it works. However, always wear gloves when applying it (you wouldn't want the smell on your hands), and keep it well away from the bird's face; products like this can be very harmful if misused.

is normally caused by fighting, or by accidental injury in the pen. It's unsightly and can take a while to heal, and always tends to show thereafter as a darker patch. Frost damage to the comb is another common problem caused during 'cold snaps' – resulting in blackened tips. The risk of it happening can be reduced by coating the comb with Vaseline, which keeps it both supple and protected. The same obviously also applies to the wattles, which can be treated in the same way.

Incidentally, I tend to use this method throughout the year, as it keeps the bird looking in good condition, especially when exhibiting.

CREST & BEARD
There are a number of breeds of chicken which feature crests and beards (for example, the crested Poland and Houdan, and the bearded Araucana). These require extra attention if the bird is to remain healthy and happy.

One common problem is that vision can be impaired by crest feather growth, and this is best dealt with by some careful feather plucking from around the eyes. This is both easy to do and will minimise the risk of potentially serious eye infections etc. This can also be caused by excessive beard growth – the feathers can actually grow upwards and cause the same problem. ❦

escape from a predator. Consequently, it's particularly important to make sure that the area in which they are kept is

Filing smooth after clipping – not essential but it greatly improves appearance.

secure. Also, if attempting wing clipping for the first time, I'd always advise doing it under the supervision of an experienced keeper who's done the job before. That way the correct technique can be demonstrated to you, and you'll feel confident about it from then on.

SPUR TRIMMING
The spur, which grows from the inside of the leg on male birds, has two basic functions. It helps the male with the mounting process during mating, and it's also a primary weapon when fighting. When on the attack, the bird rises up and strikes down using the spurs to inflict damage on the opponent.

Under normal circumstances there should be very little need to trim a bird's spurs, but there are occasions when they actually grow so large that action must be taken. If left unchecked, they can curl right back and even start growing into the leg, which is obviously very uncomfortable for the bird.

As a result of their purpose, spurs are usually very strong, which makes them difficult to cut. The best approach is simply to snip off the pointed tip of the spur, using a sharp pair of clippers. Look carefully at the colour of the spur, and don't cut back too far otherwise you'll cause a bleed.

After you finish cutting, smooth away any rough edges using a manicure file or even sand paper.

COMB CARE
Damage to the comb

Clipping tools should be the best you can afford, and sharp.

TRANSPORT POLICY

Terry Beebe advises how best to transport your poultry, to minimise stress levels and keep the birds as happy and healthy as possible.

For many years now, the transportation of poultry has been a source of great debate. Everyone seems to have an opinion; from the Government, right down to the general public. But it's far from a simple issue, and is one that's fraught with complication and conflict.

Ideas about best practice vary enormously and much, of course, depends on the sort of birds being moved and the numbers involved.

However, whatever the situation, one of the core requirements is that the birds should be transported with as much thought for their overall welfare as possible. Unfortunately, this doesn't always happen at the more 'mass market' end of the scale but, for you and me who

Whether you're an enthusiastic exhibitor of poultry, or need to get a bird to the vet, a box of some sort to carry it in is essential.

might be dealing with just a handful of birds, there really is no excuse for getting it wrong.

STRESS & HEAT
The two biggest threats to poultry on the

move come from stress and heat. Both, if allowed to get out of hand, are perfectly capable of resulting in death. The professional, commercial operators move their birds using large lorries stacked with poultry crates. These, if used correctly, are perfectly satisfactory in my view. They are designed for the job and, assuming they aren't overcrowded, work well at keeping the birds in good condition. Large doors allow the birds in and out easily (with careful handling), and the plastic construction

It's very important that the box being used matches the size of the bird being transported – the space inside must be big enough, but not too big!

quickly and efficiently after use.

However, at our end of the transportation scale, one of the traditional favourites has always been the humble cardboard box; whether birds are being taken to an exhibition or for a visit to the vet.

While these certainly offer a simple and essentially free transport solution, there are potential dangers associated with their use. Also, it seems likely that ever-tighter animal welfare legislation from the EC is likely to restrict their use sooner or later.

The more professional alternative that we should all be thinking about is the custom-built carrying box – a unit

Straightforward, two-compartment wooden box, with sliding lids and wire meshed 'windows'. This one features a shoulder strap.

means that the crates can be pressure-washed and disinfected

BOX LINING

The original, old-style carry boxes were traditionally lined with sacking. This was a great idea until it came to cleaning time, when it posed a problem.

My more up-to-date alternative is to use a piece of Astroturf. Not only does this provide a good, anti-slip and comfortable floor covering, but it's also waterproof and is simply removed for cleaning/disinfecting when necessary.

In addition, I always sprinkle a layer of clean, softwood shavings on top of the Astroturf. The birds are familiar with this, and it's effective at absorbing droppings, which helps maintain overall condition. There's nothing worse than lifting out the bird and finding it covered in smelly, poultry droppings.

plenty of ventilation. If you're using a cardboard box, then simply cutting holes in the side is fine – ideally there should be two or three high up on each side. If you're moving more than one bird, then be careful to make sure that you don't stack the boxes so close that the ventilation holes get accidentally blocked. Also, in my opinion, it's best to avoid shutting the boxes in a closed boot. Some people do this, but I don't approve.

An adapted wicker fishing basket, featuring three secure, hessian-lined compartments with individual, hinged lids.

WHICH TYPE?

Of the custom-built carrying boxes, most are made from wood; the exceptions being the aluminium, pigeon-style boxes, and the wicker-type baskets. Ease of cleaning and disinfecting is a very important issue, especially nowadays with biosecurity becoming ever-more important.

Prices vary enormously, depending on size, design and whether you buy new or secondhand. However, I think it's perfectly possible to buy a very serviceable, new carrying box for about £30, but the sky really is the limit. If you decide you want to buy secondhand, then take care to disinfect it thoroughly before using it for the first time – you never know what may be lurking in the

designed and built to match the requirements of various breeds. Most of

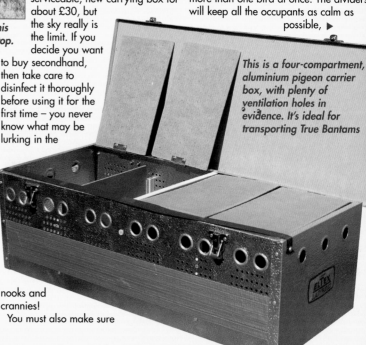

A variation on the wooden box theme. This design has a central carrying handle on top.

these are based on tried and trusted designs, often modelled on the units used in the days when most breeders transported their birds by train. Typically these are built to carry one bird, but they can often also be divided into compartments to carry up to four.

They provide solid and secure accommodation that's carefully sized to best suit the bird being transported. The basic idea is that the space inside should be large enough not to cramp the bird, but not so big that it slides around, can flap, get stressed and possibly injure itself. However, it has to be said that a properly prepared, sturdy cardboard box can do the job just as well as anything else, certainly for the time being.

To combat the risk of heat build-up within the box, it's vital that there's

nooks and crannies!

You must also make sure

that the box you buy is correctly sized for the birds you intend to put in it. If you're in any doubt about this, then make a point of consulting an experienced breeder for some specific advice; remember that boxes which are too small or too large are bad news.

When birds are put into a carrying box, and the lid is closed, the darkness inside has a great settling effect, calming the bird and usually encouraging them to sit down and go to sleep, which is the ideal, least stressful state.

Boxes that are subdivided inside really are the best option if you need to move more than one bird at once. The dividers will keep all the occupants as calm as possible, ▶

This is a four-compartment, aluminium pigeon carrier box, with plenty of ventilation holes in evidence. It's ideal for transporting True Bantams

approach. Although these can be bought in a variety of sizes, are made of easy-clean plastic and can obviously double-up to be used for transporting cats and dogs too, I don't like the 'open front' design. This, in my view, tends to cause panic if the birds are suddenly disturbed. So, if you must use this design, at least remember to cover the front to darken the interior and prevent the bird inside from being spooked by things outside. It's for this very reason that traditional, wooden poultry carrying boxes are generally fully closed. ❧

Cardboard boxes tied up with string are still favoured by many poultry keepers. But welfare-related regulations may outlaw their use in the future.

and will prevent any nasties such as feather-pecking. They will also help control heat build-up, assuming each compartment is adequately ventilated, of course.

As I've already mentioned, heat within a carrying box can be a killer, and can strike surprisingly quickly too. So, as well as box ventilation, it makes sense to keep the car's interior at a reasonable temperature too. Better to wear a coat yourself and turn the heater down, rather than drive in a t-shirt and asphyxiate the birds by accident. However, don't be tempted to put a water drinker in the box. This really shouldn't be necessary as, if the box interior is dark, the birds will tend not to drink anyway. Also, there's the risk of the water getting spilt inside the box. If you're on a long journey, then take fresh water with you and make stops to 'water' the birds and prevent dehydration setting-in.

The pictures included here illustrate the typical range of box types available, their lid designs and the different ways in which they can be carried. My own preference is for the closed box-type, with a secure fastening and solid lid.

The use of the pet carriers is becoming more common, but I'm not a fan of this

CLEANING ADVICE

Carry boxes should be cleaned thoroughly after every use. Not only is this a good policy, but it also provides a safeguard against the chance of you being stopped and checked during transportation.

As far as products are concerned, don't be tempted to use a domestic cleaner or disinfectant. These products aren't licensed for use with poultry, and could well cause the birds harm. The best thing is to talk to a specialist provider who will be able to advise you about the safest and most effective products to use.

A simple, home-made waterfowl box – not suitable for a chicken as it's far too exposed.

BOXING CLEVER

These are the five most important aspects that need to be considered when specifying a poultry carrying box.
1. Ventilation
2. Space
3. Comfort
4. Control of heat
5. Slip-free base

BAD HABITS

Poultry vices can be very destructive and have the potential to affect any flock, whatever its size, as Bob Cross explains

In the context of poultry keeping, 'vice' is the term used to describe undesirable behaviour within the flock and, in reality, it's actually probably more of a concern to poultry keepers than infectious disease.

Primary examples of poultry vices include; feather picking, cannibalism, bullying and egg eating. What's more, apart from the instant damage caused, the big danger is that these actions will become habitual, rapidly spreading throughout the flock, unless they are nipped in the bud.

CANNIBALISM

This unpleasant vice often starts with hyperactivity and bullying, where an aggressive peck draws first blood. Similarly, it may be triggered by feather picking. In either case, though, what starts as a minor incident can soon escalate into a much more serious problem.

In young stock, it's often initially noticed at the point when the first feathers develop. As these grow through the down, they appear as blood-filled pin feathers, which others in the flock investigate, peck at and find extremely palatable. Once one bird makes the discovery, the rest start following by example and, in a short time, the feather stubs have all gone, and the aggressors begin on the skin and flesh.

The site of the initial attack is likely to be either the tail/vent region or the wings. But if the situation is left unchecked, the damage will radiate from these areas. Left untreated, the trauma is likely to result in death. Occasionally it's only feathers that are removed, but this also requires action as, not only does it spoil the appearance of the birds, but it also deprives them of the feathers' protection.

Once fully-feathered, feather picking usually becomes less of a problem, but cannibalism may be seen in adult stock as well. Open wounds – caused by spur damage or prolapsus in hens – can be enough to give birds their first taste of blood.

These common problems are more often seen under intensive conditions, but the causes are many and complex. Much can be done to prevent or lessen the incidence, and an appreciation of some of the predisposing factors and stimuli may help when looking for a solution.

Breed and strain: Certain breeds, and strains within these, are more aggressive than others. So, if a choice is available, it makes sense to pick those with a quieter, less pugnacious disposition. Also, when developing a breeding line, consider the rate of feather growth; birds that are fast to feather may prove less likely victims of feather picking because they spend less time in the vulnerable, developmental stages.

Nutrition: Deficiencies of minor nutrients such as salt and some vitamins, low protein levels in the diet and, within the protein, deficiencies of certain amino acids, may trigger outbreaks. If adequate levels of these nutrients are not available in the diet, not only will feathering be retarded, but the bird will also tend to seek out other sources; such as cannibalism. Feeding a complete and adequate diet, and ensuring there are enough feeders for all birds to eat without competing for a space, should reduce the risk.

Boredom: Birds with little or nothing to do are more likely to peck each other than those that are fully occupied. If birds are kept in fairly close confinement, they should be given something to do; green food, such as a

Although feather picking tends to be particularly likely among young birds growing their first feathers, it can be triggered by all sorts of other factors among older chickens. Watch for it at all times.

Collecting the eggs as soon after they are laid as possible is one of the best ways to prevent egg-eating.

fresh cabbage, can be suspended at 'stretch height' for them to peck at, and the main feed should be of meal rather than pellets, as this takes longer to eat. Deep litter should be just what it suggests – deep. Not only will this allow the birds to dust bathe but, if a grain feed is scattered on it, it'll take some time to scratch around and find it. Probably the best solution is to allow them access to a grass-covered range, as this is almost certain to keep them busy.

Environment: High temperatures within the house or brooder pen can cause problems. Chicks reared in too warm an environment feather slowly, leaving them prone to attack. A sudden change in the weather can result in excessive temperatures in the poultry house, causing the birds discomfort. Often this can be all that's needed to promote pecking. Maintaining the correct temperature, and adjusting it to keep the birds comfortable, can prevent such conditions.

Bright lighting stimulates activity and aggression; this may be a problem when growers are housed in sheds that receive full sun through windows – even shafts of sunlight streaming through a knothole in the timber can be enough. Shading the glass can reduce light levels (putting up curtains will have the same effect), but always make sure that you never impede ventilation. Remember, also, that weather conditions during the spring and summer often change very quickly, so it's vital to keep a close watch on these factors.

There's no doubt that overstocking is a

contributory factor to feather picking and cannibalism. Not only will it exacerbate some of the other causes, but it also makes it difficult for those birds lower down the pecking order to escape the bullies. As chicks grow, the brooder pen should be extended, or batches split-up. Where space is limited, the situation needs careful monitoring.

Point of lay pullets can be prone to these vices, particularly those that have been reared intensively. The danger time is when they find themselves having to adapt to new environmental conditions – brighter light and longer days. These changes, in turn, may aggravate nutritional stresses. Vigilance,

once again, is vital.

EGG-EATING

Although it doesn't have the same welfare implications, egg-eating is still a vice and, as such, remains undesirable. Most birds enjoy the taste of fresh egg, and the eating habit usually starts following the opportunistic discovery of a broken egg. It's a habit that all your birds can quickly develop given the chance, so many eggs can be lost or spoiled.

Reducing the chances of eggs breaking is the best way of preventing the habit starting. Attention to disease prevention and dietary nutrition should help maintain good shell strength, while regular collections and adequate provision of nesting facilities (plenty of litter material in the boxes) should lessen the chances of eggs being damaged. Siting nests in a darker part of the house may also help, as can attaching a sacking curtain to the front of the nestbox.

VICE COPS
As I've already mentioned, once any of ▶

This sort of damage must be allowed time to heal, with the affected bird being isolated for its own safety.

these vices have become a habit, they are difficult to stop. Your best weapons are the successful manipulation of husbandry and stock management. It's in these respects that your powers of observation and stockmanship will be tested fully, and can pay dividends. By watching and noting the tell-tale signs, much can be done before situations become critical.

It's inevitable, however, that problems will occur from time to time and, when they do, you must always act swiftly. These vice-related troubles never cure themselves. Victims should always be removed from the flock so that their wounds can be treated. They'll also need sufficient time in isolation to recover fully. If the damage is unfortunately beyond treatment then the bird should be culled to prevent further suffering.

Also, never forget to investigate the cause of the trouble; don't simply limit your action to dealing with the results. Take positive steps to put things right, then quieten the birds by reducing light levels in the house. This should then be kept subdued until all have progressed on to the next stage of development.

If injuries are relatively minor, the affected area should be cleaned and then dressed with either an antiseptic spray, or painted with Stockholm tar. The latter not only appears to promote

healing, but its unpleasant taste also acts as a deterrent to further trouble. However, on the downside, it stains feathers and will spoil the appearance until the bird moults out. Various grades of Stockholm tar are available, the best being an almost liquid form used in the equine world; it's best applied with a small paintbrush.

Where it's not possible to prevent pecking and cannibalism by the methods already outlined, it may be necessary to resort to other more invasive means, such as beak trimming. However, this causes pain and is not best suited to the domestic environment. Beak bits provide another option. These are C-shaped clips, made from aluminium or plastic, that fit in a similar way to the bit in a horse's mouth. The ends of the 'C' clip into the bird's nostrils, and the middle passes between the upper and lower parts of the beak. This, while still allowing the bird to feed, prevents the beak from closing enough for it to grab feathers. Three sizes are available.

Troublesome birds can also be fitted with 'specs', which resemble red spectacles, but are really blinkers that prevent the bird seeing directly in front of it. Fitting over the bridge of the beak, they are clipped into the nostrils. There is a deluxe version with a retainer which prevents the bird pulling them off on

wire netting. However, versions which feature a pin that passes right through the nasal septum should never be used. Both bits and specs can be obtained from game farm suppliers.

Finally, various sprays are available for discouraging feather picking. Applied to the bird at the first sign of trouble, these products work simply by making the feathers taste horrible. Some of them may also contain an antiseptic.

STOP EATING

Egg-eating must be stopped at the moment it's first detected. Over the years many remedies have been suggested but few, if any, have prove genuinely effective.

Some recommend blowing an egg and filling the empty shell with mustard, spice or some other unpalatable concoction. In my experience, though, the birds simply move on to the next, normal egg!

Others advocate offering the offenders an unlimited supply of eggs to eat (just like giving a child a free hand in a chocolate factory) and, by doing so, the birds will eventually tire of them. However this is more likely to end in disaster. Fitting specs may help, as it makes it more difficult for the hen to see the egg and, therefore, direct a blow at it. But, this too, is unlikely to stop all cases.

Removing temptation by using nest boxes with either rollaway bottoms, or false floors that deny the hens access to their eggs, may work. Nests like these can be designed and constructed using a bit of imagination. Unfortunately, though, they may not be so attractive to the hens, so they lay elsewhere and the problem continues.

So, essentially, successfully tackling egg-eating comes down to careful observation. By watching birds in the nesting areas, when egg-eating is first suspected, it's usually possible to identify those responsible and sacrifice them before the problem escalates. Taking this course of action may seem rather extreme, but a single hen can soon eat or spoil eggs well in excess of its value, especially if they are being produced for hatching.

In conclusion, not only does vice compromise the bird's welfare, it also spoils the appearance of the flock and can have financial implications. Responsible poultry keepers should want to do all they can to control it and lessen the overall impact. ❧

Keeping your birds happy is one is one of the keys to minimising the risk posed by vices, and ensuring they aren't over-crowded plays a big part in their general contentedness.

SUBSCRIBE

Hen House Maintenance

Terry Beebe explains the importance of getting to grips with hen house cleanliness

I'm always amazed by how quickly the years seem to rush by. With springtime, there always comes an upturn in peoples' interest and enthusiasm for keeping poultry. For existing keepers, this is the time of year for preparation; gardeners always take great care getting ready for the new season, and those

with chickens at home should do exactly the same.

Experienced poultry keepers spend the early spring setting up their breeding pens, getting the birds prepared and fit

for the summer's egg production and, if they're that way inclined, selecting for the forthcoming season of poultry shows and exhibitions.

I think it's important for us all to harness this first rush of enthusiasm, and use it to give everything a thorough once-over. The danger is that if you put things off now, they'll never get done at all! Good preparation is, as always, the key to success. This is also the perfect time to give your birds a full inspection.

Spick 'n' span

Although chickens are surprisingly resilient creatures, there are a number of diseases that can bring them down. The conditions in which they live play a vital part in their overall health and, therefore, their general resistance to problems. Birds which are forced to live in a house that's too small, dirty, damp and

Always use good quality litter. My advice is to go for soft-wood shavings, or something similar. Avoid that traditional favourite, straw, like the plague.

draughty won't remain healthy for very long. Respiratory problems can prove extremely debilitating for chickens, and these are commonly promoted by poor housing conditions. Stress levels among the birds are of great importance too. Hens living in overcrowded conditions, in a house that's dirty and badly maintained, are likely to be stressed and far more susceptible to problems. House

cleaning should form a regular part of your husbandry routine but, once a year, I think that a thorough blitz is required. It's important to return the unit to 'as

With spring in the air and the worst of the weather over, it's a great time to rattle through your poultry shed, cleaning and disinfecting both equipment and the main structure.

It's not a particularly pleasant job, but it's got to be done. You are responsible for the welfare of your birds.

very important too. With constant use the ground in here can become what's known as 'stale', and can pose health risks for the birds too. To avoid this happening the ideal thing is to move the run every few days on to a fresh area of ground. But, of course, most keepers don't have the luxury of this much space to play with. This is why those living in urban environments, where space is usually tight, should always think carefully about the size, type and number of birds they keep.

If overall space is limited, then it's even more important to be rigorous with your cleaning activities. As far as the run is concerned, if you really want to be thorough (and are feeling energetic!) then dig over the entire area, so that the birds are running on bare soil – they'll love it!

The bottom line is that there's simply no excuse for neglecting the environment in which your poultry live. Keeping hens in poor conditions raises serious welfare issues, and is something that nobody should knowingly allow. I realise that this may seem harsh but, in my view, if you can't spare the time to ensure the basic levels

new' condition, or as near to it as you can get, and doing this at the start of the season makes a lot of sense. Cleaning thoroughly will help make sure that you have reasonable control over the spread of any infection and disease. Poultry houses which are neglected, and allowed to become stale and infested, are simply bad news, both for you and the birds which have to live in them.

By carrying out a full clean and overhaul you'll remove ammonia smells, bugs, bacteria and dampness. The other main consideration must be the dreaded red mite, and now is the time to go to town on this destructive, resilient pest. It's very important to get on top of this

because, if you ignore it, it'll take control of your hen house, with potentially serious consequences for your birds.

Don't forget, though, that it's not only the house that needs your attention – the run area is

Compacted floor litter like this should be removed, and the floor below it thoroughly cleaned.

of good husbandry needed to support healthy chickens, then you shouldn't be owning birds in the first place.

External matters

With the worst of the winter weather behind us, now's the time to take stock of what damaged it caused over the past few months.

Check all the basics first – hinges, locks, slide bolts etc. Anything made of metal can rust and break, so it all needs to be inspected and tested. Really, you should replace anything that looks at all dodgy; especially anything relating to house security, as you never want to give the fox even a half-chance of getting inside.

Take a look at any windows there are as well, and make sure they move smoothly and fit snugly when closed. Also check the runners/edges carefully for signs of the dreaded red mite infestation. Pop holes need to be strong and secure when fastened, and must to open and close properly. Incidentally, in situations where the risk of fox attacks is very high, an additional security bolt fitted to lock the pop hole makes a great deal of sense. Anyone who has experienced the aftermath of a fox strike will appreciate

just how horrible it is. If 'Freddy' is allowed to get in among family birds, it can be a very hard job trying to explain to young children what's happened to their precious pet hens.

The roof of any poultry house needs checking for damage and wear. Most are covered with some kind of felt and the integrity of this needs to be checked carefully for signs of damage. Felt has a tendency to split, especially as it ages. It hardens, becomes brittle and is then prone to cracking. Once this has happened the breach obviously lets in water, and is also at risk of further damage from wind action too.

If you're in any doubt about the integrity of felt roofing, then it's probably best to replace the whole lot. Once it starts to deteriorate it goes downhill fast, so there's no point in taking the risk. Also bear in mind that the space between the wood of the roof and the felt covering is another favourite red mite haunt, so check carefully and treat as necessary.

Which wood?

Various types of timber are used to build poultry units today. Most are made

from a soft wood which is tongue-and-grooved and, typically, this will have been pressure-treated with some form of preservative. The idea behind this is to try and ensure a longer, overall life for the timber; hardwood is much more durable as a building material, but it's a lot more expensive too, so its use in poultry housing is limited.

Unfortunately, recent legislation has outlawed the use of one of the most traditional wood preservatives of all, creosote. This was a favourite for many years, but has now been classified as a toxic product, and withdrawn from the market. Today's preservative treatments are, in most cases, chemical-free, and many of the latest concoctions are actually water-based. However, while the removal of the active chemical ingredients makes these new-generation treatments safer to use, it also actually reduces their effectiveness. Consequently, it's now necessary to re-treat the wood much more frequently than used to be the case with creosote. Weather conditions are much more of a factor now as well; in bad years repeat applications will have to be made to keep the defences up.

Cleaning poultry units is never a pleasant job to perform; it's dirty and dusty, but essential. Dust, cobwebs, dirt and droppings all need to be removed from both the inside and outside of your house. This is a messy job so it makes sense to wear old clothes or overalls, and to use a dust-mask to avoid breathing in anything unpleasant. It's also important to adopt a methodical approach, working to a regular cleaning program and incorporating this into your general husbandry routine.

While it's necessary to give your hen house a really thorough clear-out just once a year, don't for a minute imagine that you can ignore things for the rest of the time. Ideally, it's good practice to clear out and replace the house litter on at least a weekly basis, and to treat any soiled areas with an appropriate disinfecting/freshening-type product.

Annual clean

But spring is ideal for tackling the big, annual clean-up. Your first job should be to remove any internal fittings that can be taken out of the house; nest boxes, perches, droppings boards etc. This instantly makes the job a lot easier, and improves the general interior allowing you to do a more thorough job. It also enables you to clean the removed parts separately, outside the hen house, which is much more effective too.

The one tool you'll find absolutely essential for this work is a good, old-fashioned scraper. The type you can buy from the DIY store, that's intended for removing wallpaper, will be fine as long as it has a sharpish, metal blade. These simple, hand-held tools are ideal for getting into all the nooks and crannies, and are particularly handy where space and access are limited. You can also buy larger, long-handled scrapers, which are great to use in bigger hen houses; they

Keeping your house in order is a vital aspect of good poultry husbandry, as Terry Beebe explains.

A pressure washer offers a quick and convenient way to your hen house and the removable bits from it.

save a lot of bending over!

The job of the scraper is to loosen and remove all the compacted dirt and old droppings from the interior surfaces. It's important that none of this is left behind as it can harbour pests (red and scaly leg mite) and disease.

Once the floor has been scraped clean, thoroughly sweep the whole interior, not forgetting the roof. If possible, use a vacuum cleaner – we have an old one kept solely for this purpose. I also tend to use it for the cobwebs and dust, but if

you don't have one, then a really through brush-out will have to do.

Which products?

The first point to note here is that you should never be tempted to use any sort of domestic cleaning product in your poultry house. Household bleaches and disinfectants aren't acceptable as they can produce fumes that can be toxic to livestock. So you must always specify recognised products that have been developed and licensed for

SPRING CLEANING

The aftermath of a thorough clean. Remember to allow adequate drying time – longer for an enclosed house – before allowing the birds back inside.

Stalosan F is a well-proven, highly respected powder disinfectant which not only kills bugs and their eggs, but also has the added advantage of eliminating ammonia fumes – this pollutant is one of the main causes of respiratory diseases in poultry – to leave the house smelling fresh and healthy.

Virkon S is a highly recommended liquid disinfectant for giving a really thorough clean although, in my experience, it can lead to the production of fumes which you need to watchful of. Nevertheless, it's a well-tried and proven product which can be used for all general hen house cleaning operations.

Red mite

One of the main reasons for keeping your hen house clean is to give you the upper hand in the constant battle you're likely to have with that most persistent of house-dwelling pests, red mite. You must spray and soak the interior of the shed with the appropriate treatment, and I've found Poultry Shield to be the best for this. You must make sure that all the joists, cracks and crevices are well penetrated, but this is an ongoing situation which, due to the breeding cycle of this mite, really needs to be ▶

animal/poultry use; read the instructions carefully before you start and, if you're in any doubt, ask your supplier for advice.

Nowadays there are many good cleaning and disinfecting products available on the market but, through experience, I've whittled this down to a shortlist of regulars that I'm happy to use because I know they are safe, effective and reasonably priced.

First on your list must be a really good disinfectant. Once the house has been scraped and vacuumed, I always use this in conjunction with an anti-louse/mite treatment – prevention really is better than cure! I spray both the inside and outside of my poultry houses, sometimes on a weekly basis, and especially now that we seem to be having so much mild weather.

My personal recommendation is to use a disinfectant such as Barrier V1 or Micro Shield VX. Both of these are suitable for standard or organic situations; they are ideal for sterilising the really soiled parts of the unit, as well as being excellent cleaners for the perches, drinkers, feeders and droppings boards. Both of these disinfectants are diluted with water, and can be used safely in the shed, even when the birds are in residence. This is a real advantage, especially if you are tight for space, as the birds won't need to be re-housed during the treatment/cleaning process.

Once the interior floor has been cleaned, I always use a dry powder disinfectant as an additional safeguard,

as this will ensure that the floor is left completely dry. Before you add the new bedding shavings, sprinkle a light coating of Stalosan F powder disinfectant over the entire area. This is especially important in any damp areas, as this product will dry and sterilise them.

Poultry Shield is one of the best products I know for tackling common parasites like red mite.

If you've got walkways between pens then don't forget to clear and clean them too – areas like this can harbour just as many parasites as the pen floors themselves.

perches isn't expensive; if the timber is square just round-off the edges slightly to make them less sharp for the bird's feet.

External cleaning

The ideal way to clean the outside of your poultry unit is to either use a really stiff brush dipped into a bucket of disinfectant, or to 'attack' it with a pressure washer. Using a power washer is a great idea as you can really remove stubborn dirt a lot easier than by hand. I find the machine especially useful for cleaning nest boxes as the pressure gets the edges and joints very clean. The only problem with this method is that the house is then soaked through and needs to dry out before the birds are re-introduced. Consequently, it's a good idea to try and have a reserve house on stand-by just in case the main house doesn't dry out as quickly as you are expecting.

Pay particular attention to all joints in the timber, especially around windows and doors. If there are any signs of insect infestation (red mite), then spray the whole of the shed just to make sure that the problem can be kept under control.

Once the exterior has been thoroughly cleaned, you can re-coat it as necessary. If you want to colour it then make sure the product you choose is non-toxic. Most of today's treatments are now

Check all house fixtures and fittings as part of the spring cleaning process, and replace as necessary. Never trust to luck...

water-based, and Cuprinol is possibly the favourite; it's available in a large range of colours. The final step is to check all the external fittings such as the hinges, bolts and wire mesh. There also

repeated at least once a week. This will help keep the adults under control and destroy the young as they hatch.

Nest-boxes, perches and droppings boards are very easy to clean once they've been removed and the principle is very much the same; a good scraping and a scrub down with disinfectant, then leave out to dry, spray with Poultry Shield and re-fit. If accessories are really badly soiled and won't clean very well then I'd recommend that you replace the parts with new. Buying timber for

Make sure you clean and treat all corners inside the house, especially where you see deposits like this – tell-tale signs of red mite.

needs to be a complete check on the general security of the unit, making sure that the important doors and pop holes are all safe and secure against both rodent and fox attack.

You should never return your hens for a night in a damp house. If the weather's particularly hot and dry, then a pressure-washed house may dry thoroughly in a day or two but, in most cases, it'll probably take more like a week. Once it's dry, spray with red mite treatment, sprinkle with Stalosan F, replace the floor litter then re-house the birds. ✤

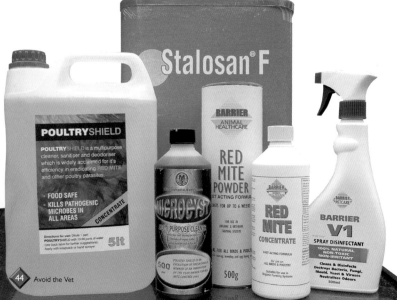

The choice about which bedding material to use in your hen house is probably one of the most important you have to make as a poultry keeper. This apparently simple decision about what to sprinkle on the floor can have all sorts of important, knock-on effects on the general welfare of your birds.

Poultry house bedding is available in various forms, with popular options including wood shavings, sawdust and straw. But there are more 'exotic' options too, such as hemp and dried grass, both of which have arrived from the equine market. The pros and cons of the most common types of bedding are explained in detail below.

Shavings

The best sort of shavings are dust-free and made from softwood. These, in my opinion, represent the best option of the lot. I've used them for years and, although I've tried other materials, I always return to shavings as the easiest and safest option. The fact that they are dust-free is one of the most important considerations; dust inside a poultry house greatly increases the risk of the birds developing respiratory problems.

However, it's vital to make sure that any shavings you buy are made from softwood, not hardwood. The latter tend to produce splinters, which are bad news. Birds jumping from perches on to a floor covered with hardwood shavings run the risk of injuring their feet. So, pick your shavings carefully, making sure they are both clean and soft.

The use of shavings also provides an easy way to keep an eye on the all-important condition of your birds' droppings; these should stand out very obviously against a background of clean shavings. Coccidiosis, for example, which is one of the more serious potential problems facing domestic poultry, will show up instantly on clean bedding, as the blood content in the droppings will be very easy to see.

Another advantage is that clean shavings will also help prevent birds' feet from becoming clogged with dirt. But the key word here is 'clean'. Shavings, of course, have a service life and degrade like anything else. Consequently, it's very important that

BETTER BEDDING

It is acceptable to used straw bedding in nest boxes, but make sure you change it regularly otherwise parasites and disease will become a problem.

course, you can buy it in bales which makes it pretty economical. Also, there are now companies chopping straw and marketing it rather like shavings; some are even scented, which is nice.

But the use of straw – a traditional favourite among poultry fanciers – does throw-up significant problems in my opinion. Primary among these is the fact that it's very effective at disguising potential dangers. It nearly always looks clean and fresh on the top, giving the false impression that all's well. However, use a fork to dig into the layer and you'll often find a very different story. Moisture and mildew tend to be held under the surface, with serious consequences. Inexperienced keepers using straw bedding can all too easily assume that everything's fine when, in reality, dampness below the surface is actively promoting potentially deadly respiratory problems for the birds. It really can be as serious as that.

The use of straw in nest boxes is quite common, and this is perfectly acceptable as long as it's changed on a regular basis without fail. It should also be powdered well to prevent insect infestation. The dreaded red mite loves a straw-based environment as it provides just about the perfect hiding place.

I've found the chopped straw, which is sold and packaged for an assortment of different types of animals, to be acceptable but once it becomes damp and dirty it can create a problem and get smelly.

Alternatives

There are quite a few bedding alternatives available nowadays, some of which have jumped into the poultry ▶

you establish a regular cleaning routine which ensures that all bedding is kept fresh. Areas of wet shavings – caused by a leaking drinker, for example – are easy to identify and remove; they appear darker in colour, and are simple to shovel away.

When you buy shavings, always opt for the large, compressed bales – typically costing about £6. Not only are these more compact, convenient to store and easier to work with, but they work out cheaper too! You can buy softwood shavings in smaller quantities if that suits you better, but you will pay a good deal more for the privilege.

Sawdust

This can be bought very cheaply and, sometimes, you may even find that lumberyards are prepared to give it away for nothing. People are attracted to it for this reason, imagining it to be a much more cost-effective alternative to shavings. However, my advice is to steer

well clear of it, whether it's free or not.

Having tried it once as bedding for my birds, I'd never use it again under any circumstances; it's dusty, clogs easily, and can often cause problems with the birds' eyes. Not only is the latter serious for the birds, but this sort of trouble can be very expensive to put right too.

Sawdust is a complete false economy in my view, although I know there are keepers who would disagree. My trial only ran for a very short period, during which my exhibition stock – which are housed permanently indoors to keep them clean – required plenty of extra cleaning to remove all the dust and particles from their plumage. It also greatly increased the amount of time I had to spend cleaning out the drinkers and feeders as they were soon contaminated too.

Straw

This is a slightly more acceptable bedding option than sawdust and, of

this type of bedding material can work out a little more expensive, I feel that it's worth the extra cost, especially if you don't keep large numbers of birds. Aubiose, unlike some of the previous types of bedding I've mentioned, will break down when raked over, and there's a good chance that if you use a good quality product it'll tend to stay fresher for longer. This obviously helps to keep the flooring fresh and dry.

One other chopped straw I've tried, is a scented one which, while it does smell great, doesn't, in my opinion, warrant its extra cost. The scent doesn't seem to last for long, and I'm sure that the chickens don't really care about what their bedding smells like! Of course, with correct maintenance and good husbandry levels, there shouldn't really be any need for anything more fancy than shavings.

Stalosan F

As regular *PP* readers will know, I strongly believe that Stalosan is possibly the best powdered disinfectant available on the market today. Its regular use will ensure protection from both insect infestation and disease. I've used this superb product on my own poultry for more than 10 years and most of my visitors are amazed by how fresh and ammonia-free my poultry sheds are inside.

There's really is a serious need to keep your poultry houses clean, especially with today's generally warmer weather and bio-security issues. I am totally convinced that the use of a specialist product such as Stalosan F provides valuable assistance with all aspects of poultry hygiene, disease prevention and general day-to-day welfare issues.

What's more, using Stalosan couldn't be simpler; all you need to do is clean out the unit, sweep and scrape the floor as required, then sprinkle the powder over the entire floor area, so that the whole area is lightly dusted. The product doesn't need to be heavily spread or worked-in in any way, but do make sure that any damp areas are covered well. I usually spread it by hand, then add the layer of clean, dry softwood shavings over the top to finish the job.

Stalosan can be used with all types of bedding but, if you do decide to use straw or hay, especially in nest boxes, make sure there's a really good covering of it underneath. If you must use straw then please ensure that you check very regularly for damp, mildew and red mite; all of these are easy to miss, but have serious consequences for your birds. Prevention is definitely always much better than cure. 🐦

market from other livestock areas. Generally, these tend to be more expensive than the options already discussed, and the fact that they aren't really produced specifically for poultry can sometimes mean their practical application is rather limited.

My testing of some of these products has thrown-up a tendency for them to become lumpy and even solid, which is a worry as it severely limits their effectiveness as a poultry bedding material. This sort of end result provides an ideal hiding place for all sorts of insect infestations, and a possible source of disease too.

I've seen newspaper and cardboard used under the bedding to help keep the house floor clean, but I don't agree with this practice either. In practical terms it creates an environment worse than that produced by a layer of straw. Acting like blotting paper, the cardboard or newspaper quickly becomes damp and smelly; it never gets a chance to dry and so can harbour all sorts of nasties. My advice is to avoid using either of these options.

There are a few well-known horse bedding products which I think are suitable for use in a poultry house. One of these is called Aubiose, which is a bio-degradable, chopped-straw product which works very well. Although

House litter must be kept clean and fresh-smelling, which means regular changing.

PREVENTIVE MEASURES

Stalosan F is an environmentally-friendly product that can make a big difference to the general welfare of your birds. Terry Beebe reports.

As poultry keepers, we live in challenging times these days. Heightened awareness of biosecurity, in the face of the threat posed by Avian Influenza, has brought all sorts of other poultry health issues into focus. This greater awareness while, on the face of it, resulting in extra work, is probably a good thing overall. Anything which encourages keepers to take more interest in the birds they keep, has got to be a plus point in the long run.

So I thought it might be useful to introduce a product that I've been using for many years, to great effect. It's called Stalosan F, and is a proven disease preventative that helps to create first class hygiene for poultry, but reduces the use of antibiotic and medication cost as well.

Even on a small scale, trying to maintain and keep conditions such that outbreaks of disease are prevented, is no easy task; the growth of pathogens under ideal conditions of moisture and temperature can occur very quickly. Constant attention is necessary to avoid this, but the use of traditional liquid-based disinfectants can actually increase the likelihood of problems by creating

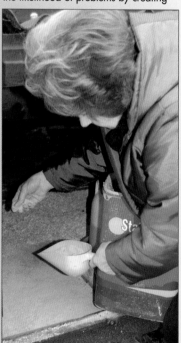

Stalosan F can be used safely with no risk to stock or keeper.

damp conditions which the bugs love. Using a powder-based alternative – such as Stalosan F – offers a major advantage in this respect.

A very significant added bonus with this product is that it's non-toxic to stock, and so can be used on and around the birds without problems. This is a great, practical advantage. Also, using the powder on wet spots created by leaks or spillage from drinkers, both saves on bedding and keeps the coop fresh and healthy.

NATURAL HYGIENE

Stalosan F is a natural product which contains no chemicals; it's completely safe to use with all types of animals and birds. What's more, there's no risk to the environment or the user. The powder is designed to be applied either before new bedding is laid down, or to the bedding directly (even when the stock is present). It's simply sprinkled wherever needed, and that's that!

As we all know, bedding should always be kept dry to avoid problems, and Stalosan F helps achieve this. It also assists with the neutralisation of ammonia, making the atmosphere inside the house better for the birds, and their keeper.

During the breeding season, this product really is a must for use in the brooders. Young chicks are extremely vulnerable to infection, so anything which helps reduce the risk is good news. I've heard stories from many keepers – both dedicated showmen and keen amateurs – about how Stalosan F has helped with the rearing and health of their birds. Some of these individuals are among the most successful and well-respected poultry exhibitors in the UK, and they swear by it!

PEST CONTROL

As well as the neutralisation of ammonia, and the drying-up of moisture in the house/pen, Stalosan F has a proven record in terms of its efficiency against dangerous bacteria such as E. coli and salmonella. It's also effective at tackling viruses like coccidian oocysts and Protozoa like trichomonas, worm

eggs and fungi. Independent veterinary tests have backed-up these performance claims, and it's also been shown that Stalosan F kills beetle and house fly eggs, both of which cause their own problems in the summer.

However, when using the product, the idea isn't to kill all the pathogens, but to reduce them to an acceptable level. In this way, while the medical challenge to the birds is reduced, their immune systems are still encouraged to function properly, which is a very important factor in terms of long-term health.

Often with poultry, it's not the initial complaint which causes the problem, but the secondary infection which follows it (E. coli and salmonella, for example). But Stalosan F offers such a wide range of control capability, that it provides an extremely valuable weapon in the poultry keepers' armoury. ❧

HYGIENIC TIPS

Follow these guidelines to help maintain hygienic conditions for your poultry.

1. Keep bedding and living conditions clean and dry.
2. Ensure the atmosphere is as free from ammonia as possible.
3. Reduce the level of 'challenge' from pathogens to your birds.
4. Reduce the risk of disease transfer by controlling rodents.
5. Use Stalosan F at a sprinkle rate of 5 per square metre, at least once a week. Pay attention to potential dampness 'hot spots' around drinkers etc.

Life-Guard™
Domestic Poultry Tonic

Maintains
Healthy Birds Naturally

Natural Animal Feeds

- Maintains healthy birds
- Optimises egg production
- Supports feathering & plumage
- Veterinary Approved
- Enriches diet

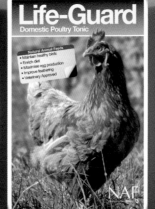

CHILLY CHOOKS!

Terry Beebe provides some practical advice about how best to help your hens through the dark and cold winter months

The cold winter weather never fails to provide a test for the poultry keeper, both in terms of personal resolve and husbandry levels. Those freezing cold early mornings are an annual chore, but we're all responsible for our birds and so must make the extra effort. As far as I'm concerned, though, I always get a terrific amount of satisfaction and pleasure from bringing my stock safely through another winter.

Fortunately, though, most of what's involved in shepherding your birds through the cold weather is based on good, old-fashioned common sense. The majority of popular chicken breeds are hardier than you might imagine so, generally, drastic measures simply aren't required. Don't imagine, for example, that you'll need to bring your prized birds into the house for extra warmth. I've seen it done, but it really isn't necessary!

The priority, as soon as cold weather strikes, is to make sure that your poultry house is providing solid, draught-free and dry accommodation. Your chickens will be perfectly happy as long as the bedding in the house doesn't get damp or dirty. But remember that good ventilation is a vital requirement too. Don't go mad trying to seal-up the house completely; a supply of fresh air must be maintained at all times to keep the birds healthy.

SHUT UP!

During the winter your birds need to be put to bed early in the evening, which inevitably means they'll be spending more time under cover than at other times of the year. Once the weather chills down, they'll need to be shut up by about 4pm, and kept inside until 7am or so the following morning. These extended hours of 'incarceration' are what make ventilation inside the poultry house such an important issue.

Fortunately, adequate ventilation is easy to organise. If you're using a properly designed hen house then allowance should already have been made and everything will be fine, assuming you haven't overcrowded it, of course. Houses with Onduline roofing can make use of the contours in the material to provide plenty of air flow, and opening windows can achieve the same effect. With the latter, however, make

A smear of Vaseline on a bird's wattles and comb works wonders as a preventative measure against frostbite.

Most chickens are actually a good deal hardier than you might imagine, assuming they are fit and healthy. Cold weather isn't necessarily a problem as long as their house is clean, dry and draught-free.

sure they are meshed and secure against wild birds and predators. I leave my poultry shed windows open throughout the year; they tilt outwards which provides air flow and weather protection at the same time.

The use of shavings inside the house (dust-free, softwood, to avoid the risk of splinters in the birds' feet) is another essential requirement, as far as I'm concerned. Another reason for opting for good quality, softwood shavings is that they will absorb moisture much more effectively than the hardwood alternative. A layer on the house floor is easy to turn and keep relatively fresh. It's also easy to burn or compost afterwards and, with the use of Stalosan F (one of my favourite products!), the reduction in ammonia and insect problems is almost guaranteed. Softwood shavings will be readily available from your local feed merchant – costing about £5.50 for a large bale – so there really is no excuse for not using them. Don't buy from pet shops unless you want to pay a lot more!

Using the more traditional straw bedding alternative is, in my view, asking for trouble. The danger is that it disguises just how damp it is by appearing fine and dry on the surface. Meanwhile, it starts to sweat which, if left, will promote the formation of fungus that can lead directly to respiratory problems for the birds. These can be serious enough to cause death, so be warned.

FOOD & DRINK
Your feeding methods need not really alter during the winter months, although you may like to consider the use of nutritional additives to give the birds an extra dietary lift. Basic vitamin supplements are cheap to buy and simple to administer. They will also help the birds to start laying again and to feather-up after the moult.

In the world of pigeon fancying, vitamins are one of the most important items on the shopping list, and this should also apply to the poultry keeper. Also, I've found that it's well worth treating chickens to a little split maize every afternoon. They love it and it's great for generating a bit of internal body heat that'll help them through the cold nights. Remember, though, only feed a small amount as a treat.

Vitamins can be added to

For the best results, use good quality, softwood shavings as a poultry house litter material. Keep it clean and fresh as the birds spend more time inside during the winter.

the feed or water; both ways are effective. If you choose to add a powder product to the feed, try mixing in a bit of cod liver oil first. Not only is this good for the birds, but it makes the individual pellets sticky too, so the vitamin powder will stick to the food rather than ending up as wasted dust in the bottom of the container. Personally, though, I prefer to use a vitamin additive in the drinking water; it's the simplest solution in my view!

BIRD TROUBLE
Virtually all chickens have some sort of wattle, comb and ear lobe – the fleshy, usually red bits attached to their heads. The nature of these means that they become vulnerable in very cold weather, and can suffer from frostbite. While this doesn't usually cause serious problems, it will turn the parts affected an unsightly black, and so is best avoided. Prevention is always better than cure and, in this case, it takes nothing more ▶

Cod liver oil is a good winter condition booster. Mixed into pelleted food, it also helps with the delivery of powdered vitamin additives.

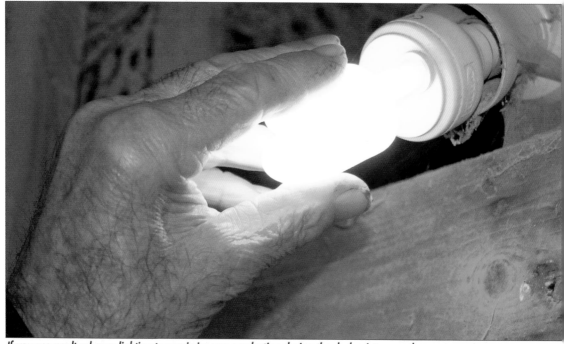

If you use poultry house lighting to maximise egg production during the dark winter months, check bulbs and wiring condition.

than a smear of Vaseline to do the trick. I always treat birds' legs in the same way (not the feathered legs, obviously!) for added protection.

We've looked at mite-related problems in recent issues, so I won't repeat myself in too much detail here. However, it's certainly worth re-emphasising a few of the core points. While the activities of red mite fall away dramatically during cold weather, they will survive in the relatively warm hen house during the winter if allowed to do so. Northern mite happily continue being a nuisance through even the coldest weather, as they live on the bird. The same applies to lice.

So my approach is always to

Check all your run fencing at this time of year, making repairs where necessary.

undertake a thorough cleaning session before the weather gets too cold. I spray and powder everything, then check every bird carefully to make doubly sure. When using anti-lice powder, don't forget to sprinkle it in the nest boxes as well, and always to carry out repeat treatments. You can't do it too often in my view; anything to keep these invasive pests at bay. Finally, when powdering a bird, it's no good simply sprinkling it over the feathers; that will limit effectiveness dramatically. For the best results you must ensure that the powder is worked right down on to the bird's skin.

When treating the hen house with anti-red mite and lice sprays – something which you should do regularly – make sure you're finished before the weather turns really cold. It's very important that

the structure is allowed to dry out completely (you don't want your birds to be cooped-up in a damp environment), and this is something which can take ages if ambient temperatures are low. Following on from this, it should also be common sense never to wet the birds themselves when the weather is cold, unless you're prepared to dry them thoroughly afterwards. I once knew an exhibitor who washed some birds before a show, and left them to dry naturally. Unfortunately, there was a frost overnight and his error turned into a fatal mistake.

Windows are a great source of ventilation, but they need to be secure against predators and wild birds.

As far as product choice is concerned, my advice is to be guided by your vet, experienced keepers or members of your local club or poultry society. There are all sorts of treatments out there which aren't licensed for use on poultry, and these should be avoided.

WHAT, NO EGGS?

Traditionally it's during the winter months that most domestic poultry keepers start to find their egg supplies getting a little thin on the ground; many birds simply stop laying altogether. Of course, commercial poultry units use timed lighting and heating all the year round, and so the shortening days and cold temperatures of winter make no difference to overall production.

The backyard keeper can take a leaf out of the industry's book, though, and install a winter lighting system to maximise egg production at this time of year. You'll need a safe, professionally-installed electrical supply of course and, as a guide, the lights should be set to come on between about 8am and 9pm. This will effectively counter the reduction in natural light, and encourage the hens to continue eating their regular amount of food. In this way, egg production should continue more or less normally, although much depends on the breed of birds you have. The results will be best from established, healthy utility breeds, or hybrids.

Finally, we should spend a few minutes considering the problems posed by rodents during the winter months. With the harvest finished and the colder

weather with us, this is the time of year that rats and mice start looking for warmer accommodation; hen houses provide the ideal winter refuge. Keeping poultry attracts rodents – we all know that – and it's a problem that everyone must be constantly aware of.

Poison and traps are the only way to combat the problem; you must never become complacent because if rodents become established they're very difficult to clear. Once again, there are plenty of product options for dealing with problem rodents. Traps come in all shapes and sizes; some which kill the occupant, others which don't (disposal is then an issue). Poisons are many and varied too and, obviously, care is needed with their handling and use. Always follow the manufacturer's instruction to the letter, and check on any likely effects there might be on children, pets and other wildlife.

One of the most effective that I've come across recently – and one that's organic and environmentally-friendly, is called Eradirat (there's also a 'mouse version' called Eradimouse). It's the only product that I know of which kills only the intended target. So, if you are concerned about the environment, or you're running an organic system, then this could be the

Re-double anti-rodent efforts. Cold weather will make a poultry shed an even more attractive winter haven for rats and mice.

poison for you.

The risk to poultry posed by badgers and foxes is a constant, year-round one but, as food becomes more scarce in the winter, your hen house can represent easy pickings. Unfortunately, there's not a lot you can do against a really determined badger. They are very strong animals that can dig and chew their way past all but the most heavily fortified defences if they want to. So all you can really do is minimise the temptation by keeping your birds securely housed at night, and hope they'll pick an easier target elsewhere.

The fox, on the other hand, is a more cunning adversary. It's a predator that's quick and quiet, and one that will kill for fun if it wants to. It's an opportunist too; they do the rounds looking for hens that haven't been shut in, or house doors that haven't been properly secured. They only need one chance. If you live in an area where foxes are common, then electrified fencing may be just about the only way of keeping them out of your poultry run.❦

I always use Stalosan F on house floors – it's great for combating dampness and ammonia levels.

NATURAL SOLUTIONS

Chris Graham investigates a natural and environmentally-friendly treatment
that might just have the power to change the way your poultry lives

"They don't make 'em like they used to!" It's a plaintive and increasingly common cry nowadays as people bemoan modern manufacturing shortfalls. So much of what we all buy just doesn't seem as good as it once was; everything from three-piece suites and electric toasters to roast chicken and Jelly Babies!

Thankfully, though, some things do last. They may drift in and out of fashion as the years pass, but they endure. A prime example of this is apple cider vinegar (ACV), which has been around for literally hundreds of years as a treatment for all sorts of ills – both in humans and animals. In fact, the use of cider vinegar as a medical treatment can be traced right back to the ancient Greeks. However, this tremendous history is actually one of the greatest stumbling blocks for ACV. The very fact that its origins are lost in the mists of time, and that many of its effects are difficult or impossible to explain in straightforward scientific terms, makes people suspicious. We live in a cynical age. Modern medicine produces explanations for almost everything, but anything which defies understanding tends to get branded 'alternative'.

OPEN-MINDED
Acupuncture, spiritual healing and reflexology are just three of the many approaches to medical problem-solving which are generally dismissed by society at large as little more than quackery. And yet, for many thousands of people these techniques have provided answers to seemingly unsolvable problems. In its way, ACV suffers in a similar manner; it's not understood and so it's frequently dismissed.

It's against this background of inherent scepticism that David Tavernor, managing director of animal health and nutrition specialists Labtec (tel: 01270 214004), has to operate. David, together with Mark Beach of M & M Natural Foods Ltd (tel: 01256 702058), are the men behind the marketing of an ACV product called Supar-Gar, which is aimed specifically at poultry. The claims they make for their product are quite amazing – there seems little that the golden elixir can't do. So it was that, with an open mind, I arranged to meet the two men to find out more.

"Apple cider vinegar is a by-product of the cider-making process, and the best comes from red-skinned apples which have a high tannin content. It takes about six to eight weeks to make and ours is sourced from the Merrydown cider makers in East Sussex.", explained Mark.

The secret of the product appears to be its ability to increase acidity levels in the gut, which aids efficient digestion and raises general resistance to all sorts of infection. "In addition to this", he continued, "ACV has a high potassium content which is also a vital factor in boosting cellular wall strength, again enhancing resistance to bacterial infection."

David added: "In Scandinavia the use of organic acids in the poultry industry is widespread because the breeders and growers there appreciate the importance of lowering pH levels in the body. The higher acid levels help control the development of pathogenic bacteria, which require a more neutral or alkaline environment to thrive.

In this country we have found that organic acids are just starting to become accepted as a legitimate and worthwhile treatment. At the practical poultry keeper's level, we are finding the same swing towards the use of apple cider vinegar. Enthusiasts are realising that it provides high levels of bacterial protection, as well as a host of other benefits.

In the past, all sorts of chemical alternatives have been used in a bid to force down pH levels – things like lactic acid. Cider vinegar does the job, but in a completely natural way. It provides all the necessary minerals and electrolytes that the bird requires in a safe, organic manner."

DIETARY SHORTCOMINGS?
My next question concerned why the average bird should require additional minerals and electrolytes at all. Surely a sensible feeding regime provides everything necessary for healthy living. Well, it appears not, according to Mark: "Often birds that are kept in a limited space, and which aren't able to 'free range' in the way they would naturally like to, show a poor balance of these important requirements. Apple cider vinegar will help put this right by enhancing feed intake and conversion."

"The product can have great benefits when administered at important times in a bird's life cycle. For the best results treatment should be provided in blocks of seven to 10 days at a time, during the most stressful periods. These include; the first three weeks of a chick's life, while birds are moulting and during the breeding period. ACV can also be used as a tonic during long spells of miserable weather. It helps in the breeding season to boost fertility levels, leading to higher numbers of stronger chicks."

By now even new enthusiasts who've only read a few issues of Practical Poultry magazine should be aware of the importance of keeping stress levels in poultry to a minimum; it's an aspect we've touched on many times already. All types of poultry are prone to stress

Supar-Gar is a 5.5% apple cider vinegar product developed specifically for use with poultry

caused by many factors including transportation, poor husbandry, bad handling and environmental changes. Birds which suffer like this can go downhill quickly, so controlling it is important. This is another of the core performance claims made for ACV. Mark says: "Apple cider vinegar can be a great de-stresser. It can be very effective to use on new birds which may have been transported a long way, or which are generally stressed because of a change in environment; hot weather can induce heat stress."

CLOUDY IS BEST

In its natural state, apple cider vinegar is crammed with a rich cocktail of vitamins, minerals, trace elements and organic acids, and it's these ingredients which are claimed to give the product its potency. However, the cider vinegar you find on the shelves of your local supermarket is likely to be a very different liquid indeed. Filtered and treated until it becomes crystal clear, the 'sanitised' version that's expensively bottled for sale as an interesting-tasting cooking ingredient, is little more than that. Most of the useful ingredients, from a medicinal point of view, have simply been processed out. While unfiltered, cloudy, ACV is widely available in mainland Europe, it's not a product that's particularly easy to find on general sale away from specialist outlets here in the UK.

Concentration is another important

Macerated garlic is added to apple cider vinegar to produce Gar-Rich – a product claimed to be particularly effective against respiratory problems as well as being an all-round poultry tonic

issue, as Mark explains, "Cider vinegar is available in different strengths, depending on how it's manufactured. Through experimentation we've found that 5.5% is just about the optimum strength for use in the poultry market." As far as dosage is concerned, it's a relatively economical product to use, especially if you adopt the 'block treatment' approach. David says: "We recommended that ACV is added to the birds' drinking water at a concentration of just 2% – equivalent to 100ml of ACV per gallon of water. This level of dilution will be sufficient to effectively reduce the pH of the water and, therefore, control the level of pathogenic bacteria in the birds' guts. It's important that this happens because, not only will the right sort of bacteria in the gut improve the food conversion ratio (FCR), it'll also enhance overall body function and development."

THE BOTTOM LINE

A five-litre bottle of ACV costs about £10 from Labtec, and should be sufficient to provide a small flock

with treatment for several months. At that price it's got to be worth a go. In practical terms, the effects it will have on your birds remains open to debate – there are so many variables involved. Many of the claims made relate to subjective issues and so may only be apparent to those who really know their birds inside out. But the one thing you can be assured of is that ACV is unlikely to cause any harm, so there really is nothing to lose. It's a natural product that's unprocessed and free from preservatives, colouring, antioxidants or any other chemical nasties. While the results of its use may be subtle to the outside observer, they could mean a lot in terms of that all-important quality of life for the birds themselves. ❧

CLAIMED ACV BENEFITS

- **Improved fertility and stronger chicks**
- **Quicker feathering and improved growth rates**
- **Increased resistance to disease**
- **Reduced stress**
- **Improved digestion rates**
- **Eggs with harder shells**
- **Tenderised and more flavoursome meat**
- **Cleaner, algae-free drinkers**

It's important to note that apple cider vinegar should not be used with galvanised drinkers, but with plastic or stainless steel ones instead.

GREAT GARLIC!

Peter Josling, director of the Garlic Centre in Battle, East Sussex, introduces an interesting new garlic-based product that could offer significant benefits for all backyard poultry.

Ancient myth has it that garlic wards off bloodsucking vampires, but initial trial results suggest that this humble spice can also be used to defend against the dreaded red mite, offer quick and efficient minor wound healing properties and help poultry to produce more and bigger eggs.

Most experienced poultry keepers know that garlic is good for hens; it's a product that's been used raw for thousands of years to help treat infection and, in particular, birds with sneezes. Many old wives' tales have grown up surrounding the overuse of, for example, garlic powder – people fear that while it may help the hen to lay bigger eggs, if it's fed for too long then the eggs will surely become tainted with the smell of garlic!

FRESH OR PROCESSED?

The most common question we get asked here at the Garlic Centre is; which is best; fresh, raw garlic, or processed garlic powder? The answer, in truth, isn't as simple as some would have you believe. We can draw a large parallel from the world of human health, where this argument has been raging for years. Yes, nationality groups like the Spanish and Greeks, who consume large amounts of fresh and cooked garlic in their diets, do have lower rates of heart disease and are less likely to suffer from various forms of cancer. But the obvious downside is that smell! This is why scientists and manufacturers around the world have always tried to get the main benefits of fresh garlic, but without the social consequences. Until recently, most had failed miserably.

The vast majority of garlic extracts are designed to begin a chemical reaction in the gut, and start producing a sulphur-based compound called Allicin. Unfortunately, stomach acid destroys an enzyme found in the garlic powder so, in reality, very little Allicin can be produced from these products. However, new technology and a simple bit of

chemistry, has led a small Sussex-based company to the invention and production of a stabilised Allicin extract from fresh garlic that doesn't make humans or animals stink of the stuff! The amount of deliverable Allicin is also much greater than could be gained from eating (or

Garlic is said to offer many health advantages; why shouldn't our chickens benefit too?

feeding) large quantities of fresh garlic. Today, the company, Allicin International Limited, is selling stabilised Allicin worldwide in a range of forms including powder, creams, capsules and sprays, aimed at both retail veterinary and medical sectors.

Behind this success is a wealth of independent research data demonstrating the product's antimicrobial and wound-healing properties. Laboratory tests by Dr Ron Cutler, at the University of East London, show that stabilised Allicin is effective against a wide range of microbes, including Eschericia coli, Listeria monocytogenes, Bordetella, Salmonella enteriditis, Clostridium perfringens and Methicillin-resistant Staphylococcus aureus. A lot of work has been completed in human subjects, showing just how effective stabilised Allicin could be as a wound-healing agent, capable of completely resolving resistant bacterial infections.

REGULAR DOSAGE

The key poultry product is called Nopex BK®, and is a liquid Allicin that can be added in small quantities to the drinking

Director of the Garlic Centre in East Sussex, Peter Josling.

water of poultry flocks. Provided it's dosed on a regular basis, the birds begin to absorb plenty of this beneficial compound, and a number of advantages are seen in a relatively short period of time! Birds are generally healthier, free from infections and initial trials have shown improvements in egg size and quality.

These first commercial trials in poultry compared two barns, each containing 10,000 birds. One group were given their usual water requirement, while the other received an additional, small daily dose of liquid-stabilised Allicin (Nopex BK®). The results revealed that the treated birds were free of E. coli infection, while control birds showed signs of infection in liver samples and in their eggs. But a more noticeable benefit became apparent only days after starting the trial. Treated birds appeared healthier and had redder combs.

Control birds had white combs, a typical symptom of red mite leading to anaemia. The result was that the treated birds had a 2% higher egg production!

Although the improved performance was not surprising, as high levels of mite infestation can cause increased stress to laying hens, reducing egg production and potentially leading to anaemia and even death, this did represent a simple, safe and natural treatment for the birds. Infection has also been implicated with elevated levels of E. coli.

A survey in 2003 indicated that 92.5% of the flocks contacted (commercial laying hens, parent stock and fancy fowl in England, Wales and Northern Ireland) had experience of red mite infestations. Red mite (Dermanyssus gallinae) is a blood-feeding parasite that attacks resting hens – mainly during the night – for a short (1-2 hours) blood meal. After feeding, the mites hide in cracks and crevices away from daylight, to await their next strike.

A follow-up, nine-month trial using the stabilised Allicin extract, compared two further groups of 10,000 hens. Detailed examination of birds in this trial revealed that mites at the nymph stage were being repelled by the taste of Allicin in the blood of treated birds. The result is that nymphs didn't feed, dropped off and eventually died. This breaks the cycle, with fewer nymphs reaching the adult stage. Consequently, the birds had more vitality and improved comb colour, plus they were laying 2-4% more eggs.

TAINTED WATER?

When talking about garlic, producers often question whether the taste of this stabilised Allicin puts birds off drinking. However at a rate of just 30ml per 10 litres of drinking water, there's no problem with water intakes. Laboratory tests also confirm no traces of Allicin in eggs or meat. Because of the benefits to

One of the most important active ingredients in fresh garlic is Allicin; thought to be a deterrent to red mite.

general well being, it seems sensible to treat birds all the way through the laying cycle, perhaps resting every fourth day. Another concentrated formulation of Nopex BK® has also provided poultry keepers with a simple non-chemical treatment for minor wounds, cuts and abrasions. This is a common problem in small poultry flocks, and can often lead to the death of birds since there are not many treatment choices that actually work. However, a simple, regular application of this stabilised Allicin compound appears to offer very fast wound-healing, and further studies on this are currently underway across Europe. ❦

Nopex BK®; doubles as a simple, non-chemical poultry treatment for minor wounds, cuts and abrasions.

WANT TO TRY IT?

Further details can be obtained from the exclusive suppliers of Nopex BK® at Mantel Farm in Sussex, by calling 01424 830357. You might also like to visit the Garlic Centre's website at: www.garlic.mistral.co.uk for more information.

Read and Feed

Chris Graham discovers the importance of feeding poultry the right food at the right time

Those of you who use computers at home or work will no doubt be familiar with the snappy and appropriate Americanism, 'garbage in, garbage out'. It refers to the fact that any computer, whatever its specification, is only as good as the data it has to work with; load it with rubbish and that's exactly what it'll produce. Well, the same idea applies to poultry as far as feeding is concerned. Chickens, ducks, geese, turkeys, quails – whatever you care to mention – are all essentially food processors. They use their feed to live healthy lives, produce often wonderful plumage and, in most cases, manufacture a regular supply of eggs.

But if you feed them the wrong sort of diet then all these benefits can begin to slide, which is disappointing for you but, more importantly, bad for the birds. Unlike wild birds which, having laid a clutch of eggs, go broody and hatch their young, most domestic hens are prevented from doing this. They are encouraged to continue laying regularly throughout the season as eggs are removed on a daily basis. While the hens are happy to oblige, they can only maintain such performance if supported by good levels of husbandry, which includes effective feeding.

So, to discover the secrets behind a good feeding regime, I went to see the experts at W & H Marriage & Sons Ltd, whose Chelmsford-based business is one of the oldest and most traditional combined flour and feed milling operations left in the country. Director Peter Marriage and salesman Paul Fields were my guides,

and they began with an explanation of the basics.

FOOD FOR THOUGHT

Poultry feed is a very general term used to describe a whole range of products covering a multitude of applications. The choices you make should be determined by the type of poultry you own, the stage of life it's at, and what you intend to do with it. The most popular types of feed these days are sold in pellet form; a simpler and more manageable alternative to the more traditional meal or mash versions.

The arrival of modern hybrid chickens – the 'laying machines' of our time – have changed feeding requirements somewhat, because these birds demand a much more precisely-balanced and nutritionally rich diet than the older, pure breeds. This means that owners will only get the best results by feeding their birds on a high quality, commercially manufactured poultry ration. 'The Darling Buds of May' approach, where the hens thrived on kitchen scraps, a handful or two of corn and not a lot else, is becoming ever more limited in its usefulness, however much it might tug at

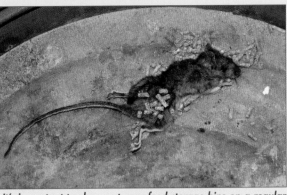

It's important to clean out your feed storage bins on a regular basis otherwise you can't be sure what you might find. They should always be rodent-proof too!

our nostalgic emotions.

To maintain adequate levels of egg production and good health, hens must be assured a good intake of food every day. This way they'll be guaranteed the protein, fats, calcium, vitamins and trace elements needed for their well-being. For this reason we'd always recommend the use of a product from an established and well-known producer. While cheap poultry feed isn't necessarily a bad thing, it may well fall short in terms of ingredient quality and mixture proportions.

If you wish to feed kitchen scraps – and by all means do so if you like (excluding meat) – then the best advice is to regard them as a treat, feeding them after the birds have eaten their pelleted ration. However, be very careful to steer clear of any leftovers containing salt; birds are sensitive to this. Also, while on the subject of what not to do, be careful with lawn cuttings – these can cause potentially serious internal blockage problems.

The danger with feeding extras over and above the normal ration is that you risk making the birds fat. Modern feed is formulated to provide a complete diet so, when it's fed in the correct quantity, all dietary requirements should be met. Much depends on the situation of course; birds that can free-range will use up more energy rushing around the place than those which are confined to a small pen. But, as a general rule, Marriage's suggest you work on the basis of feeding each bird 125g a day. They also advise that the food should be available all the time, so it can be eaten as and whenever the birds fancy it during the day.

RIGHT FEED, RIGHT RESULT!

As I mentioned earlier, an effective ▶

"They can only maintain such performance if supported by good levels of husbandry."

PELLETS OR MASH?

Mash is the traditional approach; a coarsely-ground mix of ingredients which can be fed dry or wet. Pellets are essentially the same product that's been steamed and pressed into tiny, universally-sized pieces, and pellets now outsell mash by a significant margin.

Pellets are more convenient to deal with and they flow though the feeder better, assuming they're kept dry. Another important advantage of pellets is that the birds aren't able to feed selectively – picking around and eating only what they fancy at any one time. Pelleted food ensures that the full diet is delivered with every beakful!

Mash is slightly cheaper to buy in large quantities, and is favoured by commercial concerns. It takes longer to eat, which is good for confined, bored birds that might be prone to feather-pecking, but wastage levels are inevitably higher because there's a lot more dust.

Use a vacuum cleaner to remove all dust from feed storage bins. Do this on a regular basis and your feed should remain mite-free.

It's important to store your feed somewhere that's dry, secure and out of direct sunlight.

feeding regime is one of the keys to ensuring your birds remain happy and healthy; it's a core aspect of good husbandry. Getting it wrong can introduce all sorts of problems, especially for breeding birds. Trouble with chicks can stem from a weakness with the mother bird, although lots of owners fail to make this connection. Undernourished hens are likely to lay sub-standard eggs which, in turn, will produce weak and vulnerable chicks. In such cases the young bird will often run out of steam before it's had time to start eating properly, and it'll die. So the canny keeper will bolster his breeding hens by feeding them a specially-formulated breeder pellet, containing slightly higher levels of protein and vitamins.

The important thing with newly-hatched chicks is to start them eating as quickly as possible. Mother Nature provides them with a natural reserve of food but this only lasts for a few days after hatching, by which time the young birds need to be taking solids if they are going to survive and develop properly. These solids are best provided in the form of a specially formulated and finely ground feed known as Chick Crumbs. There are different varieties available for chickens, ducks, geese, turkeys, quail and game. It's also possible to buy medicated versions – for fighting worms and conditions such as coccidiosis. However, it's important that these medicated feeds aren't fed across species, or to laying birds; they should only be consumed at the right time, by the intended poultry type.

One of the beauties of chick crumbs is that the young bird can't selectively feed (picking out only the bits they fancy at the time), so they are guaranteed to take in a well-balanced dietary combination. Size is the key to a good chick crumb. If the pieces are too large then the chicks simply won't be able to eat them. The best examples are also as dust-free as possible.

TIMING IS EVERYTHING

Chick Crumbs are usually fed for the first five or six weeks, and followed by a switch to 'growers' pellet. This carefully balanced feed is designed to take the birds through to the point of lay (POL), at about the 18-week mark. It's important not to overfeed during this period, which is why growers pellets usually have a slightly lower energy and protein content than other rations. Hens which are allowed to get fat can suffer with all sorts of nasty problems, including prolapses, when they come into lay. The next feeding stage rather depends on what

"Marriage's suggest you work on the basis of feeding each bird 125g a day."

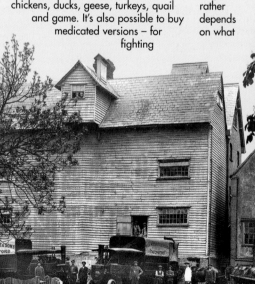

Marriage's established itself as a Chelmsford-based, family-owned, milling business in 1824, and proudly guards its independence to this day.

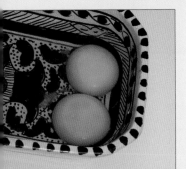

Yolk colour is affected by diet. The larger yolk here is from an egg bought at a free-range farm. The paler one came from a supermarket.

WHAT'S IN CHICKEN FEED?

	Chick crumb	Growers pellets	Layers pellets	Cockerel fatteners	Breeders pellets
Oil	3%	3%	3.5%	4.2%	5.5%
Protein	18.5%	15%	17%	16%	17%
Fibre	3%	4.7%	6.4%	3.7%	3%
Ash	5.5%	5.3%	11.4%	5.1%	12%

Common types of feed (from left to right): chick crumb, pellets and mash.

can help. The sales staff at feed producers such as Marriage's provide an obvious place to start, but you should also be able to source useful advice from the staff at your local feed barn, or from your vet.

you have in mind for your birds. If you're purely after egg production then you can switch the birds on to a traditional 'layers' pellet or mash feed. This provides a wholesome, balanced diet that'll see them happily through the rest of their lives. The choice between

mash or pellets really is a personal one (see separate panel). Mash or meal is the more traditional approach and pellets are made from a finely ground meal. Typically mash is fed to the birds dry, but it can be mixed with warm water in winter to aid food intake levels during the shorter days.

If, on the other hand, you're keeping to breed or for meat, then you really should make use of one of the specific 'breeder' or 'finisher' pellet mixes. Marriage's produce a specialised 'cockerel fattener' which is intended for use from seven weeks up until the point of slaughter. There are similar feeds available for ducks/geese and turkeys.

Of course, if you remain in any doubt about which approach is best for your birds, there are plenty of people who

SAFE STORAGE

The freshness and quality of the feed you give your birds is another important issue. You can buy the best product in the world but if you don't store it properly it can quickly become ruined. Dampness is the big enemy, as far as feed is concerned. It leads to the formation of mould and, while some moulds are harmless, others can be really dangerous. Consequently, they're best avoided altogether. Never let paper sacks get wet, or allow feed contained in plastic bags to sit in the sun (this will produce mould-promoting condensation).

Stale food is another no-no, for two basic reasons. Key ingredients such as the vitamins (particularly A and D) degrade with time, so the product loses it's effectiveness. Also, old food can suffer with mites (particularly if the weather is warm and damp), which can spoil the food and may even taint the

> *"Dampness is the big enemy, as far as feed is concerned."*

eggs. The mites live in the dusty corners at the bottom of the feed container and, in bad cases you will actually be able to see the dust 'creeping' with the naked eye!

The answer, of course, is not to let the feed hang around for much longer than about three months, and to make sure that any containers you use are completely emptied, and then vacuumed out, on a regular basis to remove all traces of mite-carrying dust.

Finally, poultry feed should always be kept in a rodent-free environment (mice and rats can carry Salmonella), so it's not a good idea to leave it in its paper sack on the floor of an outbuilding. One of the best methods is to stand the sack in a plastic dustbin (not a metal one which might promote condensation) and to store this in a dry and secure place, away from direct sunlight. ❦

HOW YELLOW?

Yolk colouring, and its relationship with food, has become an area of controversy in recent years. Fat-soluble colours consumed by the bird are what give the yolk its characteristic yellow. Hens that free-range will eat plenty of green foliage and this is what helps to make their yolks look so rich and attractive. However, birds kept more intensively, or in less rural surroundings, tend to produce eggs with a paler, more watery-coloured yolk. To counter this undesirable effect, many egg farmers add synthetic colouring agents to the feed their birds eat, which causes concern among customers who find the chemical additive idea an unpleasant worry.

This, of course, simply provides yet another benefit for home keepers, who can insulate themselves and their families from such things by buying their poultry rations with care. Quality producers use natural ingredients; Marriage's add a Maize-based product to enhance yolk colouring, and have been doing so for the past 10 years.

FEEDING KNOW-HOW

Bob Cross looks at the importance of proteins and carbohydrates

Make sure lids are tight or prevent feed getting damp from rain

As keepers of livestock we have a legal responsibility to look after our animals properly. The Welfare of Farmed Animals (England) Regulations require us to, among other things, feed a wholesome diet in sufficient quantities to maintain good health, to satisfy nutritional needs and to promote a positive state of well being.

It's in everyone's interest to get it right because the crux of the matter is that poultry simply won't prosper if you adopt a poor feeding program. A diet of grain alone just isn't good enough. Birds need a complete and balanced ration. Research over the past 50 years or so has given us a wealth of knowledge about the precise nutritional requirements for all classes of poultry stock and rearing purposes. The commercial feed mills make use of this information to produce and make available to us an excellent range of feeds. The notes that follow are intended to give an insight into poultry feeds and, perhaps even more importantly, nutritional requirements. So, the information's here on a plate for you. Make use of it!

WHAT'S IN A BAG OF FOOD?

The first point to realise is that there's a lot more to poultry feed than most people. A typical mix will contain: protein, carbohydrates, fats, oils, fibre, vitamins, minerals and water. The proportions and exact ingredients, of course, vary from product to product. Some ingredients are rich in protein while others are regarded as carbohydrate foods. However, most

	Crude	Argenine	Glycine	Histadine	Leucine	Iso-leucine	Lysine	Methionine	Phenylaline	Threonine	Tryptophan	Valine	protein
PROTEINS %													
Fish meal (white)	65.5	42.6	56.4	12.1	44.6	26.2	49.0	18.8	19.7	25.6	5.9		30.2
Full-fat soya	37.9	37.6	19.4	11.6	36.1	20.2	29.9	6.4	24.7	18.9	5.1		21
Pea meal	27.1	20.6	11	6.5	18.6	18.1	20.9	4.9	11.7	10.6	2.2		11.4
Bean meal	22	17.6	10	5.1	16.6	8.9	14.1	1.7	9.2	8.7	2		10.3
Maize gluten meal	40.4	13	15.2	8.4	62.8	17.3	7.1	9.6	28.4	15.2	2.7		21.8
Maize germ meal	19.2	9.7	6.9	3.8	10.4	3.6	6.7	2.8	5.4	4.7	2.1		6.5
Sunflower	32.1	26.5	18	7.3	19.5	11.8	10.4	4.1	14.6	11.6	4.1		14.5
Grass meal	17.8	7.5	7.4	2.7	12.1	5.6	7.1	3.1	7.1	6.2	3.1		7
Wheatfeed	14.9	10.4	7.9	3.8	8.7	4.5	5.9	2.4	5.8	4.6	2		6.6
ENERGY													
Wheat	10.4	5.4	3.8	2.7	7.2	4.1	3.8	1.8	5.2	3.2	1		4.4
Barley	11.3	6.8	4.8	2.4	7.8	4.2	4.2	2.1	5.3	4.2	1.5		5.6
Oats	10	8	5.5	2.6	8.3	4.4	4.7	1.7	5.6	4	11.2		5.6
Maize	8.2	4.3	3.2	2.6	10.6	3.2	2.7	1.8	4.2	3.2	0.5		4

Table 1: A range of feedstuffs and their crude protein and amino acid assays

foods contain a mix of both to best meet a bird's dietry requirments.

Poultry feeds are made by milling and mixing a blend of cereals and other ingredients, the mix being formulated to produce a complete and balanced diet. They are formulated to a set specification, although the recipe varies as the availability or price of ingredients makes them more or less attractive. In general terms, though, most poultry diets consist of 65-70% cereals. But, to gain a proper understanding of which ingredients are used, and why, it makes sense to look in more detail at the constituent parts, and the roles they play.

BODY FOOD

Proteins are complex substances made up of amino acids; which are either 'essential' or 'non-essential'. Essential amino acids must be provided continually in the diet in the correct amounts. Not all proteins are the same, nor is the animal to which it is going to be fed. Different stock types require different amounts of protein and, thus, different mixes of amino acids. For example, a bird in lay needs more protein than one that is growing, and also higher levels of amino acids. Similarly, chicks need a more concentrated feed because their overall

intake is low. Protein is required by the bird to maintain its body – replacing cells as they wear out and repairing damaged tissue. Any protein that maybe left over after this work has been done, is used to grow feathers, muscle and/or to produce eggs. Excess protein is broken down and some is used for energy (rather inefficiently), while the rest is excreted with the faeces.

Foods rich in protein include fishmeal, soya-beans, peas and field beans, maize gluten meal, wheatfeed etc. Of these, fishmeal is an animal protein – the rest are of vegetable origin. Animal protein has a higher biological value than the vegetable-derived alternative, and the relative values of these feedstuffs can be seen in the tables.

MEAL RESTRICTIONS

In the past, both meat and bone meal, together with plain meat meal – by-products of the meat industry – have been used in feed but, as a result of BSE, these products have been outlawed and are no longer available. They were an excellent source of essential amino acids and vitamin B12, and they also helped with overall palatability of the feed.

The essential amino acids are: Arginine, Glycine, Histidine, Leucine, Isoleucine,

Tryptophan, Threeonine, Lysine, Methionine, Phenylalanine and Valine. Synthetic amino acids are available to cover shortfalls in the formulation. It's important not only to ensure that all are there, but the correct ratio is vital too. A bird is incapable of storing amino acids which means that, to ensure good health, its total requirement must be available all in one go, and on a daily basis.

If you look at the label attached to the top of a bag of feed, you'll find a reference to protein percentage. In fact, this actually refers to what's known as crude protein, and so not all of it exists in a form that poultry can use. Hopefully, though, the miller will have taken this into account when formulating the ration and selecting the source. The methionine content will also be stated and maybe other amino acids. You should compare these values with those included in the table here, to see if the feed you're looking at contains enough.

Diluting a bird's diet with wheat will reduce the levels of amino acids and, while this may have little effect if the bird has a large appetite, smaller birds can suffer a reduction in egg size. It's also been suggested that low amino acid levels (together with several other factors), are a possible contributory factor towards feather pecking.

If you study Table 2, you'll see that the nutritional requirements of a chicken changes as the bird develops. Not only does it require different amounts of protein at different stages of its life, but the amino acid content and ratios change as well. A chick, which is growing feathers, will need sulphur in its diet, and particularly good souces of this are the sulphur-bearing amino acids, such as methionine. This, then, is especially in demand at this time. As the bird grows its daily food intake increases and the nutrient density can be reduced somewhat. With modern hybrid layer types the rearing period is only about 18 weeks and body weights are difficult to attain in such a short time. As a consequence, modern chick starter and grower rations need to be potent and may exceed the requirements of traditional poultry breeds.

So far we have looked at protein and the foods we use to supply this constituent. But remember that proteins can also provide energy. Some protein foods, especially fish meal, maize gluten meal and soya bean meal, are a good source of essential fatty acids.

ENERGY FOODS

Carbohydrates, fats and oils are the main providers of energy in poultry food. Energy is needed to power the muscles and, as a by-product of digestion, heat is generated which helps keep the bird warm.

Energy is found in all the cereal grains of which the most widely used in this country is wheat. It's also found in greater concentrations in fats and oils; these contain about two-and-a-quater times the amount found in cereals. It's usually expressed as M.E. (Metabolisable Energy), this being the amount that the bird can use – ie. the digestible energy minus the energy that passes out in the faeces. Energy is measured in Mega-Joules/Kilogram (MJ/Kg) or, as it used to be, in Kilo-calories/Kilogram (Kcals/Kg). These days, with dieting and calorie-counting being so popular, the latter units are probably easier to understand for most people.

Filling an 'on-demand' barrel feeder

Examples of the cereals used as energy foods in poultry feed are; wheat, barley, oats and maize. Currently in the UK, wheat is the most commonly used cereal. It has a widely varying composition and some of the Canadian bread-type wheats have a high (14%) protein content, containing gluten. This is a gluey substance which causes a dough in the crop and gut, leading to digestive problems. Other wheat varieties grown in this country are more suitable, with a protein level of around 10% and a relatively high energy value.

NAKED CEREALS!

Barley is less popular than wheat becuase it has a husk attached which increases the fibre content. 'Naked' varieties have been developed with energy levels almost equal to those of wheat, but the protein content is not so digestible which makes them less attractive. By adding enzymes to the feed, digestibility can be improved making them more usable.

Oats are rarely used in great quantities as they contain too much fibre. Once

again, naked varieties have been bred and these are of greater value. Traditional oats can be clipped to remove the glume (husk) at either end, thus reducing the fibre content. However, whatever is done, oats remain relatively high in indigestible organic matter. They are sometimes used in growers' rations because there is some evidence suggesting that they seem to promote good feathering.

Maize is useful. It has very little indigestible organic matter and a high starch content. What's more, for a cereal it has a high oil content which gives it a very high M.E. value. Yellow maize provides a natural pigment for yolk colour, and the yellow in the beaks, legs and skin of certain breeds of chicken. ❧

DIETS

Nutrient	Chick St	Grower	Layer
Cr. protein %	20%	19%	17.5%
Energy	12.3 MJ/kg or 2,940 kcals/kg	11.7 MJ/kg or 2,796 kcals/kg	11.8 MJ/kg or 2,820 kcals/kg
Dig. lysine	1.02	0.84	0.83
Dig. methiorine	0.48	0.37	0.41
Tryptophan	0.22	0.20	0.21
Threonine	0.75	0.67	0.63
Calcium	1.00	1.00	4.10
Avail. phosp.	0.45	0.43	0.35
Sodium	0.16	0.16	0.18
Chloride	0.25	0.24	0.24
Lin. acid	1.40	1.20	2.00

Table 2: The dietary requirements of a modern brown hybrid chicken at various stages of development.

FEEDING KNOW-HOW

Bob Cross explains why fats, oils, vitamins and minerals are so important

Fats and oils are energy foods in a very concentrated form, nowadays originating from vegetable sources. The energy content is in excess of 9200kcals/kg (38.57MJ/kg). They are used where very high energy rations are required and it's difficult to attain such levels using other food ingredients, eg Broiler finisher diets. They may also be used for cost reasons, allowing the use of a cheaper, lower-energy food to replace one that was rich in energy.

Where oils are used they reduce dust and improve palatability, which in turn improves food intake and growth rates. On the downside, though, oils are somewhat unstable and tend to go rancid. To a certain extent this can be prevented by the use of antioxidants, which is an important factor because oxidation of the oils destroys some of the vitamin content, and deficiency signs may be seen. Oils are found, to a greater or lesser extent, in all feed ingredients (even dried potato contains some, albeit only 0.2%). Richer sources include maize germ meal and full fat soya and, while these are essentially used for their protein content, they also have a significant energy content. To boost the energy level pure oils are used, these are either added to the ration as it is mixed or sprayed on after pelleting.

Boiled vegetables can not replace your regular feed but are a welcome supplement for your birds

VITAMINS AND MINERALS

Vitamins are needed in small amounts to maintain health and body function. They are found in most feed ingredients, and where enough cannot be supplied in this way, they can be added from synthetic sources. Shortages of vitamins will lead to deficiency diseases. While it is unlikely that you will see severe deficiency symptoms, it is possible that bird performance will not reach its full potential. Grass meal is used as a rich source of vitamin A and K, while biotin yeasts and cereals contribute other B-group vitamins. Wheatfeed is mentioned here as it's found in many rations. It actually makes a bigger contribution towards vitamins than wheat, and it's other useful property is that it 'opens up' a diet to prevent it becoming doughy and indigestible. Minor excesses of vitamins are unlikely to harm the bird and should be regarded as a bonus. Vitamins do not last forever, they are destroyed by heat, sunlight, oxidation and time. Somewhere on the bag of feed you'll find a 'Best before' date, after which many of the vitamins will be depleted and possibly some of the oils will have gone rancid. The lessons to be learnt here are; do not buy food that is out of date or is nearly so; only buy what you can use before it is out of date and, having bought it, store it in a cool dry place to maintain it in good condition. Minerals are required for similar reasons but also for bone and eggshell formation. Calcium and phosphorus are required in the greatest quantities and in the correct ratio. The relatively high levels of calcium in layers diets is provided by limestone flour (35% calcium) but this contains no phosphorus. Phosphorus must come from elsewhere such as di-calcium phosphate Cereals also contain phosphorus but in a form which the fowl cannot use, so enzymes are now added to help with this. In terms of calcium, an eggshell contains about 2g. The hen is only 50% efficient at absorbing it so to produce a shell it must eat 4g. If it's laying at 85% the daily requirement is 3.4g which, over a typical year, equates to about 600g of calcium or 3,250g of limestone. However, it should be noted that shortages of calcium are unlikely to be responsible for poor shell.

FIBRE

In theory, fibre is another source of carbohydrate energy. It would normally be broken down by bacteria in the gut, however, very little is derived from this source because the food passes through too quickly for much microbial action. Foods with a high fibre content have low energy values and vice versa. But despite it's virtual indigestibility, fibre does have a purpose. Its bulky nature helps the passage of food through the gut even though, to most poultry, it does not contribute anything nutritionally.

MOISTURE

The moisture content of newly harvested cereals is around 15-20%, depending on the weather conditions when they were gathered. This will fall to 12-13% over storage periods of up to a year, or more rapidly if the product is artificially dried. When the grains are milled, heat is generated which also has a desiccating effect, leading to the loss of a further 2% or so of moisture content. Of course, lost moisture can be replaced simply by adding water during the process. If the moisture content of feed is too high there is a risk of moulds developing. Storage can play a big part in preventing this. If temperatures are kept below 20° all well and good, although this can be difficult at a practical level during the summer months when ambient temperatures are well above this. Organic acids, such as proprionic acid, can be used to help prevent mould growth.

	Energy MJ/Kg	Energy KCals/kg	Fibre	Ether extract (Fat)	Ash (Minerals)
PROTEINS %					
Fish meat (white)	11.46	2,740	0.5	4.2	21.5
Full-fat soya	14.69	3,510	5.0	17.4	4.9
Pea meal	11.05	2,640	5.9	1.7	2.8
Bean meal	10.0	2,390	5.0	1.2	4.3
Maize gluten meal	10.29	2,460	3.0	4.7	4.1
Maize germ meal	9.75	2,330	9.0	11.5	2.5
Sunflower	8.83	2,110	6.0	2.7	6.4
Grass meal	5.82	1,390	10.0	3.7	7.7
Wheatfeed	9.75	2,330	7.5	3.9	4.2
ENERGY					
Wheat	12.18	2,910	9.0	1.4	1.8
Barley	11.13	2,660	9.0	1.5	2.7
Oats	11.05	2,640	13.0	4.9	2.7
Maize	13.22	3,160	12.0	3.2	1.2
Veg oil	-	-	-	-	-

Table 3: Energy content for a range of feedstuffs and their relationship with fibre

ADDITIVES

Several things may be added to feed, they include enzymes, anti-coccidial supplements, pigments, amino acids, vitamins and minerals etc.

Enzymes are included to make the digestion of certain parts of the diet more efficient. Examples include Natuphos and Roxazyme (trade names). Anti-coccidial supplements are added to Starter and as an aid in the prevention of coccidiosis. They do not guarantee to stop an outbreak of the disease but, when used in conjunction with good husbandry, they go a long way to doing so. A typical example of an ACS drug is Avatec (trade name).

Where these drugs have been included they must be withdrawn, as per the recommendations on the bag, before the meat or eggs from the birds can be sold for eating. Pigments are used in layer diets to ensure a good yolk colour. Birds on range should not need additional pigments, however, there are times during the hot summer months when the pasture has turned straw-like and the pigment is not present. Similar conditions may exist at other times of the year when vegetation is growing very slowly or not at all. The diet may contain adequate natural pigments as found in grass meal and yellow maize, but if for some reason these products are not used in the feed, colorants such as Citranaxanthin, Zeaxanthin and lutein are available. Additional amino acids may be required where the contribution from the feed ingredients is insufficient, in which case one or more will be added to correct it. Vitamin and mineral supplements are often added to ensure that these vital ingredients are present in sufficient quantities, this is especially important in diets for breeding stock and for those birds kept inside.

Rations produced to Organic standards will not contain additives or animal proteins and other conventional diets are available without them. No standard feeds contain antibiotics – these require a veterinary prescription for their inclusion and would only be given where there was a specific need. Again, if antibiotics have been used, a withdrawal period must be observed before produce is sold for consumption.

When formulating a ration there are certain constraints involved. There are maximum inclusion levels for any one ingredient. In some cases this can be because of the risk of taints, while in others it may cause palatability and or digestive problems. For a layers diet a maximum of 10% fish meal and probably no more than 50% wheat would be advisable.

WHAT FOOD DOES A CHICKEN NEED?

First of all it's important to feed the correct food at the right time – chick starter to chicks, grower to growing stock, laying food to layers etc. Also, food should not be given to species it was not intended for.

In terms of quantity and quality, a bird's daily food requirement will depend on a number of factors; its age, size, rate of lay etc. A modern hybrid laying bird kept in the warm (20°C on average) requires about 19.5g of protein and around 330-340kcals of energy each day while laying at its maximum. This is needed for egg production and to maintain growth (poultry continue to grow all through their laying year, albeit at a slower rate than in their early life).

Should the temperature drop the bird will require more energy, so it will eat more, taking in both energy and protein, even though most of the latter will be wasted. By studying the figures in Table 4 it can be calculated that on a 17.5% protein, 2,820kcal diet, a hen eating 120g of food a day will fulfil its requirement in terms of energy and protein. If it eats less, or if the diet is not up to the above

Mixed grit and Oyster shell - helps with digestion and shell formation

specification, then it will not take in sufficient nutrients and performance will suffer.

The traditional larger fowl require similar amounts because, although they are much larger, they are less productive. Their intake will be much higher so they can be fed a lower density ration, or the bagged feed can be diluted with a cereal such as wheat or oats. Bantams and miniatures are not so demanding in their maintenance or production requirements, so they too can be fed these diets.

Take a look at the ticket attached to the top of the bag, do not be overly concerned if the specification is not quite up to the standards described above – some diets are designed to be less forcing.

I hope these notes have helped explain some of the mysteries from within the bag. And finally, dictionaries define 'Chicken feed' as being something of trivial value and of poor and trifling stuff. Nowadays nothing could be further from the truth! ❦

	Vit. A (IU/g)	Vit. E (IU/g)	Choline (mg/kg)	Nicotinic Acid (mg/kg)	Riboflavin (mg/kg)	Vit. B12 (ug/kg)	Biotin (mg/kg)	Folic Acid (mg/kg)	Calcium (g/kg)	Phosphorous (g/kg)	Manganese (mg/kg)
PROTEINS %											
Fish meat (white)	-	21	3,100	62	6.6	100	0.26	0.2	66	35	7.0
Full-fat soya	-	1.0	2,840	32	4.0	-	0.32	3.6	2.2	3.0	31
Pea meal	0.5	3.0	2,210	24	1.8	-	0.11	0.3	0.7	4.0	14
Bean meal	-	1.0	1,110	29	3.1	-	0.11	1.3	1.3	2.0	16
Maize gluten meal	26.6	24	1,660	44	1.6	-	0.15	0.2	0.4	2.0	8.0
Maize germ meal	-	87	1,550	31	3.3	-	3.0	0.2	0.7	1.0	6.0
Sunflower	-	6.0	1,200	250	4.0	-	-	-	2.0	2.0	23
Grass meal	327.5	150	890	74	15.5	-	0.17	-	12	8.0	53
Wheatfeed	0.5	20	1,110	100	2.2	-	0.37	1.1	0.7	4.0	84
ENERGY											
Wheat	0.4	16	730	58	1.1	-	0.11	0.4	0.4	1.0	21
Barley	0.7	5.0	1,110	52	1.3	3.3	0.15	0.6	0.4	2.0	12
Oats	0.6	5.0	930	16	1.1	3.3	0.11	0.5	1.0	1.0	44
Maize	5.0	4.0	1,110	21	1.1	0.2	0.05	0.3	0.1	1.0	3.0

Table 4: Vitamin/mineral content of a range of feedstuffs

FEEDING KNOW-HOW

Bob Cross shares his views on the feeding of scraps

The modern hybrid laying hen is a small creature with an enormously high output in terms of egg production. The nutritional demands for sustenance and egg-making, coupled with a small appetite, mean that there is little scope for substituting part of the ration with home-produced feed. However, if the birds being kept are of traditional type, with a larger appetite and/or you are prepared to accept less from them, then it's possible to source feed from elsewhere.

Firstly, let's consider what is usually referred to as 'household scraps'. This could include plate scrapings, vegetable peelings and leaves, stale bread etc. Here we have a problem; anything that contains, or is contaminated with,

"Bread is possibly the best of the kitchen waste products."

animal matter (meat or fish of any kind, fat or gravy etc.), comes under the Swill Feeding Regulations. Swill feeding used to require a licence – issued by the local authority – but, in the wake of the last Foot and Mouth epidemic, itself the result of swill feeding, this approach is no longer allowed at all.

GREENS ARE FINE
However, vegetable waste can still be used. Cabbages and cauliflower, or just their outer leaves, can be either finely chopped and fed in a trough or hung in a net. While birds with access to grass will

probably ignore them, those not so lucky and kept inside will eat them once they realise what they are.

Root vegetables and their peelings are also suitable as poultry feed. They are

Cabbage suspended above the floor in a poultry house

or, if used whole, they can be hung up in a basket or against the house wall. Offered to the birds in this way gives them something to peck at. The thing to avoid, though, is throwing them down on to the litter.

Bread is possibly the best of the kitchen waste products; it can either be fed as it is, or soaked immediately beforehand. Soaked bread is a very palatable food for poultry, and will be eaten almost as fast as it can be distributed. It can be

Bread – hens love it and will eat it as quickly as you can put it out

best cooked first, then mixed with the compound meal or fed separately in a trough. Some, such as carrots, can be fed raw. In this case they may be grated

A range of acceptable and unacceptable raw and cooked scraps. The two marked with an 'X' contain meat and so are not acceptable as poultry feed

trough-fed inside, or spread on an uncontaminated grassy area outside.

What else is available? For those with time to spare, the hedgerows in the autumn contain hips and haws along with an array of berries; most of these if eaten by wild birds are safe to feed to poultry. These are not worth storing, but they remain on the plants for some time. For intensively-housed birds, sprouted grain used to be a popular food especially in the winter; oats are probably the first choice but barley or wheat are also suitable.

To sprout, grain is laid on a tray after soaking for 24 hours, and then kept moist at a temperature of 15°C to grow. When the

Sprouting cereals just beginning to shoot. Feed these when the sprouts are about two inches long

sprouts are 2 inches long they are fed.

WHAT'S THE POINT?
It's difficult to put a precise nutritional value on these alternative feeds. Cabbages will make a contribution to the vitamin requirements and may well contain small amounts of enzymes that aid a bird's digestion.

Potatoes are mostly water but they're also a source of energy and, while bread is certainly an energy food, it also contains about 10% protein. The hips, haws and berries will provide vitamins and energy, and I'm sure that poultry benefit from their five portions of fruit and or vegetables every day just as much as we do!

"It's difficult to put a precise nutritional value on these alternative feeds."

As to how much of the diet can be substituted, I would advise offering normal compound ration ad lib and the home-procured as a bonus, allowing the birds to adjust intakes according to their own needs.

Finally is it all worth it? If the object of the exercise is to save money then the answer is probably no. What you might save on feed bills could well be spent on extra electricity for cooking. Then, if you factor-in time and effort, the savings certainly won't stand scrutiny. The practice of feeding in this way was probably perfected during the Second World War, when it arose simply because other products were not available. Nowadays we live in times of plenty, in fact too much. I try to avoid waste and to recycle where possible, so to me this is justification enough. ❧

GRAINS OF TRUTH

Mike Hatcher extols the virtues of using good, old-fashioned grain as a dietary supplement for your poultry.

Grain is the main component of all the poultry mashes, pellets or crumbs we feed to our birds, but it's also a useful feed on its own – especially if you have free-range birds, or if maximum egg production or quick growth aren't your main priorities.

Before the advent of scientifically-designed formula rations, the feed for birds was much simpler, and had very few components. Take, for instance, the feed used for fattening the Surrey fowl. This consisted of just three main ingredients; good quality ground oats, fat trimmed from meat and skimmed milk – note the stipulated high quality of the oats. This is a grain which must always be of a good quality to avoid it having too high a fibre content.

USEFUL GRAINS

By far the most widely-used of all cereals in 'straight-grain' feeding is wheat. It's readily available as a home-grown grain and, assuming it's round and not pinched, should have a good feed value. This applies to all grains, although it's maybe not always as obvious with the others. Grain can have a high protein content too. Wheat, in common with other grains, typically contains around 10% protein. It is, however, much lower in fibre, at about 3%. This is why, when used as a ration, its by-products from the milling world (such as bran) are introduced to bulk-up the fibre.

My favourite grain is oats which, with its high fibre content of typically around 10%, does keep the digestive organs working. Most people, if buying oats on their own from a feed store, will choose the crushed variety. However, a man who worked at our local feed store, where they produce much of the country's crushed and bruised oats, certainly used to recommend the latter. Oats are generally less palatable than wheat, but are higher in a number of vitamins.

Barley is found in mixed grains, and a number of waterfowl breeders feed it in quite high quantities. The grains are similar in shape to oats, but have a more yellow colour, although not as pronounced as the colour of maize. Its fibre content is between that of oats and wheat, and it shares the same type of palatability as oats.

Maize is usually imported, and most people use the cut version for feeding. When I was over in the USA I found many poultry keepers feeding whole maize, and even saw bantam ducks eating it in that form. It's felt that when the grain is cut, the gluten is lost and this is the part of the grain which contains the most protein.

Maize is highly palatable and you will see birds pick it out from among the other grains. Our American friends use it almost to the exclusion of other cereals as a winter feed in the Northern States; it's very useful in combating the cold conditions. But we don't use too high a proportion in our rations as it can produce fat, which is not healthy especially in laying fowls.

Meal or pellets are usually offered in troughs or hoppers and so all the bird has to do is stand and eat. Birds which are kept on intensive or semi-intensive conditions, can be given grain as a supplementary 'scratch feed', which has a twofold purpose. First, it keeps the birds active as they scratch to find it among the litter. What's more, the knock-on benefit is that this process helps prevent the litter from compacting, which means it absorbs the droppings more easily. If your birds are free-range, a feed of grain in the evening will help encourage them home, and will also mean they go to roost with full crops. However, I would add that if you have a decent lawn surface, it's probably not the best idea to feed on that as, unless your grain is cleaned, it may contain some weed seeds. Also, of course, the birds' scratching action can destroy the grass.

WHERE TO BUY?

If you live somewhere rural, I would always recommend getting to know your local farmer, especially if he grows his own grain. If you have the facilities for storing it in any quantity, when he empties his stores the last ton or so, which doesn't go on to the lorry, can often be bought at a decent rate. You know, the middleman is the one who makes the profit, so get in there first!

Alternatively, if you go to a feed store, look around at the prices. Bags often vary between 20kg and 25kg in weight, and some stores do special offers at certain times. Also, if you're on good terms with your merchant, broken bags can be bought at lower prices. They are inconvenient to the seller, and every time they have to move them more spills out on to the floor. They usually have rolls of sticky tape to cover the holes, so it doesn't need to go all over your car's boot. Another advantage of buying grain is that it doesn't go out of date like feed compounds. However, I wouldn't recommended feeding grain straight from the field, as the birds don't like it.

So, to sum up, good grain is a valuable feed source. But always be on the lookout for any which is mouldy, or has signs of mite, and don't feed it to your birds. Mites can be found in the last grains in a bin, with the most obvious signs being that the grains are stuck together. In these days of good biosecurity, it should come from a source under cover, shielded from wild bird or rodent contamination.

One species which can survive fairly well on a grain diet is geese, when they are out of production, but they must also have access to grass or fresh greens. If you have pure breeds, and you want to get a good strong, healthy frame, then a high percentage grain diet will help. An old friend of mine says that you can rear healthy birds on grit, grain and grass. Finally, if you feed grain you'll need to make sure that you have plenty of insoluble grit available to your birds, so that their gizzards can do an efficient grinding job. ❦

Popular grains (from left to right); wheat, barley and oats.

MARRIAGE'S

Quality

TRADITIONAL

Rearer, Grower and Breeder Diets for Poultry

CHICK CRUMBS AND ACS

Oil 3%
Protein 18.5%
Fibre 3%
Ash 5.5%

*Day old to 5 weeks
100 birds eat
approximately 150kgs*

TYPICAL ANALYSIS

POULTRY GROWERS PELLETS/MASH

Oil 3%
Protein 15%
Fibre 4.7%
Ash 5.3%

*Pullets 5 weeks to 18 weeks
100 birds eat
approximately 760kgs*

TYPICAL ANALYSIS

COCKEREL FATTENERS PELLETS

Oil 4.2%
Protein 16%
Fibre 3.7%
Ash 5.1%

*7 weeks to kill
100 birds eat
approximately 400kgs*

TYPICAL ANALYSIS

POULTRY BREEDERS PELLETS

Oil 5.5%
Protein 17%
Fibre 3%
Ash 12%

All breeding birds

TYPICAL ANALYSIS

Please contact the sales office on
01245 612000

Visit our Websites on
www.marriagefeeds.co.uk
www.countryclick.co.uk

W. & H. Marriage & Sons Ltd.,
Chelmer Mills, New Street,
Chelmsford, Essex CM1 1PN.

The complete range of high performance quality traditional feeds

FOOD ADDITIVES

Lindsay Sissons, gets stuck into the additives issue, with a look at what's available and why your birds may or may not need it.

The range of products sold for inclusion in either poultry food or drinking water is enormous, as is the range of benefits that are meant to follow. I'm firmly of the belief that 'if you haven't tried it, don't knock it', so most of what's included here is based on research, rather than personal experience. Many keepers swear that their birds' good health, top condition and high fertility rates are achieved solely thanks to the carefully selected extras that are added to the standard diet. But then there are others who swear that all supplements are a waste of time and money!

What's certain is that it's impossible to detail the pros and cons of every supplement currently available – there are simply too many. So what I'll do here is just lift the lid on a few of the reasons why some may or may not work, when they should be used and what, if anything, we can expect from them.

There are several broad categories of additive – vitamins and minerals, non-veterinary supplements (given for health reasons), veterinary additives (also given for health reasons) and miscellaneous supplements that offer wide-ranging actions.

VITAMIN & MINERAL SUPPLEMENTS

There are literally hundreds of these available for use by the poultry keeper. Some are aimed at specific problems, such as poor eggshell quality, slow moult, the treatment of stress etc. Others are designed for use on individual species, such as game birds and turkeys. Still more have been developed for helping to prevent, or treat, health problems. These can include 'fatty liver', for birds on a high fat or oil diet, bone growth disorders in fast-growing birds and Encephalomalacia (Crazy Chick Disease), to name a few.

The vitamin and mineral requirements of most breeds of poultry at various stages of life have been researched and calculated by several organisations. Feed companies use these figures to produce a balanced diet that will give the birds optimal dosages in a form that they can best utilise (refer to the table on page 74). If the food offered is fed correctly, and the birds eat the normal amount expected for that species, then it can be assumed that the correct levels of vitamins and minerals will be taken in.

However, trouble can arise if appetite becomes depressed, if there are problems with the gut (causing poor digestion and/or absorption), or if some birds in the group are not being allowed to feed properly. Also, trouble will strike if insufficient food is provided in the first place, or if the feed is unpalatable. The latter can occur if the feed is past its 'use by' date, which can also mean that some of the vitamins will start to deteriorate.

Generally speaking, feed manufacturers put higher than recommended levels of nutrients into their products to help ensure that each bird will get enough, and to allow for vitamin loss during processing and storage. It's vital to make sure that the correct feed is given to the right age of birds. For example, breeding stock will need breeders pellets to make sure that the chick in the egg has ample vitamins

> *"Trouble can arise if appetite becomes depressed, if there are problems with the gut."*

Inspect your birds regularly for sig of trouble. Vitamin B deficiency co show in a matter of day

and minerals from the yolk.

For those keepers who don't use a branded poultry feed, the trick is to maintain variety. A balanced diet can be achieved by feeding, or allowing access to, a large variety of plant material, kitchen trimmings, soil and insects. With plants, it's advisable to feed a choice of colours to get the full range of vitamins and minerals – though not beetroot or maize if you're feeding white birds to show! Free range birds will naturally select a range of different plant species in certain proportions – watching these can help balance the selection for feeding birds kept indoors.

Knowing the vitamin and mineral status of a flock of birds can be difficult, but deficiency is often suspected by keepers if problems start to arise. Many people blame the feed for fertility shortfalls, hatchability, poor growth, chick death, slow moult and poor performance (whether that be egg production or meat production). This reason for a bird's problems is second only to the weather!

However, each vitamin and mineral is responsible for many different actions in the body so, unless signs are marked, it can be difficult to ascertain whether a specific vitamin or mineral is lacking, or if the problem involves a combination of causes.

VITAMINS FIRST

Poultry get all vitamins, apart from vitamin C, from their diet alone. Fat-soluble vitamins (A, D, E and K) are stored in the bird's fat reserves, so a deficiency is only seen some months after the amount in the diet has become inadequate. Water-soluble vitamins (B vitamins), on the other hand, aren't stored and so signs of trouble are obvious much more quickly (sometimes only days after the deficiency in the diet begins). Severe deficiencies are actually rare, so I'll only deal with the symptoms of mild to moderate deficiencies here.

Vitamin A deficiency symptoms in adult birds vary from increased numbers of blood spots in the eggs, to emaciation and weakness. It's involved in the health of the linings of the gut, together with the reproductive and respiratory systems. Signs of impairment here can result in an increased tendency to get respiratory disease, reduced fertility or a decreased ability to digest and absorb food. Young birds show reduced growth rates, weight loss, weakness and staring (slightly lifted) feathers. Young cockerels may develop larger combs than expected. Supplementation should result in a rapid reduction in these signs.

However, care is needed when supplementing with vitamin A. Overdose can cause problems with bone growth and, if severe, generalised illness. Normal feeds contain high amounts of vitamin A; 7000iu/kg for growers and adults, 12,000iu/kg for chicks, which compares with the recommended requirements of 1,500iu/kg for all ages. So deficiency is unlikely, and overdose from supplementation is a real possibility. Always follow the dosage instructions on the supplement carefully if it contains vitamin A, and don't be tempted to give 'a little bit more' if it doesn't seem to be working.

Vitamin D is involved in bone metabolism, beak and claw

"Feed manufacturers put higher than recommended levels of nutrients into their products."

growth and eggshell formation. As in humans, some vitamin D is formed in the skin by the action of sunlight, but most of the requirement still has to come from the diet. Thin or soft-shelled eggs can be seen in laying hens with a vitamin D deficiency. This can be intermittent. Laying and growing birds are more prone to signs as their demand for the vitamin is high. Vitamin D-deficient chicks can have shortened upper or lower beaks, along with a reduced hatchability of the batch.

It's always worth cracking open a few of the failed-to-hatch

Egg numbers and shell quality provide big clues about dietary vitamin and mineral levels.

eggs to see if the chicks inside are normal or not. Rickets is the sign in young birds, where the beak softens and the birds become reluctant to walk. The leg bones can bend or become fragile. Treatment is by supplementation. Again, overdose can happen, though the amounts of vitamin D needed are 10 times those commonly added to feeds ▶

(2,500-3,000iu/kg). Signs are the opposite of deficiency, with bone being deposited in the soft tissue.

The classic sign of Vitamin E deficiency is 'Crazy Chick Disease' (Encephalomalacia), with muscle deterioration and changes (of skeletal and heart muscle) and/or enlarged hocks. Adult birds do not show any signs of a deficiency, but hatchability will be reduced. Chicks with encephalomalacia fall over on to their sides, or stand with the head twisted or between the legs. Some chicks can develop fluid in the tissues under the skin as the blood capillaries are leaky – they stand with their legs far apart and the skin appears greeny/blue. If the mineral Selenium is also deficient, then muscle signs result. Turkey poults fed inadequate vitamin E and high fat/oil diets can develop swollen hocks and bowed legs. Mild to moderate signs can be treated by supplementation.

'Curly Toe Disease' is caused by a riboflavin deficiency (vitamin B2). Chicks with a deficiency can have toes that curl inward due to paralysis, the legs may also have a degree of paralysis. Growth is slow, diarrhoea can be seen and chicks are reluctant to walk. Turkeys show poor feathering and crusty eyes and beak. Toe-curling does not respond to supplementation, though milder signs will.

Other vitamin deficiencies can occasionally be seen and, as long as the signs are mild, supplementation will usually succeed as a treatment.

MINERALS

There are lots of different mineral complexes available, but most contain the same minerals that are likely to be implicated if the birds are on a mineral-deficient diet. Again, there are lists of recommended mineral requirements that are used by the feed manufacturers to ensure that birds gain a full complement of minerals in the correct amounts and ratios, and in forms that the bird can use.

Many feed mills include minerals at a much higher rate than is recommended, to cover for losses while processing the food or in storage, and also the variable diets of the birds eating the finished product. Minerals are vital for a vast array of functions in the body of the bird, and have to be included in the diet of the bird. Again, a variety of natural foods will ensure that a good variety of minerals are ingested and commercial diets are balanced with some minerals added.

Calcium demand is high in young growing birds (for bone formation) and in laying hens (for egg shells). It's also important for many cellular processes, normal blood clotting and muscle function. A shortage of calcium in the diet of laying hens leads to poor egg shell quality and decreased egg production, along with thinning of the bones. Calcium, phosphorus and vitamin D work together in the formation of bone, and a deficiency of any of these will result in changes in the way bone is laid down, causing

"A deficiency is only seen some months after the amount in the diet has become inadequate."

VITAMIN & MINERAL REQUIREMENTS

Vitamin or mineral	Recommended requirement	Amount poultry fee
Vitamin A	1,500 iu/kg feed	7,000 iu/kg adu 12,000 iu/kg chi
Vitamin D3	1,000 iu/kg	2,400-3,000 iu/
Vitamin E	10 iu/kg chicks 5 iu/kg grwrs/adults	80 iu/kg chic 10 iu/kg re
Selenium	0.10mg/kg grwrs/adults	0.15-0.4mg/
Copper	4.0mg/kg grwrs/adults	20-23mg/

Maintaining a good balance of varied foods is very important to the overall health of your birds.

...ds on a good, varied diet shouldn't normally require dietary supplements, so ...ke professional advice before taking action.

hatchability, with weak chicks. Supplementing the iron in the diet will reverse these changes.

Copper is commonly added to poultry feed, partly due to its role in haemoglobin and enzyme function in the cells, but also due to its growth promoter property. A copper-deficient hen may lay distorted or wrinkled eggs, with variable shell thickness.

The macrominerals have another very important function. The body of a bird has to be at a certain pH to function correctly. The macrominerals either carry positive charge (sodium, potassium, magnesium and calcium) or negative charge (chlorine, phosphorus and sulphur), and these need to balance to give the pH at which the body works best. If they are out of balance, the pH of the body changes and it doesn't work as well as it should.

Too negative a balance means that the body is more acid than it should be. This can affect bone development and eggshell thickness. Too positive a balance means that the body is too alkaline, which can result in visceral gout. Supplementing a macromineral deficiency or imbalance has to be done carefully to keep the pH balance correct.

Now, many of these signs and symptoms are vague in comparison to vitamin or mineral deficiency, and could have plenty of other causes. If there is doubt about the diet of the bird, or about how much it's eating, then it may be worth supplementing as a trial. If major or multiple deficiencies are suspected, then a vet should be consulted for testing, especially if a large flock is involved.

At times of stress, when the demand for vitamins and minerals increases (illness, showing, selling), then it may be worth using a wide spectrum vitamin and mineral supplement in the short term only. For a long term solution to a problem, the flock health as a whole needs to be investigated. Factors such as underlying disease, a weaker or less productive line of breeding, poor management and husbandry and flock expectations should all be considered.

Remember that fertility in some pure-breeds is good if it's 50%. Egg production also varies considerably between breeds, and some moult quicker than others. If the supplementing helps, then it shows that the diet is not what it should be, and that there's room for improvement. If the supplement doesn't work, then a) it's not needed, or b) the problem lies elsewhere and should be investigated. Generally, for the vitamin and mineral side of things, commercial diets contain plenty of each in usable forms, while a good, varied fresh food diet should also be adequate, so supplementation should not be necessary. ❦

...inning, softening or deformation in the bone (rickets). Supplementation can help, but calcium can cause kidney ...roblems and visceral gout (where urate crystals build up in ...he internal organs) if it is given to excess. The recommended ...equirement for calcium is 0.9-1.0% in the feed, and signs of ...xcess calcium can be seen at just 3.0% calcium in the feed.

Potassium is often included in the mineral mixes available. ...n the bird it is involved with nerve activity, heart muscle ...unction and keeping cell membrane ...alance and function correct. Deficiency ...esults in generalised weakness, with ...owered production of eggs, with thin ...hells.

Iron is part of the haemoglobin ...nolecule that is contained in the red blood cells and carries ...xygen. It is also important in many enzymes and the ...igment in coloured feathers. Deficiency results in anaemia ...nd reduced colour in feathers. Eggs from breeding birds ...vith inadequate iron in their diet will have reduced

"It may be worth using a wide spectrum vitamin and mineral supplement in the short term."

NATURAL HELP

Lindsay Sissons, investigates food and water additives, with a look at four of the more natural options.

The range of non-veterinary supplements available to poultry for health reasons is very large so, in this article, I'm limiting myself to four of the most popular options – garlic, aloe vera, probiotics and apple cider vinegar.

Garlic is a member of the lily family, and a species of the onion genus (Allium sativum). The ancient Egyptians used it for a wide range of medicinal purposes, including the treatment of worms, snake bites, haemorrhoids and eye diseases. Over the centuries it's also been used in dentistry, for vermin control and as an aphrodisiac. In fact, there's very little that garlic hasn't been thought to aid, at some time or other, and it remains in wide medicinal use today.

Garlic's antibacterial properties were first confirmed by Louis Pasteur in 1858, but research into its other properties continues to this day. Allicin is released when cloves are cut or crushed, and it's this (together with the allicetoins) which is responsible for the bulk of the plant's antibacterial performance. However, Allicin is an unstable chemical, so preparations must be used quickly for maximum antibacterial benefit. Phenols are also released from a crushed clove, and have antiseptic and anti-inflammatory benefits when used

Aloe vera plants originate in Africa, but can be grown indoors here.

internally. The flavenoids in garlic are thought to be of bene in the prevention and treatment of cancer, while the vitamin A, B1, B2 and C are a useful part of the diet. The essential oils (allyls) probably play a part in the insecticidal propertie of the plant. When using members of the onion family as companion planting in organic gardens, it's this allyl that is taken up by neighbouring plants, preventing insect damage

Garlic is mainly used by poultry keepers for its anti-parasi effects, although concrete evidence of its effectiveness is har to find. Some claim a strong effect, while others suggest a weak one is all you can expect. Either way, I wouldn't advis that you rely implicitly on garlic or any other herbal anti-parasitic agent. Birds should always be closely monitored, with conventional medicines being used if required. Howeve it's worth remembering that a combination of garlic and goo management was used as a suitable preventative method fo centuries before the widespread use of chemical parasiticide took over.

Garlic can be used internally for worm control, where it ha been shown to work by preventing the worm larvae developing into adult forms. Externally, garlic can also be applied to prevent mite, lice and other insect infestations, where the allyl essential oil makes the animal unpalatable to the insects. So, there are no claims made that the garlic kills the parasite, it just renders the habitat unfavourable, thus preventing large numbers of parasites accumulating.

To use garlic to prevent (and some say to treat) worms, the minced clove can be added to the food, or the garlic can be planted within reach of outside birds, so they can help themselves. You can also buy proprietary garlic powders tha can be added to the feed, according the the pack instructions. There's little information available on the quantities of fresh garlic needed daily for effective treatment. An alternative to adding to the food is to make a decoction o garlic. Do this by adding 25g of garlic to one litre of boiling water, and letting it cool. Then remove the garlic and let the birds drink the liquid.

To prevent or deter surface parasites (mites, lice etc), a liquid to be applied topically can be made up by steeping four cloves of garlic in one cup of olive oil overnight, then discarding the garlic before slightly warming the oil and applying to the skin of the bird. Care should be taken with this, as one research source warned of a possible skin irritation developing in some cases. A poultry house spray can also be made by finely mincing 10 cloves of garlic, and mixing them with 500ml of mineral oil. This can then be sprayed around the house.

Garlic is also thought to act as an immune system stimulant, and so is used to help prevent viral and other diseases. Its antibacterial properties will inhibit many bacteria including E. coli, Salmonella and Staphylococcus species. It's also effective against many fungi and yeasts. For cleaning infected wounds a mashed clove can be placed directly on to the damaged area. For poulticing, the clove of garlic should be crushed on to a piece of gauze (extracting as much of the juice as possible), then be fixed over the infected area and left for 10 minutes. An infusion (a clove of garlic in boiling water for a few minutes, much as tea is made) can be cooled and then dabbed on to wounds and burns.

Aloe vera leaves are very fleshy and the extracted juice is believed to have many beneficial constituents.

Garlic is also mentioned quite strongly for its effects on the respiratory system, as an antibacterial, an anti-inflammatory and as an expectorant. The bird can be 'steamed' with garlic in boiling water, to help with breathing, and to get the active ingredients of the garlic into the lungs. Place the bird in a small show pen, put the bowl against and outside the bars then use a towel or bin bag (taped all round to prevent leakage) to keep the steam in the pen. This treatment should last for 10-20 minutes.

There are countless other uses listed for garlic. It can be effective as a cardiovascular tonic – it's been shown to act as a blood thinner, by reducing clotting activity and increasing the breakdown of clots that do form, and will also reduce blood cholesterol. It may also lower cholesterol levels in the eggs, though this is of less importance now that medics have found that this doesn't increase the blood cholesterol of the humans eating them. Garlic does, however, reduce the sulphur content in the egg, giving a milder eggy taste that some people may not appreciate. If garlic is included in the birds' diet at a level of 3%, the poultry house will smell

garlicky, but lower levels will still reduce the normal odour of the manure.

Anything that is being added to the birds' diet should be considered and researched thoroughly before use, and the pros and cons weighed-up carefully. Some people swear by the use of garlic, while others are disappointed.

ALOE VERA

This is another member of the lily family, and there are several species of Aloe that can be used medicinally. Seen as pot or garden plants in this country, the Aloes are succulent with thick, fleshy leaves and originate from East and South Africa. They've been used in medicine since at least 4,000BC (by the Greeks), and are still extensively used today. Aloe vera is prized for its anti-inflammatory, antibiotic, antiseptic and immune-boosting properties. It's widely available commercially as a drink or juice that can easily be added to drinking water.

Mucilagenous polysaccharides (molecules that are part mucus-like gum, with carbohydrate added) are the constituents in aloe juice that have a wide range of medicinal properties. Also called 'mannans', they act as anti-inflammatories, can help restore and increase immune system function, can accelerate the healing process and have direct antibacterial, anti-viral, anti-fungal, anti-yeast and anti-parasitic effects. Other constituents, including anthraquinones, have strong laxative effects if used internally.

If given in food and water, Aloe vera is said to improve appetite, keep joints supple and boost energy. It's also thought to help in cases of generalised infection or inflammation. The juice has been shown to change fluid production in the large intestine (producing more fluid so loosening faeces), thus causing marked diarrhoea. It was, at one time, the preferred purgative for horses. But, it is useful for reducing gut inflammation and accelerating healing in gastrointestinal infection and disease. It's not advisable to use fresh aloe sap internally, but commercially-prepared juices and drinks have had the laxative elements removed and so are safe to use internally, following the manufacturer's ▶

Both garlic and Aloe vera can be used on a bird's skin, to help fight parasites and heal wounds respectively.

ACV dilution must be carefully controlled in poultry drinking water – only use it in plastic or stainless steel drinkers.

guidelines.

The stimulating effect that aloe has on the immune system is well known. Acemannan, one of the mucilagenous polysaccharides in the juice, has been approved for use as an adjuvant for the Mareks vaccine. The role of an adjuvant is to increase the immune response at the site of the vaccination, and so ensure that a good immune response is formed to the vaccine that has been injected (to make sure the vaccine takes, if you like). The aloe also has anti-viral effects so it may help prevent the live, inactivated Mareks vaccine becoming activated. If Aloe vera extract is given on a regular basis to the bird internally, it's said to improve immunity by raising the number of a certain type of immune system white blood cells. This is thought to give improved resistance to viral diseases, such as infectious bursal disease (Gumboro disease), where there is a destruction of a certain white blood cell type. Aloe vera extract is a concentrated preparation and is available commercially. If using this, the manufacturer's guidelines on dosage should be closely followed.

Aloe vera reduces inflammation by inhibiting the migration of the immune cells to the site of damage, and reducing the amount of inflammatory chemicals that they then release. This effect is strong, and the anti-inflammatory action is the most common reason for the use of this plant. For external application there is a commercial gel widely available or, for those with a suitable aloe plant, it's a case of snapping off a bit of leaf and applying the sap where necessary. Some aloe species need to be at least four years old before they are medicinally mature. If you're in any doubt, it's worth talking to a herbalist. The gel is soothing, moisturising and will speed the healing of skin wounds. It's now becoming more frequently used in veterinary surgeries, especially for burns and sores.

There is also a tincture available – which is the Aloe vera prepared in ethanol. For use in poultry, 1ml of this (1:1 strength) should be added to one litre of water, and offered as drinking water. It should be changed daily. For individual dosing, two drops of tincture in 200ml of water can be given directly into the beak, once or twice a day. It's also possible to apply the diluted tincture (two drops in 200ml water) directly on to the skin (rubbing into abdominal or head skin) where it will be absorbed.

Once again, like garlic, certain elements of the medicinal properties of Aloe vera have been confirmed scientifically, and many of the constituents are used in veterinary medicine. But, as before, careful thought must go into the reasons for using it on a bird.

PROBIOTICS

There is much research going on at the moment in the field of probiotics and prebiotics, in an effort to steer away from the feeding of antibiotics to commercial stock, as well as to try and reduce the incidence of food poisoning in humans.

The gastro-intestinal tract of a bird contains millions of bacteria that form part of the intestinal flora. This flora, as well as playing a part in the digestive process, also maintain a balance which generally prevents pathogenic (disease-causing) bacteria from taking hold. It therefore acts as an important local immune system. If a bird is immuno-compromised, ill or has had a course of antibiotics, the balance of the intestinal flora will have changed, with overgrowth of some components, possibly the disease-causing bacteria. The theory behind the use of probiotics is that the bacteria in the probiotic will artificially bring the intestinal flora back to its correct balance, and so restore the proper functioning of the gut. The probiotic bacteria work by occupying the sites in the gastro-intestinal tract where the disease-causing bacteria would normally attach and multiply – this is called 'competitive exclusion'.

The main benefit of probiotics at the moment is that of the increased food conversion – the improved digestion by the correctly-balanced gut bacteria means that the bird will get more out of its food than a bird with an imbalance. Birds that have a healthy gut flora initially may not show any changes when given probiotics. The use of probiotics is advised by manufacturers at times of stress, such as showing and breeding, where the balanced gut flora will help prevent illness and increase water intake.

Probiotics are available in liquid or powdered forms, to be added to the drinking water. There is also a sprayable version which can be used on new-hatched chicks. Prebiotics can also be added to feeds or water – these are non-digestible foods or nutrients that are required by the probiotics to colonise the gut and correctly balance the intestinal flora. Some research has shown that the use of probiotics can increase the food conversion efficiency, and give increased body weight in intensively-farmed birds, under environmental stress (among others), that probably have a somewhat compromised immune system. The trials being undertaken now are to find non-disease-causing bacteria that are suitable for use as probiotics, that will displace specific disease-causing bacteria. Some feeds are now available with actobacillus johnsonii added, with Clostridium perfringens (the cause of Necrotic Enteritis) as the target to be displaced by competitive exclusion.

The future use for probiotics is thought to be that of reducing the levels of Salmonella and Campylobacter, for example, in poultry, so that the subsequent risk of food poisoning in humans can be reduced.

APPLE CIDER VINEGAR

Vinegar has been used medicinally, and as a disinfectant, for thousands of years, with apple cider vinegar (ACV) recorded as being used by the Egyptians 3,000 years ago. Some of the reported uses include; antibiotic, antiseptic, antifungal and, some say, antiviral. Apple cider, with no fruit sugars remaining, is taken and the alcohol is broken down into acetic acid and water by the bacterial action. A 6% cider will yield a 6% vinegar. Apples contain many different vitamins, minerals and trace elements (among other 'beneficial' components, 93 in total according to some sources), and all of these remain in the vinegar. The main component of the ACV is acetic acid (usually about 8%). The body of a bird has a set pH (level of acidity or alkalinity) that can be affected by its diet. Each part of the body is designed to be most effective at a certain pH, so diets that change this level can effect the functioning of the body. The theory behind ACV is that it reduces the pH of the body (makes it slightly more acidic), and brings it back to a better level of function. Very small pH changes can have quite an effect. It's believed that most modern diets tend to make bodies slightly more alkaline.

According to BF Miller's paper *Acidified Poultry Diets and Their Implications to the Poultry Industry*, decreasing the pH below that in which a specific organism can survive, will lead to the eradication of that organism. So, for gut flora, if the gut pH is decreased by a small amount, then it may well control the disease-causing bacteria that need a slightly higher pH to survive. It may also wipe-out some of the beneficial gut flora. There is a change in gut function involved as there is said to be a noticeable reduction in odour from the birds droppings. Some trials with ACV have found that the incidence of bacterial infection is reduced, while others have stated that the incidence of sour crop is also lower.

ACV is also reported to be a good detoxifying agent. The betacarotene will mop up free radicals (highly reactive by-products from cells, that contribute to ageing and damage to the immune system etc) and so the functioning of the immune system will often improve, bringing higher resistance to disease and reduced levels of infection. ACV also affects the blood circulation; it's said to increase the amount of oxygen carried in the bloodstream as well as balancing the clotting mechanism, reducing internal clot formation, while speeding the clotting of wounds.

Other suggested benefits include that of improved egg shell quality – the potassium in the vinegar apparently regulates calcium deposition and helps prevent soft-shelled eggs. ACV is also said to improve fertility and increase egg production. It can even help to break down and remove fat, mucus and phlegm deposits.

If given daily in the water to young birds, some trials have shown that birds will grow more quickly and bigger, while feathering-up faster than untreated birds. This is due to a higher feed conversion efficiency. On killing, there is more meat with an improved fat distribution, and some sources state that the meat is more tender too.

To use ACV in young birds, the initial dilution is given as $^1/_4$ teaspoon in 4fl/oz. As the birds grow, the dilution can be very slowly increased to a maximum of $^1/_4$ cup per gallon of water. Alternatively, the ACV can be sprinkled or sprayed on to the food. Remember, though, that metal drinkers and feeders cannot be used with ACV, unless they are made from stainless steel. The ACV will reduce the build-up of algae in drinkers, and generally sanitise the water (though that should not be used as an excuse not to change water frequently!).

ACV should not be used on birds with intestinal problems (it's too much acid for cases of diarrhoea or inflammation, and may cause further damage). Measuring of ACV in the dilution should always be done carefully to prevent overdosing (too acid is a real problem for birds).

ACV can also be used topically for superficial wounds and burns – it's said to reduce pain, and assist with healing thanks to its antiseptic and antibiotic properties. However, never use neat ACV; it should always be diluted as recommended ($^1/_4$tsp per 4fl/oz of water).

At the end of the day, if the birds are not quite right and the keeper has ruled out infection, a diet that may be lacking in nutrients and incorrect management, then it may well be worth trying these types of supplements. Some people do swear that they give their birds that little bit 'extra' but, at the same time, others report no benefits at all. So it's probably a case of 'try them and see', providing there is a reason for using them in the first place. ❧

A mineral oil and garlic mix can make a useful poultry house spray.

FOOD AND WATER ADDITIVES

Lindsay Sissons, outlines the extensive range of veterinary additives that are available for use with poultry.

There are five classes of drug commonly added to the feed or water of poultry: vaccine, wormer, coccistat, antibiotic and growth promoter. The number of available products is enormous, so here I shall deal only with the basic types, plus how, when and for how long to use them. And don't forget, further information can always be obtained from your vet, or the drug manufacturer.

VACCINES

Many vaccines can be given in the drinking water. The diseases covered by these are Gumboro Disease (Infectious Bursal Disease), Newcastle Disease, Infectious Bronchitis, Avian Encephalomyelitis, Swollen Head Syndrome (Avian Pneumovirus) and Salmonella. These are live vaccines that have been altered to ensure that they will trigger an immune response, but will not cause the disease in a healthy bird. Most of these vaccines will come with a data sheet providing precise instructions on the method of preparing the water source, how to dilute the vaccine, and time guidelines for the age of vaccination, the length of withdrawal and the time before the vaccine should be used.

There are a few steps that are common to all of these vaccines. The water in which the vaccine is to be given should be non-chlorinated and low in metal ions. These substances will make the virus of the vaccine less stable and, therefore, the vaccine less effective. Some data sheets recommend that mains water is left to stand for 12 hours

before use, or that de-ionised water is used. The usual way of ensuring vaccine stability is the use of skimmed milk powder (added at a rate of 2-4g per litre) or skimmed milk (added at one pint per litre). The milk proteins 'tie up' the metal ions and so prevent them interfering with the vaccine.

Ideally, the drinkers used should be plastic; metal drinkers, especially if rusty, increase the metal ion concentration in the water and reduce effectiveness. Also, don't use drinkers that have recently been cleaned with disinfectants or detergents. These products may damage the virus in the vaccine; direct sunlight has the same effect. If the birds are receiving antibiotics, then these must also be stopped during the vaccination period, especially when vaccinating against Salmonella. Usually, 24 hours off the antibiotics, either side of the vaccination, is advised.

On a more practical level, some of the vaccines are diluted according to live body weight, or volume of water drunk – each data sheet is normally quite clear about calculating the dilution, with some giving set dilution rates. But should a volume of water drunk by the birds be needed, then it pays to measure this volume the day before to make sure that the dilution is accurate and the vaccine effective. When diluting the vaccine, the vial should be opened under the surface of the water and both vial and lid rinsed well in that water.

Withdrawal of water from the birds before vaccination varies between 30 minutes and two hours. For the 'backyard' keeper, the easiest way to ensure rapid uptake of the vaccine is to change the drinkers at dawn, as the birds rise – they have withdrawn themselves all night already, and will drink well. For birds kept indoors, the lights can be turned off/down so they roost and don't drink while the

You should only ever vaccinate healthy birds, like these Welbars, as they'll need a functioning immune system to mount a response to the vaccine being given.

providing that the suggested dosage on the data sheet is not exceeded. But there is a seven-day turkey egg and all meat withdrawal period.

COCCISTATS

Coccidiosis is caused by any or a combination of intracellular parasites, mainly of Eimeria protozoans, and results in diarrhoea and dysentery with severe outbreaks, or reduced productivity in mild infections. Many commercially-available chick crumbs will contain coccistats that reduce the challenge that the young birds come up against, while still allowing the bird to contact enough coccidia to build up a resistance to them. Each coccistat is active against several Eimeria species – they're all licensed as active against five major chicken species and/or three major turkey species, with some active against other species too.

Most of the existing coccistats are only available to manufacturers to be incorporated into feeds, so buying treated feed for young stock is the best option. Baycox 2.5% solution is available (albeit in a litre bottle) for addition to the drinking water to treat coccidiosis in chickens. The birds to be dosed should be weighed, in kg, then the volume of Baycox calculated (weight in kg x 0.28) and this volume gently mixed into the drinking water for the day. This dose is repeated for the second day, and can be repeated again after five days if necessary. The data sheet also contains warnings about disposal of manure from treated birds, because of the persistence of the coccistat in groundwater.

When using feeds containing coccistats, it's important to always mention their use to the vet, should there be a need for

Many treatments, including vaccines, can be successfully administered in the birds' drinking water.

vaccine-containing drinkers are placed inside. If food is offered at the same time as the water with the vaccine, the birds will drink well. Enough drinkers should be placed so that two thirds of the birds in the house can drink at once. Note should be taken of the length of time that the vaccine is offered. Some vaccines are only effective for one hour after dilution, while others last much longer.

Only healthy birds should be vaccinated, as a bird needs to have a functioning immune system to be able to mount a response to the vaccine that's offered. These vaccines can be used as preventative medicine, or in the face of disease that is present in the flock or the local area. Different vaccines against the same disease (Infectious Bronchitis, for example), are based on different strains, so it may be worth contacting your vet to see which strains are in your area.

WORMERS

Flubendazole is available for use on feed for worms in chickens, geese, turkeys, pheasants and partridges. It's available in a small tub that will medicate 200kg of pelleted chicken and goose feed, or 300kg of turkey feed. Flubenvet can be used as a top-dressing, and should be given daily for seven days. There's no chicken egg withdrawal needed,

additional medication of any sort. Monensin, narasin and salinomycin, for example, should not be used alongside the antibiotic tiamulin, because of the severe growth retardation or death it can cause. All of the data sheets carry warnings about mixing with other coccistats, or other medications, so advice should always be sought.

The maximum age to which a coccistat can be used varies according to the drug used and the bird species. Monensin is used up until three days before slaughter in broiler chickens, or up to 16 weeks old for turkeys and replacement layer chickens. Lasolacid, used in pheasants and partridges, is only fed to 12 weeks maximum, while nicarbazin can only be used to four weeks old in broiler chickens. The data sheet should always be checked.

ANTIBIOTICS

There's a wide range of antibiotic available in formulations that can be mixed with feed or water. As long as birds are still eating or drinking, it has to be the easiest way for the poultry keeper to medicate birds. The major plus points of using this method are that the birds are not stressed by being caught, handled and treated, plus their daily routine essentially remains unchanged. A minus point of feed and ▶

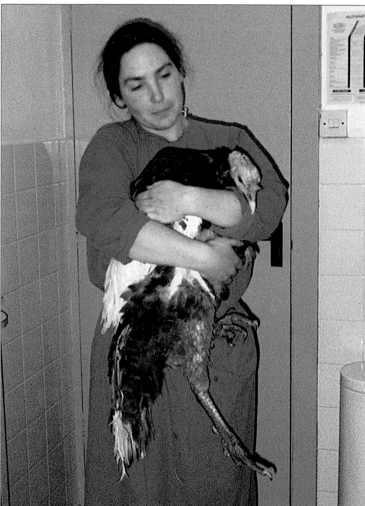

Vets should always be made fully aware of existing treatments to avoid potentially dangerous drug clashes.

bird unless he has prior knowledge of the flock. Discussion of symptoms, numbers affected, numbers dead, timescale and the like will all narrow down the possible causes, and help the vet to choose an effective antibiotic. If the problem is severe with high mortality, then a post mortem and/or blood samples will be advised. The results may take a while to come back, but can be useful in cases where vaccination may be appropriate in the future.

The vet will usually start with a broad-spectrum, first-line antibiotic, as this will help in many cases, unless a specific diagnosis with a specific antibiotic is obvious. If that doesn't work within a few days, then the situation should be assessed and different antibiotics prescribed with activities different to the ones already used. There are many bacteria or other organisms that are resistant to one or more classes of antibiotic, so the first antibiotic tried may not be effective. The only way to definitely get the right antibiotic is to culture the bacteria and test it against different antibiotics so that the effective ones can be chosen. While waiting for results, the vet will usually prescribe a suitable, broad-spectrum antibiotic.

Tetracyclines are a broad-spectrum, first-line antibiotic family. They are effective against many bacteria, and have some activity against mycoplasmas and chlamydia. Tetracycline and oxytetracycline are available as soluble powders from the vet for addition to drinking water; tetracycline being licensed for use in cases of necrotic enteritis (Clostridium perfringens), and oxytet for use in respiratory disease (E coli and Pasteurella). Chlortetracycline is available as a pre-mixed feed only, and is suggested for chronic respiratory disease (including mycoplasma) and E coli septicaemia secondary to Gumboro in chickens and TRT in turkeys.

Sulphonamides potentiated with trimethoprim (TMS) are broad-spectrum antibiotics usually only available pre-mixed in feed. One is formulated as a soluble powder for use in drinking water, and is indicated for use in cases of enteric or respiratory bacterial infections caused by sensitive organisms. As with the tetracyclines and, indeed, many of the antibiotics, there are problems with resistance, but there are many bacteria that are still susceptible. This soluble powder is designated a POM (prescription-only medicine) and, as such, can be prescribed and supplied by the vet.

A POM combination of lincomycin and spectinomycin provides a broad-spectrum mixture that is recommended for use in chronic respiratory disease (mycoplasma), and coliform infections of growing poultry. Neomycin is a more narrow-spectrum antibiotic available POM for use in the treatment of E coli bacterial enteritis. Both of these are powders for addition to drinking water. Apramycin soluble powder is suggested for use in cases of E coli septicaemia and salmonellosis in young birds, and is a prescription-only medicine too.

water medication is that it's impossible to guarantee that every bird has taken enough antibiotic to have a full dose, as individual intake in a group of birds cannot be monitored. Another drawback is that the amounts of antibiotic required in food and water, to achieve the correct dose, can sometimes be a bit tricky. Advice can always be obtained from your vet.

Several families of antibiotic are available for this use. Most of them are first-line, broad-spectrum products, which are active against a wide variety of bacteria and other organisms. These are good in cases of mixed infections – those caused by lots of different bacteria, or just one initially, which is then followed by more afterwards. Where there are specific infections, then a narrow-spectrum antibiotic can be used, aimed at that purpose (histomoniasis, for example). In some cases, where bacteria or other organisms (mycoplasma, say) have become resistant to some antibiotics, then a narrow-spectrum antibiotic can be chosen that's effective against that bacteria/mycoplasma, then a broad-spectrum antibiotic may be given alongside to ensure that other involved bacteria are not missed. Vets will advise on useful combinations for this purpose.

When starting antibiotic therapy, the vet will need to see a

Tylosin is a soluble powder available POM, that's stated for use against Mycoplasma synoviae airsacculitis and Mycoplasma gallisepticum infections. It can also be used to reduce the level of infection after live vaccination. The data sheet also states that the diagnosis should be reviewed after five days, if treatment is not working. Tylosin has a narrow range, and is not effective against many bacteria, so may need a broad-spectrum back-up when it's being used to target mycoplasma in a mixed infection.

Tilmicosin is another antibiotic that's active against mycoplasmas in chickens and turkeys. Again, POM and given in water, it has a short dosage length of three days only, with long meat withdrawal times. There are also data sheet warnings about manure disposal. Several medications have implications for the environment, so the data sheet should be read thoroughly and adhered to.

Tiamulin, available POM, is used in drinking water, and is now licensed for use in cases involving mycoplasma. Care must be taken if feeds containing coccistats are being used as certain coccistats, if used with tiamulin, will cause severe growth retardation and death. Always mention any in-feed medication to your vet.

Nifursol is available only as pre-mixed medicated feed, and is used long-term for the prevention of histomoniasis in turkeys. The drug is only allowed to be incorporated into feed by registered, category A manufacturers. There is a five-day meat withdrawal period for this product.

GROWTH PROMOTERS

These are antibacterials that are given as part of the feed ration, to increase the feed conversion efficiency and growth rate of young birds. They work by either altering the bacterial flora of the gut (reducing possibly pathogenic bacteria, altering the bacterial by-products that are useful to the bird, and so on), by changing the metabolism of the bird or by increasing the absorption of digested food from the gut. Each feed must only contain one growth promoter, and no other antibiotics should be used as treatment while birds are being fed this medicated feed – the feed must be changed to non-medicated so that birds can be treated. There is no meat withdrawal necessary from the poultry-licensed products.

Avilamycin and flavophospholipol are the two poultry growth enhancers available as pre-mixed feed. Licensed for broiler chickens, turkeys and laying hens, the age limit for feeding varies with the species – turkeys can be fed to 26 weeks maximum, chickens to 16 weeks. Some feeds have no maximum age limits for feeding.

Growth promoters, or enhancers, are widely used in the commercial poultry rearing world, to decrease the amount of feed needed per kg of meat produced, while getting to killing weight quicker, and so reducing production costs. Pure breed birds, or birds to be used for breeding, really need to develop naturally and at the correct speed; forcing these birds will only hamper them later on.

AND FINALLY...

Responsibility when medicating birds is of utmost importance. We have all of these drugs at our disposal that are all useful in some way or other. Irresponsible use will only serve to reduce the effectiveness and usefulness of these medications. ☙

Growth promoters in feed are used in the commercial sector, but are not really suited to pure breeds in the domestic environment.

Nutrition and Vitamins

Bob Cross investigates nutritional deficiencies, and the practical effects they can have on your poultry

Nowadays, thanks to all the careful development work that's gone into modern poultry feed formulations, you might imagine that nutritional deficiencies are a thing of the past. Unfortunately, though, they aren't – people still make mistakes. The consequences of a dietary imbalance can prove costly, both in monetary terms and for the birds involved. We have enough knowledge regarding the nutritional requirements of poultry to provide them with a balanced and adequate diet. All commercial flocks are fed on branded feed, or a home-mix that's been formulated by someone 'in the know'; tailored to the precise needs of the stock in question.

There's also a wide range of complete and wholesome diets available to the domestic poultry keeper and, as a result, deficiency disorders should rarely be seen. This is just as well, as serious deficiencies of one or more of the essential nutrients will be seen as disease, often resulting in mortality. Where the deficiency is only marginal, the consequences can be depressed production in terms of growth, egg yields and hatchability. The danger, of course, is that these symptoms may go unnoticed, or be attributed to some other cause.

Predisposing factors such as parasitic, viral or bacterial infections and stress may affect the absorption of nutrients. Climatic changes and environmental conditions will alter the requirement or balance of the diet, and result in a previously suitable diet becoming deficient.

ENERGY

Where a major component of the diet, such as energy, is lacking the bird will tend to compensate by eating more. As long as food is available little harm will be done although, at the same time,

protein intake will be increased as well. But little of this extra will be used, resulting in an expensive waste. Also, situations can arise when lightweight, high-producing modern hybrids are kept on range in the winter; with their small size and frugal appetites it's physically impossible for them to consume enough food to sustain themselves and produce eggs.

PROTEIN

This may be deficient in two ways; either in terms of the amount or the quality. In the former, problems may arise when economising on the bag feed by diluting it with grain and overdoing it – effectively reducing protein intake. High poultry house temperatures, or hot weather, will reduce food (and protein) intake. Birds at 'peak lay', and those high producers with meagre appetites, are most vulnerable. When these factors coincide, the situation is exacerbated. In both cases, production will suffer and if the situation continues, the bird may be forced to use its body tissue to sustain production until it decides enough is enough, and stops.

Marginal deficiencies will present themselves as a reduction in average egg weight (which should increase daily from the first egg laid through to the end of the season). Where it's more marked and left unchecked, it can lead to poor egg numbers and even a cessation in production for a time.

Deficiency in protein quality (one or more amino acids in short supply) produces similar effects. Feather pecking and cannibalism have also been associated with a shortage of the amino acid, lysine.

VITAMINS & MINERALS

Vitamins are chemical compounds required for normal body function, including involvement with the body's enzyme system, hormone and chemical regulator production. They are needed for the build-up of body tissue, and the breakdown of waste and toxic substances. Minerals are chemical elements required in varying – usually small – amounts to maintain health.

Most vitamins are derived from the

Naturally birds get vitamin D from exposure to sunlight, but this can be a problem for those kept entirely inside. Supplements are required.

diet; the majority of foodstuffs contain small but adequate amounts. Shortages can be rectified by natural or synthetic supplements. If the birds are being fed a proprietary ration, it's unlikely that deficiencies will occur, although it is possible if the feed is stale or mouldy. Discovering one or two birds displaying symptoms in a flock doesn't necessarily mean there's a problem with the diet. The cause could be another disease, a management issue, or the fact that those individual birds have a different dietary requirement.

On the other hand, where most of the flock are affected (showing signs of a gross deficiency), it's probably safe to assume that the feed is at fault. The services of analytical and veterinary laboratories should be used for confirmation and treatment advice. Similar action should be taken where the provision of the mineral element is suspected.

Excesses of vitamins and minerals can be equally harmful. Not only are they wasteful but some, when taken in excess, may lock-up the availability of others, or even prove toxic. Vitamins likely to be deficient in the diet include A, D, E and K (fat-soluble), riboflavin, nicotinic acid, vitamin B12, pantothenic acid, folic acid, biotin and Choline (water-soluble). These are the ones required in the greatest amounts, or that are scarce in many foodstuffs.

VITAMIN FUNCTION

Vitamin A: Required for good growth and can also play a fundamental part in disease resistance, possibly being involved with the production of antibodies.

Deficiency causes a condition often referred to as 'Nutritional Roup'. Chicks receiving a diet deficient in vitamin A will show signs at about a month old. The timing is dependant on the degree to which it's lacking; it may be as early as the first week, especially with chicks hatched from eggs laid by parents also receiving inadequate supplies of the vitamin. The feathers of affected chicks are poorly developed, the plumage ruffled and the bird's appearance is unkempt. The chicks are drowsy and reluctant to grow. Pigmentation of the legs and beak will be less than in healthy birds. Cheesy material will be found under the eyelids, and the eyes appear watery at first but, latterly, become dry if the bird survives long enough.

In adult birds, where stock has

Vitamin D deficiency can slow or even stop egg production, depending on the severity.

previously received an adequate diet, it may take many months for signs of a vitamin A deficiency to become apparent. Initially, only one or two birds are affected, but then the signs spread throughout the flock. The birds appear ragged and lose condition. In laying flocks, egg production falls and in breeding flocks hatchability suffers, with an increase in embryonic malpositions.

There's a watery discharge from the eyes and nostrils, the eyelids become 'gluey', with the bird appearing to be suffering from a heavy cold. In the latter stages there's a white discharge from the eye and, if the eyelids are parted, the eye itself may be covered in a white material. In some cases the eye will have been destroyed.

With turkeys (poults and adult stock) the signs are similar, but also the brown spots on eggs laid by breeding turkeys may be much paler in colour. Ducklings show a nasal discharge and may display some signs of paralysis. In breeding ducks, hatchability is reduced and those that do hatch have watery eyes, impaired vision and suffer high early mortality.

Vitamin A is found in both fresh and dried grass, other green food, yellow maize and fish liver oils. It can also be

added to the ration as a dry supplement. The vitamin is readily destroyed, especially under poor storage conditions – strong sunlight and warmth. Even under good conditions much of the potency can be lost in a matter of months. Worm infestations and coccidiosis severely damage the intestine wall, reducing its ability to absorb the vitamin. So, during such outbreaks extra vitamin A may prove beneficial.

Vitamin D: Vitamin D3 is involved with the metabolism of calcium and phosphorus and, where a deficiency is noted, these two minerals should also be checked. With chicks, rickets is usually seen as a sign of vitamin D deficiency. From about two weeks old, leg weakness is seen with many chicks sitting on their hocks, which may be swollen; a faltering gait is all they can manage. The beak and claws become pliable, the toes spread out and the legs bowed. Feathering is poor and ragged, and growth is retarded.

In adult chickens, egg production decreases and may even stop. The number of thin and soft-shelled eggs increases, and these changes occur over a number of weeks, unlike similar signs associated with viral infection such as infectious bronchitis and Newcastle▶

disease. Hatchability declines too.

The beak, claws and keel bone become pliable, and the rib bones turn inwards. Some laying hens may temporarily become unsteady on their legs after having laid an egg. Similar signs will show in turkeys and ducks although, with the latter, the beak can become bent back on itself.

Birds can synthesise Vitamin D3 (the form in which it's required) from a precursor if exposed to sunlight or ultraviolet light. So those kept outside will get much of their requirement in this way. Ordinary foodstuffs contain little vitamin D, so it must be provided in some other way; fish liver oils are one source and, alternatively, a dry vitamin D preparation can be added to the diet.

Vitamin E: This acts as an antioxidant, protecting vitamin A in the gut. In the body it's part of the cellular respiratory enzyme system, and may also be involved with the synthesis of DNA within the cell.

Deficiency is commonly referred to as 'Crazy Chick Disease', or Nutritional Encephalomalacia. It normally affects chicks aged between three and four weeks, causing nervous derangement; chicks are ataxic – unsteady on their legs and in walking. Backward and downward retraction of the head – sometimes between the legs – can also occur. In the early stages, they appear drunk and will fall over backwards, lay on their backs paddling or jerking their legs before appearing to recover. The performance is then repeated. Death will follow shortly after these signs are seen.

The other disease associated with this deficiency is Exudative Diathesis. Accumulations of fluid – sometimes bloodstained – under the skin, particularly beneath the wings and the lower parts of the body, is indicative that birds are suffering from this condition. It has little effect on egg production, but a significant one on hatchability; many embryos die on the third or fourth day of incubation.

Turkeys and ducks can suffer similarly, but can develop muscular dystrophy too. On post mortem, light-coloured streaks of muscle will be seen throughout the normal coloured breast muscle. The embryonic mortality in turkeys tends to occur in the latter stages (between 24 and 28 days). A small percentage of the poults that do hatch will have eye problems, some being blind.

The best sources of vitamin E are wheat germ oil and maize germ oil. Green foods also contain useful quantities. Dry preparations made in a similar way to Vitamins A and D are also available. Normally Vitamin E is stable, but it is rapidly destroyed in the presence of rancidifying fats.

Vitamin K: This is involved in the production of the blood-clotting component of prothrombin and so deficiencies result in poor clotting. Chicks can suffer with massive haemorrhaging almost anywhere on the body, especially on the breast, wings and legs. In extreme cases bleeding to death from a comparatively minor injury can occur. Anaemia, due to blood loss and a reduction in the bone marrow also results.

The blood takes longer to clot in adult birds too, so injuries take longer to heal. In laying stock there may be a relationship between blood spots in the eggs and vitamin K levels, but it may be that adequate levels cause the blood to clot and show as spots, while deficiencies allow it to diffuse in the albumen. Where eggs are saved for incubation, hatchability will be reduced; most of the mortality occurring after the eighteenth day (chickens).

Vitamin K is ubiquitous, but major sources are found in green food such as grass or Lucerne, either in fresh or dried form, or in other plant material. The vitamin can be synthesised by the bird in the alimentary tract, and feed supplements are also available to make up shortfalls should they occur.

It's unlikely that deficiencies will occur, but the vitamin is readily destroyed by sunlight. Certain drug treatments may induce signs of deficiency, and the bird's requirement for it may change in the event of an outbreak of disease.

Despite the fact that modern feeds offer a nutritionally-balanced diet, keepers still make mistakes, as a consequence of which birds can suffer.

The water-soluble vitamins are an important group, and include the vitamin B complex, choline, folic acid and biotin. Most of these are required to sustain health and promote normal growth, so are important as part of a well-balanced poultry diet. Consequently, deficiencies in any of them present problems, as we'll see.

RIBOFLAVIN B2

This is necessary for growth and the normal function of the nervous system. It's involved in the metabolism of carbohydrates, fats and protein, and is required for egg production, embryonic development and, therefore, hatchability. Chicks reared on a diet deficient in riboflavin grow very slowly, responding in a positive way to supplements of this vitamin. Where the deficiency is less acute, chicks will be seen walking about

on their hocks and this develops into Curled-toe Paralysis (CTP); the signs of which are the toes turning inwards under the bottom of the foot. This problem is usually seen between the second and fourth week. On post mortem examination, the brachial and sciatic nerves are found to be grossly enlarged.

A riboflavin deficiency in adult chickens causes lower egg production and reduced hatchability in breeding birds (many embryos die around the 12th day of incubation). Those that survive this early mortality die in the latter stages of incubation, probably on the 20th day, and it can be seen that the down follicle has failed to split, giving rise to the characteristic 'clubbed down' associated with riboflavin deficiency. In the case of turkeys, growth rate is much reduced. Other symptoms include

dermatitis, poor feathering and perosis (slipped tendons). With ducks the main signs are poor growth rates and increased mortality.

It's important to note that CTP shouldn't be confused with crooked or bent toes, where the bird will still walk on its feet. The latter deformity is more likely to be of genetic origin, and is also more prevalent where chicks are reared under bright emitter infrared lamps.

The richest sources of riboflavin are dried grass, dried milk products, dried yeast and other fermentation by-products. In the past, meat products – especially dried liver meal – were useful, but the inclusion of these is no longer permitted. It should be noted that cereals are poor sources of the vitamin. Additional riboflavin can be added in a synthetic form. Bacterial action in the droppings produces the vitamin, and this may prevent problems in chicks reared on litter where the deficiency in the feed is marginal. Riboflavin is relatively stable under normal storage conditions, but is rapidly destroyed by ultraviolet light.

NICOTINIC ACID/NIACIN

Nicotinic acid is necessary for growth, good feathering and to maintain the upper part of the alimentary tract.

Chickens lacking it show reduced growth rates and poor feathering. The mouth cavity and the upper end of the oesophagus become inflamed and dark red, producing the condition known as 'Black Tongue'. Turkeys present similar signs. Poults may also suffer from perosis and diarrhoea. Ducks show the same, plus bowed legs (the bones are hard, not rubbery). The chick can synthesise the vitamin itself, but not fast enough to satisfy its demands under certain conditions.

Most diet formulations will ensure an adequate supply of the vitamin, but those based around a high proportion of maize may be problematic. Rich sources of nicotinic acid are found in sunflower meal, rice polishings, bran, middlings and dried yeast. It's fairly stable under normal storage conditions.

PANTOTHENIC ACID

This is necessary for growth, good feathering and hatchability. It's also required for the maintenance of nerve tissue and healthy skin.

Chickens lacking it show reduced growth rates (as chicks), and dermatitis – especially around the eyes and the corners of the mouth. In severe cases it ▶

Birds enjoying access to plenty of natural greenery are unlikely to suffer from folic acid deficiency.

may be seen on the dorsal (back) surfaces of the feet. Similar signs will be seen with biotin deficiency, although this will be evident on the feet first. Minor deficiencies of pantothenic acid may not adversely affect hatchability, however, the resultant chicks will benefit from a supplement of the vitamin to prevent dermatitis developing.

A turkey's requirement for pantothenic acid is twice that of a chicken's, so deficiencies may occur. Reduced growth rate will result, but not the dermatitis. Egg production isn't affected in adults, but hatchability is. Many of the latter stage embryos and chicks have wiry down, plus leg abnormalities. In ducks expect depressed growth rates.

The best natural sources of pantothenic acid are dried yeast and other by-products of fermentation, groundnut (peanut) meal, dried milk products, dried green crops and molasses are also good sources, while all the grains will make a contribution. Packet forms are available to supplement rations which otherwise would be deficient.

VITAMIN B12

These vitamins are cobalamins, and used to be referred to as the 'Animal Protein Factor' (APF) because birds fed on diets including animal protein outperformed those where the protein was of vegetable origin. The vitamin is required for growth and hatchability. It's also involved with the maintenance and performance of blood.

Chicks with a deficiency show poor growth and feathering, often accompanied by increased mortality (unattributable to any particular cause). There may be signs of kidney damage and perosis. Adult birds show few signs, but the hatchability of their eggs is markedly reduced. Most embryo mortality occurs during the second and third week of incubation (chickens). Dead-in-shell embryos are dwarfed, with many other anatomical abnormalities. It has been reported that the hatching of affected turkey eggs may be delayed by up to 30 hours.

Birds on litter can get the vitamin via bacterial action on compounds in the droppings. Those with access to range may obtain some from animal protein, in the form of grubs and worms. Where fish meal, and especially herring, is included in the ration formulation, it makes a useful contribution. It's made commercially by a fermentation process for inclusion where diets would otherwise be deficient. The vitamin is

Feeding your birds a balanced diet based around a modern, professionally-formulated poultry ration, should mean that nutrient and vitamin deficiences are a thing of the past, but it's not always the case.

fairly stable under normal conditions.

CHOLINE

While not strictly speaking a vitamin, I've mentioned Choline here because it's usually included when discussing vitamins. It forms a structural part of lipid (fat) and nerve tissue. It's necessary for fat metabolism, prevention of fatty livers, bone development, growth and egg production.

Chicks that are deficient will show poor growth rates, and this can also be the case if it's taken in excess. Perosis is also likely; it may be that there is enough choline in the diet for growth, but not enough to prevent this condition. Adult chickens can usually synthesise enough choline to support normal egg production and hatchability. Turkeys and ducks present similar symptoms.

Choline is present in all grains and seeds. Rich sources are found in fish-meals, yeast, soya bean and wheat germ meals. Fed otherwise good diets, the bird can synthesise it from precursors present in other ingredients. Synthetic choline is also available, and both these and natural forms are quite stable under normal storage conditions.

FOLIC ACID

This is required for growth, the normal development of feathers and is essential for the maturation of red blood cells. Chicks without it will grow poorly, have poor feathering perosis and anaemia. Adults birds will suffer with reduced egg numbers and hatchability.

In young and growing turkeys, leg weakness may be seen around the 8-10-week stage; cervical paralysis has also been reported. Poor and brittle feathering and, in the case of coloured birds, feather pigmentation may be affected. Ducks show reduced growth, anaemia and enlarged livers.

Folic acid is found in green leaves, so deficiencies are unlikely to be seen in birds with access to range with a good cover of vegetation. Other sources include yeasts; dried brewer's yeast being especially rich in the vitamin and useful contributions are made with the inclusion of soya bean, dried grass and lucerne meals to a ration. Most cereal grains will contain some, and synthetic folic acid is also available. The vitamin is affected by heat so a ration that is just adequate may become deficient on pelleting due to the heat generated during this process.

BIOTIN

This used to be known as vitamin H, and is required for growth and hatchability. It, along with a number of other factors, is involved with the prevention of perosis and a type of dermatitis.

Chicks deprived of biotin show retarded growth rates, poor and brittle feathering. Scaly dermatitis develops on the underside of the feet, which become cracked and bleed – the dermatitis later spreading to the eyes and the corners of the mouth. An increased incidence of perosis will be noted.

Egg production may remain normal in adult birds, but hatchability will be reduced. Embryonic mortality will be increased in the first week and, again, in the final three days. Among the chicks that do hatch, perosis and other skeletal deformities such as 'Parrot beaks', chondrodystrophy (where cartilage fails to grow properly), micro-melia (shortened limbs) and syndactyly (fused toes) will show.

Similar signs are seen in turkeys. Those between eight and 20 weeks old develop dermatitis on the feet, and adopt a stiff-legged gait. Hatchability from breeding hens is reduced, embryonic mortality peaking during the first week of incubation.

Good sources of biotin include maize germ meal, safflower meal and yeast products. Cereals are poor providers and, while the amounts present in dried green crops aren't as good as some, the vitamin is fully available. Synthetic forms are available for inclusion to rations where fortified levels are desirable.

MINERALS

These are inorganic, chemical elements. They are found throughout the body, but not uniformly. For example, most calcium and phosphorus is found in the skeleton, iron is a constituent of blood, iodine is essential for thyroxine and silicon is needed for feathers. Some minerals are required to ensure others can work.

CALCIUM & PHOSPHORUS

The skeleton contains about 99% of the calcium, and 80% of the phosphorus, in the body. The metabolism of both is influenced by levels of vitamin D and manganese in the diet. The amount required by poultry will vary according to type, age, size, rate of lay etc. A laying hen stores calcium in the long bones of her body, drawing on it (and that taken directly from feed digestion) to produce egg shells. After the egg is laid, calcium is replaced in the bones to restore the balance.

Only about 50% of dietary calcium is retained in the body or voided as egg shell, and levels of around 4% calcium in a diet should be adequate for most domestic flocks where relatively high appetites are a feature, and high egg production is not. If birds are fed a low calcium diet for some time, shells will become progressively thinner and eventually laying will stop. Feeding extremely low calcium diets will lead to a cessation of lay, although the hens will remain apparently healthy in other respects, coming back into lay when the calcium is restored.

Manganese is also essential for bone formation. Together with vitamin D, it helps with the transfer of phosphorus from body tissue so that it can be combined with calcium to form bone material. While minor deficiencies of one can be dealt with by a slight excess of another, they are all vital in the correct proportions and a failure to achieve this will result in problems as already described above. Rickets is another possibility.

MANGANESE

Manganese deficiencies are especially associated with perosis, although the condition is not uniquely caused by a lack of it – it's also seen when vitamins are in short supply, and there may be some genetic involvement too.

Perosis – also known as 'slipped tendon' – develops in the growing bird and is usually seen between two and ▶

A chicken's bones contain about 99% of the calcium, and 80% of the phosphorus in its entire body.

10 weeks old. Birds fed an adequate diet for the first three months are unlikely to develop the condition. Chicks suffering from perosis tend to sit around for long periods, and inspection will reveal slightly puffy hock joints. These will become quite enlarged as the condition progresses, then the tendon will slip out of the groove at the back of the joint. Continued attempts to walk pull the lower leg sideways and backwards, crippling the bird. On examination, the bones will be found to be thickened and shortened, rather brittle but well calcified, with the upper end of the tibia conical in shape.

In adult birds deficiency results in reduced egg production while, in breeding stock, fertility and hatchability are lowered. Many of the embryos from eggs laid by these birds die in the latter stages of incubation – in the case of chicken eggs, on 20/21st day. Many of these dead-in-shells show shortened, thickened legs and wings, 'parrot beaks', domed, oedematous heads and short wiry down. Hatched chicks, if fed a manganese-deficient diet, will develop perosis as early as two weeks old.

Egg shells will be thinner and, as a consequence, more water will be lost during incubation, again leading to a further depression in hatchability if compensatory measures aren't taken.

MAGNESIUM
This is found in bone and egg shell. Severe deficiencies in chicks have been reported to cause symptoms similar to Vitamin E deficiency. Where the birds have access to green food they will get sufficient from the chlorophyll, and any supplementation may be harmful.

ZINC
Zinc is a constituent of insulin, some enzymes and an activator of others. When diets low in zinc are fed to chicks, growth rate is reduced and feather development is poor. Dermatitis, similar to that seen with deficiencies of biotin or pantothenic acid, can occur. Birds affected adopt a 'goose-stepping' gait.

Symptoms in poults include reduced growth rates, shortening and thickening of the long bones, thinning of the web of the secondary flight feathers and a perosis-type condition.

MINERAL SOURCES
Most ingredients of bagged feed will contain a mineral element contributing (some more than others) to the birds' needs. Special mineral mixtures are available for inclusion by the miller to make up for shortfalls. These include ground limestone, di-calcium phosphate (DCP), sodium chloride (salt), manganese sulphate, iron sulphate, cobalt sulphate, copper sulphate, zinc sulphate and potassium iodide.

When feeding a proprietary brand of feed, vitamin and mineral supplements shouldn't be required. Occasionally, though, the use of oyster shell grit is justified on the grounds that it improves shell appearance. Likewise water-soluble vitamin mixes may be beneficial in times of stress, or to aid recovery after disease.

The deficiency symptoms of many of the vitamins and minerals are either the same or similar to each other as a result of an inter-relationship and interdependency between them and, as a result, it's often difficult to identify the specific cause. Where nutrition is suspected it may be worth consulting the feed manufacturer for further guidance or, if welfare is being compromised, it is always advisable to seek the expert services of a vet, who may refer you to a laboratory for final diagnosis.

The egg provides a very valuable indicator about the overal health of a hen. Factors such as the number produced, shell quality and thickness, fertility and hatchability all offer clues about potential problems.

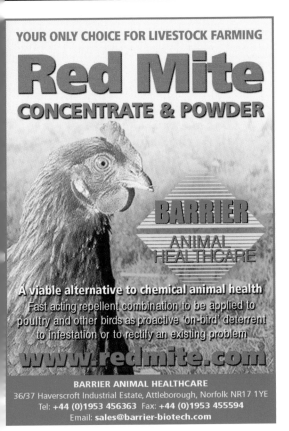

David Spackman NDP, BVSc, MRCVS, explains the threats posed by rats and mice towards the small poultry flock

RODENT ALERT!

Everyone seems to know at least two basic facts about rodents, and rats in particular. The first is that, if you live in a town, you are always within just a few feet of the nearest one; an interesting statistic promulgated on television by popular programmes like 'A life of Grime'.

The second thing most people know is based on an anecdote that's been handed down over the generations. Common opinion has it that for every rat you see, there are 15 more that you don't!

The situation regarding the first is that, while in the rural environment the ebb and flow of the rat population does not alter much year-on-year, several surveys have shown that numbers in urban conditions are increasing annually. This should come as no surprise given the explosion of fast food, supermarkets, restaurants and other outlets which encourage population multiplication, coupled with less vigourous pest control action by local authorities.

TOO MUCH FOOD

Compared to many other North European countries, the UK is less than efficient at keeping towns and cities clean and free from edible debris. Then, on top of this, there's the problem of supermarket design and layout. When applying for planning permission to build a new outlet, the major retailers are told that they must incorporate plenty of trees and shrubs in the design, ensuring that islands of vegetation abound in the car parks. All of these offer ideal environments for rats to set up home among the roots. Combine this with the overflowing waste bins and the large amount of rubbish left by consumers, and ideal conditions prevail.

The increased use of plastic piping for water supplies and drainage close to modern houses, rather than the more traditional clay pipes, also allows rodents not only easy availability to water, but also easier access to the houses themselves. In more recent times a lack of pro-active baiting with poison in sewers has also allowed numbers to increase and, even where baiting does take place, failure for the bait to be consumed frequently leads to the misinterpretation that there are no animals about.

What should be remembered is that rats in particular are neophobic; very suspicious of new things suddenly appearing in their environment. They simply will not approach strange, new objects or features. Also, there may be other far more tempting foodstuffs near

"For every rat you see, there are 15 more that you don't!"

at hand to be preferentially selected.

RAT ATTACK

So which rodents are most likely to be encountered by the small poultry flock owner here in the UK? Well, leaving aside squirrels and other more exotic rodents, there are essentially three species which are likely to cause problems.

Before the mid-1700s, the only rat resident in the UK was the Black Rat (Rattus rattus). However, at about this time, the larger Brown Rat (Rattus norvegicus) arrived from Russia, and swiftly began to displace its smaller neighbour. It did this so successfully that today it's dominance is almost total, and its just about the only rat you'll ever see. The Black Rat still has small colonies, mostly in port towns such as Hull, Bristol, Liverpool and Glasgow, where it may also be seen around gardens. But generally it follows a different lifestyle. Occasional encounters with the species have been made in such unusual inland towns such as Stratford-Upon-Avon – it was, after all, the only rat Shakespeare would have known.

The House Mouse (Mus musculus) is widespread throughout the whole country and is the third commonly-encountered problem rodent. Brown rats are excellent burrowers, whereas Black rats are excellent climbers and nest high rather than in burrows. House mice, of course, are ubiquitous and will nest anywhere. Much of the aforementioned will convince the poultry keeper that rodents will be attracted to the areas where their birds are kept, not only for the ease of finding edible titbits, but also for suitability in most cases for setting up home.

It should not be underestimated just how much rats and mice will eat. A mouse will eat about 15% of its body weight every day (about 3-4g), while rats will consume 25g or more a day. So literally millions of tonnes of food are consumed annually throughout the world, and in some third world countries, up to 50% of everything available is lost to hungry rodents. It's a

	Brown Rat	Black Rat	House Mouse
Weight	250-500g	100-250g	15-30g
Length of Tail	15-20cm	19-25cm	8-10cm
Head & Body Length	18-25cm	16-20cm	6-9cm
Total Length (nose to tail)	30-45cm	35-45cm	15-19cm
Age at Sexual Maturity	2-3 months	2-3 months	45 days
Gestation Period	23 days	22 days	19 days
No. of Young/Litter	6-12	6-8	5-6
No. Litters/year	4-7	4-6	8
Av.No.Females/weaned	20	20	30-35

very serious problem.

In the UK we don't suffer those extreme levels of loss, primarily because our storage methods are more effective. But you can rest assured that, if the opportunity presented itself, the rodents would move in. It's estimated that there are 70-80 million rats in the UK today, so their population comfortably outnumbers that of humans. The fact that such large numbers survive at all indicates just how much food is available for them to eat.

FAVOURITE FOODS
Both mice and rats like wheat, whole or preferably cracked, so poultry feed obviously provides a strong attraction for both species. Luckily, mice prefer other foods even more. About 70-90% of canary seed will be readily consumed, 30% oatmeal and grass seed, 20%+ of wheat and 10% of peanuts. It's clear then that canary seed

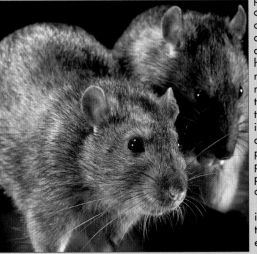

offers a very suitable base to mix poison with and is the preferred choice for pest operators.

As a rule, mice tend to prefer to pick up morsels of food as they scurry around, whereas rats will often take bait from a bait station. However, it's important that these are made from plastic, rather than metal. Rats' feet are very sensitive to variations in temperature, so a cold metal surface may well be sufficient to put them off walking across it.

Another interesting aspect of rodent life is how far the different species will range from the nest. Mice tend to stay pretty close to home, never straying much beyond 10 metres away from the nest. Rats, as you might imagine, are rather more adventurous, and will work across a larger area of anything up to 50 metres from their nest. But at times of migration, or when colonies disperse, rats have been known to travel as far as three kilometres.

> *"Rats have been known to travel as far as three kilometres."*

Of course, food consumption isn't the only aspect to worry about as far as the presence of rodents is concerned. In addition there's the actual damage they can cause by gnawing, mice being especially dangerous in that they have a liking for electric cable insulation and have caused many fires as a result. Then there is the contamination caused by both faeces and urine – mice again being particularly troublesome in that they constantly urinate as they run around, leaving long trails of urine. The potentially serious consequence of this contamination is disease, which can affect both poultry and humans. Incidentally, it's now thought that Mozart might have died due to the rat worm disease trichonosis, which had infected pork that he ate. This particular problem still causes real problems for the meat processing industry in central Europe.

Of particular importance to poultry is the risk of Salmonella, especially enteritidis, which has caused so much of a problem for the egg industry in the past few years. S. enteritidis was, after all, first found in rodents in the 19th century, long before it became a talking point in poultry, but is still easily transmitted by mice especially.

PRACTICAL MEASURES
Fortunately, there's a lot that we can all do to help keep the rodents at bay. For a start, as much close cover as possible should be removed from the proximity of the poultry house, to eliminate obvious nesting sites. The other advantage of this approach is that it gives predators such as cats, or even foxes, a good chance of dealing with the vermin at night.

Next, it's important to raise the poultry housing well clear of the ground, thus preventing burrowing underneath. The birds can easily be trained to access the houses via ladders, which are removed at night.

It's also a very good idea to have some sort of contract in place for rodent control. Farmers can attend courses which, upon certification, allow them to purchase their own rodenticides, but this is not a proposition for the smaller flock owner. Contracts can be made with both commercial companies or some local authorities. Naturally, the commercial operators will charge more for their services, but not all councils offer a full contract service. Typically you will find that a local authority will charge around £50 for the first half-hour survey and treatment, and then about £20 for each subsequent half-hour period.

However, whichever is chosen, the service must be thorough and effective. Visits should be at least monthly and preferably fortnightly. In the event of the bait being taken on the first day, then more should be deposited the next day and so on until no more is consumed. But, remember, having cleared your own premises, new colonies will move in from surrounding areas and immediate rebaiting will be required. 🐦

All photographs courtesy of Rentokil Pest Control

Resisting Rodents

Terry Beebe gets under the skin of those little furry 'friends' who delight in tormenting poultry keepers with their destructive and potentially dangerous habits.

Rodents, in particular rats and mice, are bad news for poultry keepers. Never mind whether you have three birds or 300, sooner or later you're likely to encounter these annoying and potentially dangerous pests. Poultry houses, the abundance of feed and bedding, and the birds themselves, act like a rodent magnet.

But this isn't to say that rats and mice aren't attracted by other domestic factors, because they most certainly are. People are often quick to blame the neighbourhood poultry keeper for rodent infestations, but most conveniently forget the compost heaps at the bottoms of their gardens, and all the food they regularly put out to feed the wild birds!

As well all know, rats are among the world's great survivors. They're intelligent and wily, suspicious and determined. They are quick to take advantage of a situation, and to establish themselves whenever a suitable opportunity presents itself. What's more, there are plenty of them around –

surveys have shown that wherever you care to stand, there'll be a rat no more than 10 feet away! But probably the most disturbing thing about rats is the health risk they present. This, together with the physical damage they can do, means that they are not a pest to be tolerated.

DAMAGE ALERT!

Given the chance, rats and mice will cause enormous damage, both to hardware (sheds, feed bins, electrical wiring etc.) but also to your birds. Quite apart from the cost of the repairs needed to sort out the holes they gnaw, it's quite common for rats to chew away at chickens' tail feathers. They seem to do this for fun, and usually strike at night while the birds are roosting. This, obviously, can be a disaster if your birds are destined for the show pen. Nevertheless, it's the risk of disease associated with rats that gets people most worried, and quite rightly so. One of the nastiest is called Weils Disease; it's a potential killer.

I've had an uncomfortably close brush with this myself, as I lost a friend to it a few years ago. He was out walking with the dogs, one of which caught and killed a rat. It was a wet, dirty day and so when my friend arrived home he automatically washed and dried the dogs. Unfortunately, what he didn't realise was that earlier in the day he'd cut his hand very slightly. Rat urine from the dogs infected the cut and within five days he was dead. So be warned, and always make sure you wear gloves if there's any risk that you might be touching rat-infested materials. Always check carefully when you're moving things or cleaning-out. Stay well protected and you'll have no problems.

Weils Disease starts off as a flu-like illness, with an incubation period of 3-19 days. This is followed by muscular aches and pains, loss of appetite and nausea when lying down. After this the sufferer experiences bruising of the skin, followed by sore eyes, nose bleeds and, eventually, jaundice. These symptoms last for about five days and, if left untreated, can prove fatal. Incidentally, this information was sourced from the disease section of the University of Leicester's website. It's also worth remembering that this nasty disease can easily be caught from infected water (either from contact or swallowing) that's been polluted by rats' urine.

PROBLEMS, PROBLEMS

While the risk to health should obviously be a great concern to us all, rodents can also be responsible for a load of other trouble. They can worm their way in to virtually any building if they want to. A rat is capable of squeezing in through gaps that are less than an inch wide and, even if there is no gap at all, the chances are that one will be perfectly able to dig down, then chew up through the wooden floor. What's more, they can do this surprisingly quickly, so it's all too easy to get caught off-guard. Chicken house pop-holes are a favourite entry point, especially as there are usually gaps around the edge where the sliding cover fits.

If you have a hen house like this, the small gap between the floor and the ground could provide a perfect refuge for rats and mice. Check it regularly, or raise the whole thing so it's higher above the ground.

Food kept in containers is always another prime target and a big attraction for rats and mice. Plastic containers provide very little resistance and, as for paper or plastic sacks, well... I wonder how many of you have gone to get the morning feed, picked up the bag only for the bottom to fall out, dumping the contents all over the floor? I've heard that story many times but have to admit that it's never yet happened to me. Mind you, I remember once walking into the shed carrying a 25Kg bag of feed, only to find that I'd left a neat trail as the pellets were escaping from a hole in the bottom. That sack had come straight from the feed merchant, so none of us are safe! In fact, they had a serious infestation problem, which cost them a lot of money and time to sort out.

Also, if you've got electrical power in your outbuildings, then always be sure to keep a wary eye on the condition of the wiring. Electric cables that have been damaged by chewing can cause a major fire hazard, not that this happens often but it is worth a mention.

RATS IN RESIDENCE

Rats and mice can make their homes anywhere, especially if there's a readily available supply of food. Sacks of pellets stacked in a corner and food left or spilt on the floor provide an opportunity that's too good to miss. Areas that are dark and warm are a particular favourite, which is why poultry sheds and hen houses are such

This Thornton poultry house stands at the ideal height, on sturdy legs.

an attraction. Designs which feature an internal lining offer ideal sanctuary, and rodents will happily make a home in the cavity space; it's safe and quiet, offering an ideal nesting site. Mice, in particular, love this situation.

A few years back I made the classic mistake of lining our chick shed, and using a fibreglass insulator material to fill the resultant cavity. It soon became apparent that this cosy, warm space was being used as a breeding ground for a mouse colony.

"People are often quick to blame the neighbourhood poultry keeper for rodent infestations."

When I stripped out the lining I was absolutely amazed at the number of nests I found inside. It only took a short period for the mice to become established, and the whole incident

taught me a valuable lesson. Now, in my view, poultry shed lining and insulation is a definite no-no!

Rubbish piled up in and around buildings will also provide a very suitable rodent refuge, so keeping everywhere clean and tidy is always the best bet. The more you can see the better, so try to avoid cluttered corners, and make use of your local refuse tip!

The fact that many poultry keepers raise their sheds and houses just off the ground can cause more problems than it solves, if the gap created isn't big enough. Lifting it just a few inches will create a perfect nesting spot for rodents, so my advice is to be sure and raise the building much higher. Put the structure on legs so that the space underneath is open, uncluttered and light.

STAYING IN CONTROL

Keeping on top of the rodent situation is largely a matter of common sense. Put yourself in a rat's mind and assess your set-up for likely hiding/nesting sites. Keeping everything clean and tidy goes a long way to nipping problems in the bud. Rats and mice thrive on neglect. Untidy sheds and runs, where food and rubbish are left lying around, are guaranteed to attract trouble. Also, it makes sense to site log piles and compost heaps as far away as possible from your poultry. Old gardening equipment can pose a problem too – that ancient mower you've been meaning to take to the dump for years, that's now a rusting hulk and surrounded by weeds, could be sheltering a family of rats or mice.

In many cases the unfortunate reality is that we only have ourselves to blame for rodent problems. After all, if we provide them with easy access to three meals a ▶

Rat hole very close to a feed bin.

FACTS OF LIFE

Rats usually weigh about 11 ounces, typically grow to 13-18 inches long (including a 6-9-inch tail) and live for 12-18 months. They will eat almost anything, but do prefer high quality foods such as grain and livestock feed. They produce litters of 6-12 young, with a pregnancy period of 23 days after mating. The young become sexually mature after about three months and, on average, a female rat will produce about 6 litters every year. Is it any wonder that they are so successful?

HAVE YOU GOT THEM?

The best way to check to see if you have a rodent infestation problem is by looking carefully for evidence of droppings and fresh gnawing. Diggings are usually easy to spot – fresh holes which will appear under sheds and along the sides of fences are an obvious givaway.

There will also usually be signs of the runs they create. These too will be seen down the sides of buildings and fences etc. Although rats are very agile creatures that are perfectly capable of climbing over most fences, it's usual for them to dig underneath.

They don't bother to hide the fact that they are in residence, so the signs should be plain to see if you take the trouble to look.

you'll stop them from simply walking inside. Concrete and metal are the only materials that offer a complete solution. Wood, unfortunately, will never keep rats out.

Try to assess house design – whether you're building your own or buying one ready-made – in terms of how rodent proof it might be. If there are nooks and crannies that you cannot see into, then this is where problems could arise. My own houses all stand on legs which raise them well above ground level, so I've never had trouble with rodents nesting underneath. The excellent Thornton Poultry unit illustrated here was designed by a friend of mine and is sold by us; it's typical of what I'm talking about.

There are lots of ways of dealing with rodent problems

dustbin can be just as effective. Finally, it's also sensible to get into the habit every night of bringing in any outside feeders that you may use. Leaving them out simply provides yet another attraction, so get them under cover and out of reach of the rodents.

"Untidy sheds and runs, where food and rubbish are left lying around...attract trouble."

day and comfortable accommodation, how can we then grumble when they take advantage?

Housing needs to be built strongly and, as far as possible, to be rodent proof. If you ensure that any gaps are kept to a maximum of a quarter of an inch, then at least

A fresh rat hole – a sign of trouble!

As far as feed is concerned, my advice would be to invest in a properly designed metal feed bin, which will be completely rodent proof. But, if your budget won't run to this, then a metal

This is typical of the sort of damage that a rat will cause in its efforts to get in around the base of a pop hole.

"It's quite common for rats to chew away at chickens' tail feathers."

"What have we here then?" Typical rat damage in the floor of a hen house.

Rodent Poisons

Terry Beebe provides some practical advice on how best to use rodent poisons, and assesses some of the most popular brands.

There is no doubt that rats and mice can be very bad news for poultry keepers, fortunately there are ways of getting rid of these annoying and potentially dangerous pests. The key point to remember is that you must always act swiftly.

Rodents become established very quickly, and the trouble they cause multiplies as rapidly as they do! Dealing with them effectively and safely calls for the use of the right equipment and products.

PLENTY OF CHOICE

There is a wide range of poisons and traps on the market nowadays, so choosing which approach to take can be a little daunting, especially for those of you new to poultry keeping. So let me be your guide!

Problems often start with an irate neighbour who spots a rat and comes knocking on your door. The fact that you keep chickens means that you must be to blame; that's the popular reasoning used. Sometimes it can be true, other times not. But the point is, no matter what the cause, the problem must be dealt with quickly and efficiently. Rats are bad news in every respect. Failing to tackle the problem will endanger your birds and possibly your family. It may also result in your angry neighbour reporting you to the local council, at which point things can get very

serious indeed.

Poisons are one of the best forms of attack, and there are plenty of alternative types generally available – whole wheat versions, cut wheat versions and the wax-block types. Whichever you choose, the most important thing is to use the product responsibly and safely; always follow the product instructions to the letter, and use your common-sense. Major consideration must be given to the surroundings in which you are going to use the poisons. You should make completely sure that any children are in no risk and also that the local wildlife can continue going about their normal routines without a problem.

Over the years I've found through experience that the best and most efficient way to eliminate rats and mice is to tackle them at the source; their diggings and holes. Track these down and you're halfway to solving the problem. Usually these are dug overnight, and fresh signs of these earthworks are normally pretty easy to spot if you look carefully. My advice is to put the poison straight down the most recently-dug hole, and then to cover the entrance with something heavy, like a brick or stone slab. It's important to block-off the hole to prevent other wildlife, your own pets or even children, from getting access to the poison. Then it's simply a matter of waiting. Go back and check the following day, to see if the poison has been eaten. If it has, then drop in some more, and keep doing this until it stops disappearing. Once this happens, you know the job has been done, and that that particular problem has been solved. Never assume though that, just because you've cleared one lot, you can relax. Once you've had a rat infestation, you need to remain permanently vigilant, and ready to act quickly and nip future problems in the bud.

WHICH ONE, AND WHY?
While there are certainly a number of other poison options currently available, I think that the ones detailed here

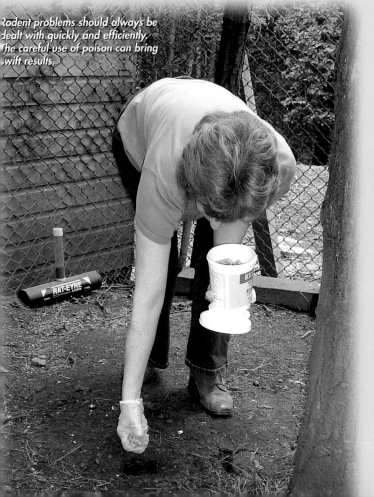

Rodent problems should always be dealt with quickly and efficiently. The careful use of poison can bring swift results.

One of the most effective methods is to drop the poison directly into a freshly-dug hole...

...and then to cover it with something heavy to prevent anything else getting access to the poison.

provide a useful enough range for the sorts of circumstances you're likely to encounter. I've used most of the poisons covered in this feature, so can comment on their effectiveness from experience.

ERADIRAT & ERADIMOUSE

This is an unusual product in that the manufacturers claim that it's totally safe to use in environments were there is a potential risk to other animals. It's hard to believe that this product kills rats and mice and yet it is completely safe for all other animals, birds and humans, but I can assure you it does.

I've used Eradirat myself on more than one occasion and have found it very effective. However, I should also point out that, because of the type of product it is, it does take a little longer to work than some of the other more traditional, anti-coagulant-type poisons (which

cause death by internal bleeding).

Rats and mice have a unique digestive system and Eradirat operates by promoting dehydration. This, in turn, causes the blood to thicken to such a degree that effective circulation eventually becomes impossible. During this process, the rodent will become lethargic, and will usually return to its burrow were it'll fall into a coma and die. Death normally occurs between four and seven days, if the poison is being taken regularly. Tell-tale signs that you can look for which indicate that the poison is having the desired effect include pale and larger-than-normal droppings (don't touch them, obviously!). This will indicate that the poison is being taken on a regular basis. One of the biggest advantages of this product is that when the rat or mouse dies, its decomposing body tends

not smell because it has died through dehydration.

For the best results, Eradirat (or any other of the poisons mentioned in this

Eradirat is a pelleted product that's safe for everything apart from rats and mice.

article) should be carefully stored so that it's kept as dry as possible. Wet bait will sometimes lose its effectiveness. Also, it makes sense to prevent easy access to other forms of food. So, during periods of treatment, make sure that any poultry feed you may have lying around is ▶

Always wear protective gloves when handling rodent poison, and wash your hands afterwards too.

PARENTAL WARNING

Someone told me the other day that one of the UK's largest supermarkets stocks rat/mouse poison in its garden department, and that it is displayed on shelves at about the same height as a four-year-old child. It's hard to believe I know, but it's true. Surely this is an accident waiting to happen; parents of young children be warned.

moved out of the area. Giving them a choice of meals isn't a good idea!

For me, though, the best aspect of this product is its safety. This is a fantastic benefit and, to emphasise the point, Eradirat is perfectly suitable for use in organic units, and is recognised by the Barn Owl Trust, which is an organisation very close to my heart – but that's another story!

ROBAN

This company produce an excellent range of products, all of which are well tried and tested. All work as anticoagulant poisons, and are flavour-enhanced to create maximum feed and rapid control.

Roban Cut Wheat is available in a variety of pack sizes, and is a very 'small-cut' poison. This makes it very effective against mice, and ideally suited to use in bait boxes for extra safety.

An alternative is Roban Whole Cut Wheat Bait, which I have used many times in the past, and still do now. It produces and almost instant effect in rats, and always seems to be taken after being placed in position. There's very little wastage in normal use and it is equally effective whether it's used in a bait box, or directly down a hole.

Roban Pellet Bait is a poison that's suitable for both rats and mice. It comes

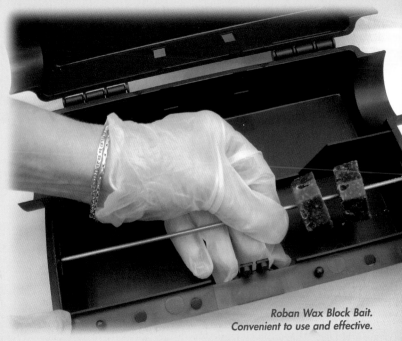

Roban Wax Block Bait. Convenient to use and effective.

in a pellet form (as the name suggests!), and is taken very easily. It's ideal for use in bait boxes and rat tunnels. I've found this one to be very effective when used inside sheds, in cases where the rats have got in by gnawing their way through wooden floors or walls.

Roban Wax Block Bait is one of my favourite poisons. Although most rats will readily consume pellets, they do seem to prefer the bait blocks in my experience, which is why this is such a good one. When used with a rat box it always works well and safely. The blocks are secured inside by being slid on to a metal rod, which holds them in place

A selection of anti-rodent equipment. Can you spot the odd one out?

BE SAFE, NOT SORRY!

The golden rules for using rodent poison include:

- Always read and understand the manufacturer's instructions
- Always wear gloves when handling poisons
- Always store poisons safely, out of the reach of children
- Always wash hands after use

Neosorexa, a general-purpose, wheat-based rodent poison.

until they are eaten.

This bait is used widely in both private and commercial environments, and seems to be more attractive to the animal than the pelleted alternatives; they eat more in a single feed. The blocks are also useful as they can be wired into place as needed, to make them totally secure.

RODEX

This is a highly effective poison, although it must always be used with extra caution. It's highly likely that a rat will consume enough Rodex in one day to provide a lethal dose – that's how powerful it is. A dose of just 5-7g is all that's needed to kill a 250g rat.

Rodex needs to be placed in dug burrows, or in rat stations, but extra care must be taken to ensure that no other animals can come into contact with this product. It contains the anticoagulant, bromadiolone, and has an antidote which is vitamin K1.

NEOSOREXA

This is bait designed for use by the amateur, and is intended as an all-purpose mouse and rat poison. It contains the anticoagulant difenacoum, and has been specially formulated to control strains which have become resistant to some other anticoagulants.

Two or more feeds are required to provide the lethal dose, and death will normally occur within 4-10 days thereafter. As with all previous baits, this one needs to be used in dry locations, and should always be kept covered and secure in a safe, dry storage place – well out of the reach of children and animals. ♥

Rodent Traps

Terry Beebe looks at the final option for dealing with the problems caused by rats and mice – the safe and effective use of rodent traps.

Writing this series has brought home to me just how big a problem we all face when dealing with rodents. The damage they cause, the havoc they wreak – in all walks of life – is staggering. As a poultry keeper, I'm pleased to say that my main problem is ensuring that the blighters are kept out of my sheds; something which I'm pretty successful at, thank goodness.

The rat trap should be an important weapon in the armoury of every poultry keeper, whether you've got rodent problems or not. These pest are unpredictable, and problems can quickly get out of hand if you're not vigilant.

TRAP CHOICE

There are many different types available and, when choosing which to buy, you must first establish exactly what you want to achieve.

Basically, there are two options. Do you want to kill the varmint, or do you want to trap it alive, and then dispose of it afterwards?

I recently met a very pleasant woman who, I discovered, left food out on purpose to feed the rats and mice. I tried explaining to her the problems she'd be bound to face in the future because of this, but she just said that she couldn't bring herself to kill them. If this is your position too, then you must get help from someone who can. Simply ignoring the problem (or encouraging it by deliberate feeding), will only lead to a disaster.

"Problems can quickly get out of hand if you're not vigilant."

The use of poisons generally leaves you remote from the final result. Working with traps, on the other hand, is a good deal more 'in your face'. Using one which kills instantly is often better although, of course, they only kill one at a time. But set a few 'live-catch' traps and you can get significant numbers in one go, if you're lucky. Young rats can be caught relatively easily, and will follow each other into the traps. Adults, on the other hand, will tend to be a bit more streetwise, and so more difficult to catch.

Before I get into the description of the basic options, there are a couple of points which everyone should consider. First, always bear in mind that traps which kill rodents on contact will also be capable of killing other animals and birds. Secondly, the 'live-catch' alternatives mean you'll have a live rat or mouse to deal with. This may sound a simple task, but the reality can be much harder. Plunging the trap into a bucket of water to drown the occupant is certainly not to everyone's taste, but the other options can be equally gruesome; giving it to a terrier to finish-off, or using an air rifle to shoot it in the trap (which can be messy).

LIVE-CATCH TRAPS

I think that these are the most basic form of trap. They are usually made from wire mesh, and come in various shapes and sizes. Some designs will have a little trap door through which the animal has to climb to reach the bait. Then, once it's inside, the door snaps closed to seal off the escape route. Others have a sliding door that's triggered when bait is taken from the trigger or plate. Some use simple sliding mechanisms, while others are spring-loaded.

All types of live-catch trap are easy to use, and are particularly suited to environments where other creatures need protection. What's more, their simplicity means that they always work effectively. One practical point worth remembering is that shiny new traps should be allowed to get dirty and tarnished as soon as

Dead victims from contact traps are easier to deal with for most people than live ones from 'live-catch' traps.

possible. Traps (of whatever type) that look brand new aren't usually very effective because rats, in particular, are suspicious of anything new, and will avoid them.

Traps should always be checked on a daily basis – several times every day if you can. It's important to avoid leaving trapped animals for any length of time. They will die of stress if kept under this sort of confinement, which is a cruel way to go, even for a rat. As far as placement is concerned, site the trap close to where the rodents are running or digging. You'll need to leave it there for a few days, so that they become used to its presence. Once they become comfortable with it, curiosity will get the better of them, and the trap will start doing the business.

I find that peanut butter is a good bait to use in live-catch traps, but I've also had good results with Mars bars! But, whatever you choose to use, make sure you place it on the metal tray inside the trap. I've known people put it on the wire floor of the trap, but all that happens then is that the rats simply dig underneath and pull the bait through that way.

The trap door-types need to be set very finely, to ensure that they go off at the slightest touch. With the tunnel-types, though, there are no settings so all you do is bait them and hope. I've used several different types over the years but, on balance, tend to favour the tunnel ones; I always find

Contact traps like this need to be secured. This one is simply screwed to a piece of wood.

them very effective and easy to use.

Unfortunately, as I mentioned earlier, catching the pest is only half the story. In my view, drowning represents the easiest disposal method. Use a deep bucket or water butt, secure the trap, drop it under the surface and walk away. It'll all be over in a few minutes. I appreciate that it's an unpleasant task but, unfortunately, it's got to be done.

"Adults, on the other hand, will tend to be a bit more streetwise."

CONTACT TRAPS

Traps of this sort come in quite a variety. There's the Fen trap, which snaps shut and kills instantly. Commonly these are called 'back-breakers', which gives you all the clues you need about how they work. The end is swift. Alternatively, there are a number of new traps on the market, which are supplied ready-baited. They are easy to set and, as with the Fen trap, they kill instantly as they snap shut.

The type you choose depends a lot on your circumstances. Some, for example, are very powerful and can injure children, the family pet, or other wildlife. So these sorts of device should only deployed under very carefully controlled conditions. Any trap that springs shut has the potential to catch the unwary (animal or human), so use your common sense and take care. Metal, wood or stones should be used to cover them over; it's important that they are not visible from above. The saddest case I've come across involved a Barn Owl. The bird had been reared in captivity, and its careless owner put a 'back-breaker' trap in its aviary – well, you can imagine the rest. It ended up having a leg amputated, and I now own it. Happily, it leads a pretty normal life now with us, but it was a needless injury in the first place.

The ready-baited contact traps are still quite new on the scene, and they certainly work. I have to admit that ▶

Baiting a live-catch trap. Always wear gloves for this sort of job.

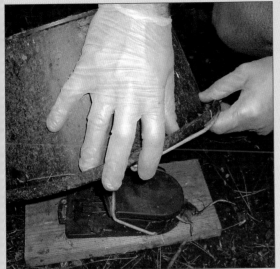

It's important to keep contact traps out of sight, to protect other wildlife, pets and children.

Examples of 'back-breakers' – watch your fingers!

don't know what's used as bait, but it's definitely attractive to rodents. The ones that I've tried, specifically for catching mice, are quite amazing. They seem last for months, and you can continue using them after all the original bait has gone. I just add peanut butter, or bits of Mars bar, which both work very well.

I also make a point of ensuring that the traps are secured so they can't be moved. If, by chance, they don't work instantly, the injured animal can drag the trap away. Not only will this cause unnecessary suffering, but it may also result in you losing the trap. So a short length of chain, or a piece of string, attached to the trap and then either tied

"Traps that look brand new aren't usually very effective."

to something heavy, or pegged to the ground, will stop any movement. Most of the traditional traps are designed to be secured in this way, but many of the new plastic ones aren't.

One other point worth mentioning is that the pre-baited traps are supplied fitted with a plastic cover which is clipped over the bait before use. Obviously, this cover must be removed when the trap is set, otherwise it won't attract anything. I've known several instances where people haven't realised this, and have then grumbled to the supplier that the traps don't work!

If, as a beginner, you stick with the sort of traps covered in this article, I'm confident that you won't come unstuck. The secret is to find the trap that best suits your own needs, and that you find is the easiest to use. If you're in any doubt talk to the suppliers or, better still, speak to other poultry keepers who can advise you from their own experience. The

effective control of rodents is a very important aspect of good poultry husbandry. Keep

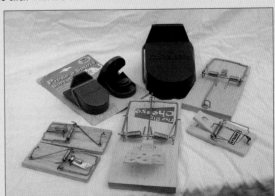

Rat trap with spring-loaded door.

things in check and then you won't have a problem. But allow the situation to get out of control and you and your birds will face all sorts of trouble. ❦

A live-catch trap in the henhouse; a perfectly acceptable trapping method.

Selection of contact traps, including the convenient, ready-baited versions.

Avoiding Poultry Poisons

Bob Cross gets to grips with the risk of poultry poisoning, then begins an overview of more general disorders, starting with sour crop.

Losses due to poisoning in poultry are small when compared to those attributed to other causes, such as infectious diseases. Nowadays, it's unlikely that poultry will die as a result of ingesting the obvious poisons – such as arsenic or strychnine – as their availability is strictly controlled. Similarly, rodent baits, if used in accordance with the manufacturer's instructions and sited with care (allowing access only to the target prey) shouldn't cause problems either.

However, there are a number of other toxic substances which it's as well to be aware of, as they can all pose a threat to the health of your birds in different ways.

SALT

In small amounts, salt is vital for the well being of poultry but, in excess, it can prove harmful. Salt tolerance varies according to the age and type of poultry. Adult chickens are able to stand inclusion levels in the feed as high as 20% (8% with turkeys) for several weeks without mortality. In the growing stage they are slightly less resilient and, in very young stock, high mortality will result from levels of only 5%. Again, poults appear more susceptible.

But the situation is quite different if salt is added to the drinking water. Levels of just 0.9% can cause 100% mortality in young chicks, and even less is needed to achieve similar results with turkey poults. Birds suffering from acute salt poisoning show excessive thirst, diarrhoea and, in some cases, an apparent paralysis of the leg muscles. Depending on the amount of salt present, mortality may be noted, with some individuals showing convulsions just before they die.

Where levels of 20% are included in the meal, birds will reduce their food intake, resulting in a drop in production. Post mortem examination shows tissue oedema, inflammation of the gut and a dark-coloured liver. Crop impaction may be a feature too, the contents of which will lack the normal semi-sour odour.

MOULDS

The toxins produced by moulds as by-products are known as mycotoxins, and the generic term for disease caused by these poisons is mycotoxicosis.

Many fungi are responsible, but the Aspergillus species feature prominently. One of this family, Aspergillus flavus, is often associated with groundnuts (peanuts), and it produces a toxin known as aflatoxin. This may also be found in other feedstuffs and materials used for litter. The presence of this toxin in the feed causes a condition referred to as aflatoxicosis.

All animals can be affected, including man, so it's advisable to avoid eating certain out-of-date foods, especially last year's nuts or those that are sold as wild bird food.

The symptoms vary according to the type of stock and the mycotoxin involved. Affected birds die suddenly and while in good condition. The signs preceding death include problems with co-ordination, lack of appetite, a reluctance to move, depression and a reduction in growth, production and condition. Before any of the above are noticeable, there may be signs that the immune system has been compromised.

Ducks seem to be the most susceptible species, closely followed by turkeys and

Don't give your birds access to long, tough grass because there's a risk that it (together with other undesirables like feathers, string and straw) may lead to crop and gizzard impaction.

If you suspect a bird is suffering from sour crop, gentle squeezing can release the characteristically rancid-smelling gas!

pheasants, where losses can reach 80-100%. In chickens the mortality may only reach 10-20%, but many survivors will turn out to be 'wasters'. Older birds are more resilient but, fed contaminated feed for long enough, they will succumb. The post mortem signs will vary according to the severity and duration of the poisoning. The liver tends to be the centre of focus, showing signs of becoming hard, pale and occasionally orange-brown or mottled. In longer term cases cirrhosis occurs. There may or may not be kidney involvement; if affected, they will be found to be swollen and congested. A gut empty of food, plus catarrhal enteritis in the duodenum, are also signs.

There may be some indications of muscle bruising and, especially with ducks, haemorrhaging under the skin of the legs and feet. As a result of its immuno-suppressive actions, secondary complications may occur such as coccidiosis, salmonellosis, mycoplasmosis etc. Confirmation of the condition requires veterinary assistance, and samples of suspect feed – together with infected birds – should be submitted for examination.

DRUGS

Some poultry feeds contain medication; the most likely supplement is one to help prevent an outbreak of coccidiosis. Fed to the stock for which it was intended, it generally does a good job. But fed to others it may have serious consequences – the inclusion rate may be too great or it may simply be toxic to that type of stock.

Occasionally the coccidiostat fails to keep the disease at bay and further treatment is necessary, or it may be that another kind of infection is present for which antibiotics are required. In either case, it's vital to get veterinary guidance, firstly because it's likely that a prescription will be needed to get the best treatment. Secondly, there's also the risk of possible contraindications – the non-compatibility of treatments running alongside each other. The vet, when making a decision about the best treatment, will take into account any medication the birds are already receiving and prescribe accordingly. Should the contraindications be ignored, the results will be just as it says on the tin!

PUTREFIED FOODS

The feeding of rotten foodstuffs to poultry will result in losses from alkaloid poisons, or the toxins produced by bacteria with which the food is contaminated. An example of such poisoning is botulism, also known as 'limberneck'.

This condition affects all species of poultry, and is caused by the birds being fed 'spoiled' tinned meats and vegetables, or eating rotten meat and or the maggots that are found in the same. Present in the decomposed food will be a toxin produced by the bacteria chlostridium botulinum, and it's this that causes the disease. The organism can live in the soil so is able to contaminate any creature that lies dead on the ground. This, when eaten, will cause disease.

A few hours after ingestion of the contaminated feed, birds become extremely weak, lose their appetite, become sleepy, and those affected look sick. Paralysis sets in, the birds losing use of their legs, wings and neck. The neck may become so flaccid that it's almost possible to tie it in a knot. The flaccid nature also makes swallowing difficult, and those affected will often be seen with the head and neck extended, resting their beaks on the ground. The feathers become loose in the follicles and, if rubbed backwards, will fall out very easily. Death is almost inevitable following complete paralysis, often preceded by a coma.

There are few internal signs to be found on post mortem examination. A laboratory detection of the toxin in the ▶

contents of the gut confirms diagnosis; a job for the vet, who will also advise regarding treatment.

PLANT-DERIVED POISONS

The list of poisonous plants is extensive, however, poultry are unlikely to come into contact with most of them. But some of those that they may encounter include: laburnum, corn cockle, lily of the valley, lupins and Deadly Nightshade (the berries and seeds of which are poisonous, and can cause high mortality).

Sprouted potatoes, and those with green skins, contain a poison called solanin. So, if used as a poultry feed, they must be boiled to remove the toxin and the water in which they were boiled discarded. Infected grain can cause metabolic disorders; grains thus affected resemble rat droppings and samples containing them should not be fed.

Linseed contains a cyanogenetic glucoside which yields prussic acid if the meal is allowed to become damp and stand for some time. The use of raw linseed to condition birds' feathering is not advised, if it's used it must be fed in dry mash, at an inclusion level of less than 3% of the diet. The toxin can be destroyed by boiling.

Cocoa residues are unlikely to be used as a poultry feed and its inclusion here is for interest only. Some of the residues are available in garden centres for use as a mulch and, as such, may be used for a litter. They contain a toxic agent called theobromine which, if eaten, will prove harmful to poultry. Similarly, household cocoa powder contains enough theobromine to cause problems if fed.

The inclusion of cocoa residues in poultry feed was trialed during WW2 to help out with the rationing, but its unsuitability was soon proven. Theobromine is completely absorbed from the alimentary tract and only slowly excreted, consequently it has a cumulative effect. After feeding rations containing it for a short period, high levels of mortality are seen – the birds displaying nervous excitability and then dying of sudden heart failure with no other apparent signs of illness. On post mortem examination, the smell of chocolate may emanate from the gut contents.

When poisoning is suspected, veterinary help should be sought and the advice followed regarding treatment. While this is forthcoming the feed should be replaced, together with the litter and any other suspected sources of contamination removed. Affected birds should be isolated and made as comfortable as possible, with ready access to fresh food and water.

SOUR CROP

Also known as moniliasis or thrush, sour crop is a descriptive name given to a condition where the contents of the crop have begun to ferment, and smell rancid or sour. A fungus, Candida albicans, is the causal organism, and where other conditions already prevail, such as pendulous crop or crop binding, it's more likely to occur. All poultry species are susceptible, especially turkeys. The disease may be due to the ingestion of stale, mouldy or putrid food material, or the food remaining in the crop long enough to ferment. Flocks that are already debilitated are more likely to suffer, with conditions such as pendulous crop and crop impaction/binding often predisposing sour crop.

Infected birds are depressed and have a reduced appetite which, in turn, leads to stunted growth and, in long-term cases, emaciation. The contents of the crop may be semi-liquid, becoming apparent if the bird is being held or carried upside down, when it's likely to drain out. It can also be diagnosed by feeling the crop. Squeezing will expel any gas that is present, with its characteristic, rancid smell. The crop itself may be grossly oversized and pendulous.

Post mortem examination reveals

Beware of garden centre mulch, as some of it may contain cocoa residues which are toxic to poultry. It's best to avoid using it as a litter material for this reason.

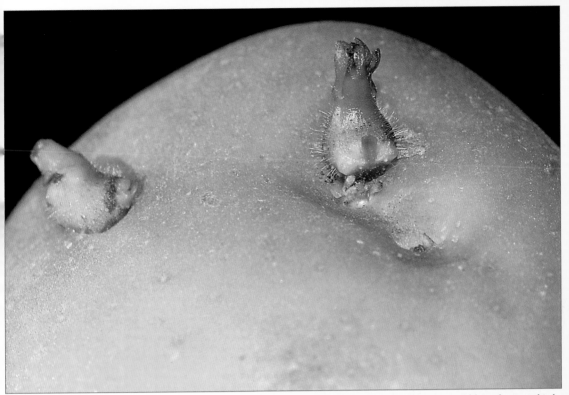

Something as innocent-looking as a sprouted potato can cause problems for your birds. They contain a poison called solanin, so mustn't be fed raw.

primary lesions in the crop, possibly through to the proventriculus, the oesophagus and mouth. The wall of the crop is thickened and ulcerated, along with haemorrhagic spots, and necrotic tissue will be evident. The crop contents will be sour-smelling; those of the intestine watery in consistency.

Any attempt to treat sour crop without the help of veterinary medicine is likely to prove futile, and the condition is likely to reoccur. Preventative measures include maintaining drinker and feeder hygiene, this being especially important where mash is fed, and even more so if it's fed wet, and not consumed in one feed.

PENDULOUS CROP

This condition affects adult chickens and turkeys (more so the latter, in which there seems to be some genetic involvement). The crop becomes enlarged either due to excessive water consumption, possibly during a hot spell and/or because of failure of the muscles associated with the organ's functioning. In either case it's unlikely to return to a normal size, and never empties properly. The food that remains trapped within begins to ferment and sour crop will follow.

The symptoms include an enlarged, flaccid crop, the contents of which are watery and sour. There is no effective treatment and affected birds should be culled.

CROP & GIZZARD IMPACTION

This is quite a common complaint in chickens and turkeys. It's caused by birds consuming long, tough grass, string, feathers, straw or other litter material, thus preventing food exiting the crop or the gizzard, and effectively blocking its passage through the gut. Nerve damage as a result of Marek's disease may cause paralysis of the muscles involved with the proper working of these organs, and is another possible cause. These problems may not become immediately apparent, only becoming so as birds lose condition.

Affected birds become progressively thinner and weaker, taking on the appearance of culls. On handling, the offending material can be felt in the crop. Records may show a tie-up between the symptoms and the introduction to range. On post mortem examination the crop and/or gizzard will be found to be packed with tangled coarse material which shows no signs of

movement through the system. The carcass will show some degree of emaciation.

Where the complaint is solely the result of birds eating coarse material, and it's only the crop that's affected, the organ can be gently massaged to move-on the material, or to manipulate it back up through the mouth for removal. Administering a teaspoon of olive oil beforehand may help. Should this fail, surgery is the other option, but this requires veterinary assistance. If the gizzard is blocked there is no remedy.

The incidence of crop and gizzard impaction can be reduced if birds are not allowed access to long, coarse grass when they are first let out on range. Likewise, litter materials of similar type are best avoided. Chicks should be given insoluble grit (either granite or flint); introduced at a few days of age, and fed in small quantity every week. This will help develop a strong gizzard, and prevent associated digestive problems. As the birds grow, coarser grit should be offered.

Vaccinating against Marek's disease will help prevent the complaint when it's of a constitutional origin, rather than a mechanical one. 🐦

HEALTHY HENS?

Bob Cross looks at poultry problems with an explanation of Blackhead, plus a handful of the most common parasites which affect poultry.

BLACKHEAD

Also known as Histomoniasis and Enterohepatitis, Blackhead is caused by a protozoa – Histomonas meleagridis. It affects turkeys, game birds and peafowl and, while chickens possess a certain degree of natural resistance to it, the disease occasionally occurs among these birds too. Transmission can be direct via infected water, feed or droppings, or indirectly through the bird ingesting the eggs of the caecal worm Heterakis gallinarum, which are infected with the histomonads.

The histomonas protozoan survive within the worm's egg, and can withstand desiccation plus high and low temperatures which, in the open, would kill it. Given this protection, the organism can remain infectious on the ground from one season to the next. When the worm eggs are eaten they hatch and the worms burrow into the wall of the caeca and, at the same time,

the heterakis are released. They multiply rapidly in the tissues of the caecal walls, causing a lot of damage and trauma. Some are picked up by the blood stream and migrate to the liver, invading and destroying it. Because of their vulnerability, turkeys used to be reared on wire floors so (in theory) they had no contact with their droppings, containing the histomonas or the infected worm eggs, thus breaking the cycle and interrupting transmission.

Symptoms: Where turkeys are affected, the birds rapidly become weak with dropped wings and ruffled feathers. They stand around with heads drooped and/or drawn into the shoulders. Feed consumption is reduced and growth stops. Watery diarrhoea will be noticed and this may be followed by sulphur-yellow droppings as the liver succumbs. As the name implies, there may be some darkening of the head parts.

This disease is normally associated

with young stock (typically 8-16 weeks) when the symptoms are most pronounced. The disease is more protracted in older stock, causing unthriftiness. Mortality in young, unchecked turkeys, may be 100% although more usually it's 20-50%; less in older birds.

In chickens the symptoms are less marked but similar, but the sulphur-coloured droppings may not feature. Mortality is much lower than in turkeys, usually less than 10%. The major losses are those associated with egg production and body weight.

Effects: The walls of the caeca are swollen and may be ulcerated – peritonitis may result where the ulcers perforate. The caeca contain a creamy-grey-coloured core, possibly streaked with blood and of cheese-like consistency. Circular, crater-like necrotic lesions (described as 'dartboard lesions') on the surface of the liver, varying in

Scaly leg mite causes very obvious swelling; the legs become deformed with a crusty build-up. Never let things get as bad as this!

Effective treatment for parasites can be achieved by spraying birds individually with a suitable product, especially around the tail and under the wings.

number from a few, to enough to almost cover it. In chickens it may be that lesions don't proceed beyond those associated with invasion of the caecal wall. But the presence of caecal cores and liver lesions appear to give a pretty conclusive diagnosis. Veterinary guidance should be sought without delay to keep losses to a minimum.

Treatment: In the past 'chemotherapeutics' have been used for the treatment, control and prevention of blackhead; Dimetridazole and Nifurzol being the two major players. However, their EU approval was withdrawn, and they are no longer available. There may be other treatments – especially where the birds are not kept for human consumption and/or withdrawal periods are not an issue. But because treatment is difficult, the emphasis is now on prevention by other methods. Strict sanitation is vital; houses must be thoroughly cleaned and disinfected before restocking.

Drinkers and feeders must not become contaminated with faecal matter. They should be physically cleaned regularly, and correctly hung and/or placed on wire mesh platforms as appropriate. Keeping the litter dry and friable will help reduce the histomona survival rate, and worming flocks will reduce the

challenge too. Where both chickens and turkeys are kept, they should be isolated, and simple precautions taken to prevent transmission on clothes and footwear. Correct management and husbandry practices will pay dividends (as always), reducing stress levels which will leave the bird more able to resist a challenge. Also, good observational skills will help early detection of the disease, thus reducing losses.

PARASITES

Parasites are classified according to whether they live outside or inside the host – 'ectoparasites' or 'endoparasites' respectively.

Ectoparasites affecting poultry include lice, fleas and mites, and all are insect-type creatures that live off the skin cells and/or by sucking blood or tissue fluids. In small numbers they cause few problems but, given the right conditions, they multiply rapidly to detrimentally affect the health and productivity of the host bird. Damage is caused by severe irritation and through anaemia. In the worst cases it can be enough to kill the bird.

Losses from parasites are not as striking as those from infectious diseases, and often go untreated. However they are probably more

common and, due to the depressive effect they have on production and welfare, they must be regarded with equal importance. These sorts of parasites are found wherever poultry are kept, but wild birds and other animals are also affected. Parasite life cycles vary. Some are host-specific, while others can live on a range of hosts including humans. Some will stay put for life, while other move on and off the host.

Ectoparasites arrive in various ways, being brought in by wild birds and on infested poultry, or by being carried on clothing and equipment. Because the generation time is so short, parasite numbers can build up extremely rapidly, especially during the warm summer months. With this in mind it's very important to be vigilant, observing and handling birds regularly to identify problems before they arise.

With regard to treatment, many effective cures are available 'off the shelf', but it's also worth consulting your vet because there may be a better option that requires their dispensation.

LICE

While there are probably 40 varieties of lice, it's only the 'body', 'head', 'wing' and 'shaft' types that are of much ▶

This bird is infested with lice. It's possible to see lumps of matted feather material, and the louse eggs.

interest to the poultry keeper – the name indicating the area of the bird where they live. The most common (and most important in economic terms) is the 'body' or large louse, Eomenacanthus stramineus, which remains on the host at all times.

These measure 2.8-3.3mm in length, are pale yellow-brown in colour and are usually found on the less densely-feathered parts of the body, especially those around the vent area. Often, if the feathers are parted in these areas, they can be seen running around on the skin. Adult females lay eggs in clusters that stick to the base of the feathers and, often, the eggs and feather material becomes matted. The eggs hatch in about seven days, then take a further 14-28 to reach maturity and repeat the life cycle.

These lice live for several months, breeding throughout the year; it's been estimated that a single pair could produce 120,000 descendants in a season! Lice feed on feather and dead skin cells, but also bite into the living tissue and consume blood, other body cells and fluid. Consequently, heavy infestations cause severe irritation, producing reduced growth rates, egg

numbers and even death. Younger birds seem to suffer more, lacking the constitution to cope with the challenge.

The 'wing louse' (Lipeurus caponis) lives on the primary and secondary feathers. producing a jagged or serrated appearance. The 'head louse' (Lipeurus heterographus) is most harmful to young birds, especially those reared under broody hens. The 'shaft louse' (Menopon gallinae) lives on the shafts of the feathers.

Control measures: Treat infested flocks with a suitable powder or spray, as per the manufacturer's directions, repeating the treatment to kill any lice that subsequently hatch, until the problem is gone. Dust bathing facilities are a natural way of controlling many external parasites, and adding insecticidal powder to them can further enhance their efficacy.

FLEAS

The poultry flea – Ceratophyllus gallinae – is similar in size to the common louse, but is obviously darker in colour (brownie-black). It also has a flattened body and, instead of running, it jumps. Unlike lice, though, fleas remain on the body of the host only while they are

feeding, and they do this by biting through the skin and sucking blood; once or twice a day. Having fed, they return to the litter and nest material. Several eggs are laid during the day while on the host, and these fall to the floor where they hatch in about seven days.

Small larvae emerge and feed on debris in the litter. The maggots develop and undergo several moults over a period of months, eventually hatching into fleas. The fleas move on to the body of the host and suck blood, becoming fully mature within a few days. In warm weather the flea can complete its life cycle in about a month. They can live fo over a year, and can survive without food for weeks.

Control measures: Fleas are not normally a problem with poultry, but infestations can occur in deep-litter houses. As fleas spend much of their life off the host, their control is difficult. Not only must the bird be treated, but also the litter, nests, house etc. In the event of an outbreak the house must be depopulated to stand any chance of eradicating the problem. The birds should be treated with one the insecticide sprays or powders available for this purpose, then moved to new quarters. All litter, including that from the nests must be burnt, and the house washed and disinfected.

Use a disinfectant with either insecticidal properties, or one that can be mixed with diesel and water to form an emulsion and ensure a more destructive and long-lasting effect.

MITES

Mites are much smaller than both lice and fleas, and there three types worthy of note here: red mite, northern mite and scaly leg mite.

The red mite (Dermanyssus gallinae) is about is about 0.7mm long with an oval body. It's yellowish-brown in colour, becoming red after it has fed. It spends most of its time in cracks and crevices in the house – particularly in perch sockets, joints and nest fittings, only living on the birds at night, during which time it feeds. During warm weather, the life cycle takes around seven days, and red mite can live away from the host for several months.

The northern mite (Lyponyssus sylviarum) is about 1.0mm long, but otherwise similar to the red mite. However, the big difference is that it can be found on the bird at all times; when picking up infested birds, the mites run on to the handler's hands and arms. They are typically found in the vent and tail area, and on the breast. The feathers around the vent may become matted.

Infestations of both northern and red mites not only cause irritation and discomfort, but also anaemia. In severe cases it can kill the host; the bird dies suddenly overnight. Other signs of these mites include brownish-red spots on the egg shells, a reduction in egg numbers, fertility, growth rates, loss of condition plus pale combs and wattles. With red mite especially, there may be an increase in the number of eggs laid on the floor of the house, as the hens become reluctant to suffer the discomfort of infested nest boxes.

Control measures: Where a red mite problem is identified, all fixtures and fittings should be treated with a suitable insecticide (preferably one with a residual action). There are a number of products on the market, so consult the supplier for advice about which to use, and the best method to adopt.

Northern mite is more difficult to control because they live on the bird at all times. However, there are sprays and powders available, and treatment needs to be applied directly to the birds, treating each one individually. It should be repeated after a seven-day interval, at least twice, to break the breeding cycle.

However, regardless of the type of mite, when the house is emptied it should be cleaned and disinfected in the same way as described for flea control, but paying particular attention to cracks, crevices and joints. When moving birds they should be routinely treated just in case they are harbouring parasites, and to prevent carry-over to a 'clean' environment.

Scaly leg mite (Cnemidocoptes mutans) affects chickens, turkeys, game and cage birds, but not waterfowl. It's a tiny, spherical creature with a diameter of less than 0.5mm, which spends its entire life on the bird burrowing into the skin of the legs. As a consequence, the scales become raised, the legs appearing thickened, rough and lumpy. If left unchecked, they will eventually become severely deformed. Close inspection will reveal dry, grey material under the scales, and affected birds will develop walking difficulties in the worst of cases. Older birds with looser scaling, and those with feathered legs, are the most susceptible, but it's not exclusive to these categories. Even chicks hatched under a hen suffering with the condition can become afflicted. The mite can also attack the comb and wattles.

Control measures: Affected birds should be isolated, and those with severe infestations should be sacrificed. The house must be cleaned as previously described. Proprietary treatments are now available, but remedies used in the past include; washing the legs using a tooth brush to get under the scales, then dressing the legs with either sulphur ointment or Vaseline, or dipping them in a solution of paraffin and linseed oil. If attempting the dipping method, it's important not to get the solution above the hock joint otherwise it'll cause sever distress to the bird.

Scaly leg mite is probably the one parasite where prevention is not only the best option, but also a realistic one. When buying-in stock check them carefully. If they are infested then walk away and find some 'clean' birds. Also, as a further precaution, my advice is to treat apparently clean birds before introducing or reintroducing them to the site. There's no point in taking chances. ❧

'Greasy' feathers around the tail are a typical sign of insect pest infestation.

HEALTHY HENS?

Bob Cross discusses a few of the more common poultry complaints, and considers some typical egg problems too.

BUMBLEFOOT

This is the quaint name given to a condition where abscesses develop on the footpad, between the toes. It's caused by bacterial invasion, and is likely to be Staphylococcus aureus. It's common in turkeys and chickens, with older, heavier birds worst affected. The bacteria, which is ubiquitous (especially so in dirty conditions), gains entry to the foot via a cut or a puncture wound, caused by the bird treading on nails, splinters, thorns or wire etc.

Typical symptoms include lameness, with the affected foot and toes becoming swollen and hot. A spherical blister may develop between the toes, and the infected areas fill with pus. If left untreated, the infection can appear to clear up in some cases without human intervention, leaving a corn at the site of infection. But, in others, the infection may spread up the leg, further complicating matters.

Treatment involves lancing the wound and squeezing out the accumulated material within; this may be pus or a harder, cheese-like matter. The wound should then be bathed with an antiseptic

Mini eggs have no particular significance, and are often caused by a tiny foreign object entering the oviduct and triggering the normal secretions, as a yolk would.

solution. The bird must be allowed to recuperate in a small coop with clean bedding, and repeated dressing may be necessary. If treatment seems ineffective, the infection spreads or the bird's welfare is compromised, then you should get veterinary assistance, or sacrifice the bird.

EGG BINDING

Obstruction of the oviduct is commonly caused by the presence of an unusually large egg in the system. Affected birds are seen repeatedly visiting the nest, and straining to lay an egg. Upon handling the bird, an egg may be felt, or even seen, just inside the vent.

Assisting the bird to pass the egg by smearing the vent with olive oil or Vaseline may be effective. Alternatively, an old remedy involved steaming the vent over a jug of boiling water. If these measures are unsuccessful, the egg must be removed by other means. Inserting a finger into the vent, while applying pressure to the abdomen with the palm of the other hand to expel the egg, should be tried initially. If this fails, the egg must be broken *in situ*.

A hole is made in the end of the egg and, holding the hen accordingly, the contents are drained and the egg shell

Setting the correct perching height inside the hen house can play a big part in helping to eliminate the risk of bumblefoot. Ramps are a good idea too.

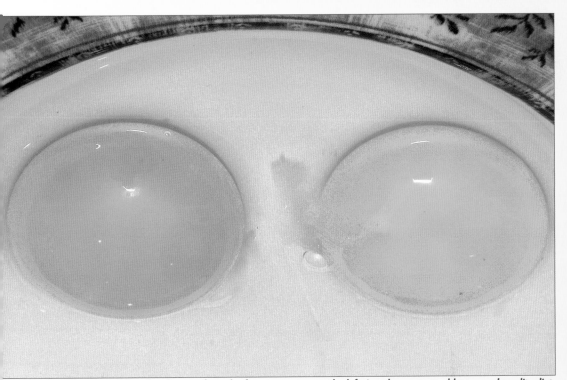

Spot the difference? Rich yolk colour, as from the free-range egg on the left, is only guaranteed by a good quality diet.

fragments removed, making sure to get all bits. Whichever method is chosen, cleanliness is vital if you're to avoid the oviduct becoming infected (most likely if you have to break the egg). Consequently, unless the bird is of particular value, it's probably as well to kill it. Egg binding may also cause muscle damage, so recovered birds may suffer further with prolapsus.

PROLAPSUS
This is an inversion of the oviduct, and it may be caused as a result of the bird experiencing egg binding, an inflammation of the oviduct, or a weakening of the muscles that retain this organ in position as a result of heavy production. As such, it's only seen in females.

It's not infectious or contagious, however, a number of cases may be seen in young pullets which have been forced into lay without having the physical constitution to do so.

One of the main symptoms is that the end of the oviduct can be seen protruding form the vent. The condition usually occurs without warning, although eggs with bloodstains on the shell can provide a valuable clue that all is not well.

Treatment is simple, but is unfortunately unlikely to be successful. The bird should

be removed form the rest of the flock, the organs bathed in an antiseptic solution, and then carefully pushed back into place. It should then be allowed time to recover in a small coop. As a result of bacteria entering, peritonitis may ensue and, even if the bird recovers, the condition is likely to reoccur when it starts to lay again. With this in mind – and especially if other birds have pecked the wound – it's probably as well to kill the bird to prevent further suffering.

Ensuring pullets are well developed before they commence lay, and avoiding over-stimulation with lighting, are measures that will lessen the likelihood of this condition occurring.

EGG PERITONITIS
Egg peritonitis is an inflammation of the peritoneum – the thin lining of the abdomen. The disorder often arises when yolk material enters the abdominal cavity, instead of passing down the oviduct in the normal manner. It subsequently becomes contaminated, and bacteria sets up the inflammation. It can also result from oviduct or intestinal ruptures.

The normal path for a yolk to take, after release from the ovary, is to pass into the 'ovarian pocket'. This is a space surrounding the ovary, and the easiest –

and usually only – way out of there is through the oviduct, entering via the funnel-shaped entrance or infundibulum. In the majority of cases this is what happens but, if a bird undergoes some physical shock causing an ovum to be released, it may be forced past the infundibulum and fall into the abdomen. The same may happen with birds as they recover from certain viral diseases, such as infectious bronchitis. Damage done by this disease to the reproductive tract may prevent the yolks entering the oviduct so, again, they end up in the abdomen.

While the bird is alive it's difficult to diagnose egg peritonitis. In acute cases, the victim will show little interest in life, blue combs, dropped abdomens, and diarrhoea may be noted, but these signs alone are not conclusive. Most casualties are found dead and, upon post mortem examination, the abdomen will be found to be inflamed, smell putrid and yolk material will be present. Where a ruptured intestine is responsible, perforations or ulcers will be present on this organ.

Unfortunately, there's no treatment. Laying birds should be handled with care, and taking steps to avoid causing panic while working among them, are key points in preventing this condition. House design, with regard to perch and ▶

Careful handling and regular inspection can reveal much about the health of your birds. It's sometimes possible, if a hen is egg bound, to feel the offending egg with your hands.

will vary according to the severity; it's likely to be at its peak during the first 72 hours after hatching. Some chicks may be found dead in the incubator while others will struggle on until the end of the first week. Those that survive are unlikely to catch up with the rest of the flock, and will appear as culls later on in life.

Upon post mortem examination, the chicks' abdomens are found to be soft or mushy, the carcass emaciated and the muscling red. The yolk may be brown in colour, being granular or lumpy and watery in consistency, as opposed to the yolk in a healthy chick, which is yellow-green in colour, and viscous emulsion-like in texture. When opening the carcasses they emit an unpleasant odour. It's advisable to submit carcasses to a veterinary laboratory to confirm diagnosis, and to eliminate other possible infections.

Treatment is not practicable, as the drugs are unlikely to penetrate the yolk – the centre of the infection. All affected chicks should be culled and the management for the survivors adjusted to give them more comfort and easier access to food and water. Maintaining strict hygiene, from the time the egg is laid through to the end of the chicks' first week of life, will help reduce the bacterial challenge. Good husbandry and careful handling of chicks after they leave the incubator should help reduce stress, and give the young birds every chance of fighting the bacterial threat.

nest box height, should also be considered; both should be kept as low as possible.

Vaccination against Newcastle disease and Infectious bronchitis will help reduce the incidence where their involvement is linked to the problem.

YOLK SAC INFECTION

This condition is also known as 'mushy chick disease', and is an infection that develops from within the chick. It's the result of contamination by a number of bacteria; Bacillus cereus, Staph. aureus and E. coli are three often involved. The first named is capable of breaking down yolk material and, once this has occurred, secondary infections set-in causing the death of the chick from bacterial toxaemia. The bacteria are likely to be present in incubators and poultry houses, and become a problem when standards of hygiene are allowed to fall. The disease is not infectious and so isn't passed from chick to chick, but contamination in the incubator can become progressively worse in

subsequent hatches, as the bacteria multiplies.

Newly hatched chicks have little resistance to bacteria. Having entered the body via the intestinal and respiratory routes, it migrates to the yolk sac where infection sets in. Unhatched chicks can become infected as the bacteria can pass through the pores in the eggshell. It's worth noting that even eggs that appear clean will be covered in many thousands of bacteria; those with obvious dirt on will be covered in teeming millions, and the conditions in an incubator are ideal for their multiplication. The bacteria responsible are fairly commonplace and, under normal conditions, not particularly virulent. However, stresses such as incubation faults, chilling and high levels of contamination, leave the chick weakened and vulnerable.

Infected chicks appear drowsy, and reluctant to move about. When they do they tend to stagger, many remain close to the heat source unless bullied away by the stronger, healthy chicks. Mortality

OMPHALITIS

Much of what has been said about yolk sac infection also applies to omphalitis, which is also known as 'navel-ill'. However, this condition is really an infection of the navel and the surrounding tissues. When the chick emerges from the egg, the yolk sac is drawn into the body through the navel. After this has happened the entry point heals over and dries out. But, until the navel is completely dry it remains vulnerable to attack from bacteria, most probably Staphylococcus aureus. If infection takes place here the navel, and the area around it, becomes putrid, the contamination spreads and the chick dies.

Again, prevention is really the only solution; contamination comes from dirty eggs being set, dirty conditions in the incubator and poor personal hygiene among those people handling the chicks and eggs. So set only clean eggs, maintain cleanliness in the incubator, with an ongoing disinfection programme throughout incubation, and wash hands in a bactericidal soap before handling eggs or chicks and between batches.

ABNORMAL EGGS

Blood spots: Those found in the yolk are caused by a haemorrhage from a blood vessel in the ovary before ovulation, while those in the white come as the result of a blood vessel in the oviduct rupturing. The amount of blood may be anything from a speck the size of a pinhead, to enough to colour the contents of the egg – the latter may be referred to as a 'blood egg'. There is no treatment, but eggs should be candled before sale to prevent any with blood spots getting to the customer.

Meat spots: These are either blood spots that become denatured and change their appearance or, in some cases, a small speck of tissue that has become detached from the oviduct wall as the egg passed down. Preventative measures are the same as for blood spots.

Double-yolk eggs: These are eggs where two yolks have been released almost simultaneously. They pass down the oviduct in the same way as a normal egg, and both yolks are encased in one shell. Occasionally more than two yolks are released, giving rise to other multi-yolk eggs. It's more common as pullets are coming into lay, and especially if this coincides with the long days of the summer months. Strictly speaking, a double-yolk egg is not of 'first quality' because, to comply, the yolk must be in the centre of the egg. If there are two yolks, neither one is.

Double yolk eggs are of no use for incubation. As long as the bird has the physical condition to lay eggs like these, no treatment is called for, and the situation should right itself after a few eggs have been produced.

Mini eggs: These are eggs often measuring as little as 1cm in diameter. They may be caused by a tiny foreign object entering the oviduct, and triggering the normal secretions as a yolk would. Alternatively, it can even happen spontaneously. These tiny eggs do not signify the start or end of lay, and it's likely that only one will be laid. Consequently, no treatment is needed.

Eggs within eggs: This is a very rare occurrence. When it does happen it results in a very large egg being laid, which is found to contain another shelled egg inside. It may be caused by the hen becoming shocked when an egg was in the final stages of development. This causes the egg to travel back up the oviduct, where it meets the next one coming down. The direction of travel is again reversed, and the two eggs come back down the oviduct and are encased together in a second shell. It's unlikely to reoccur.

Yolk colour: Deep orange is the colour most consumers desire and expect. This comes naturally where laying hens have access to grass runs. Using certain feeds, or pigments, for intensively-housed stock will achieve similar results. Occasionally, other colours of yolk are produced; pale-coloured yolks may be as a result of birds being deprived of green stuff, or it may be that they are infested with parasitic worms. Certain additives may cause yolks to become mottled. For example, green acorns result in olive green yolks, and shepherds purse and pennycress may also colour the yolk green. Prevention is simple; feed the correct diet and, where birds are kept on range, make sure there is plenty of grass so they aren't forced to eat the only green food that's available. ❦

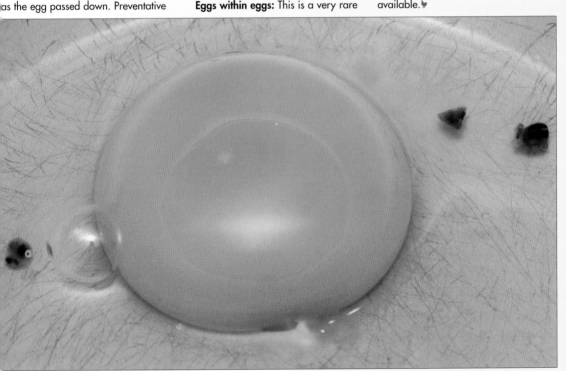

Meat spots are blood spots that become denatured and change their appearance, or specks of tissue that become detached from the oviduct wall as the egg passes down.

THE POULTRY DIGESTIVE SYSTEM

Lindsay Sissons explanatory journey from the mouth to the stomach, via the beak and crop!

Here's a little anatomy and physiology to get you started. Figure 1 shows the digestive system of a chicken. Understanding how this works helps greatly when thinking about nutrition and management. Birds have a high metabolism and have developed their digestive systems to be able to take large quantities of food in a short space of time, and then to digest it efficiently. The food travels very quickly through the gut so that flight is not hampered by a heavy load.

At the start of the digestive process there's the beak, which is formed from keratin; the same material used for horn and hair. It grows continuously to allow for wear and tear, but this can become a problem for housed birds eating soft food. Overgrowth can occur, as in Fig. 1, and this condition can affect both feeding and drinking. If this happens, then the beak needs to be trimmed using a pair of straight-bladed nail clippers.

> *"Always keep an eye out for excessive beak growth."*

CAREFUL CLIPPING

The live tissue in the beak is shown by the shaded area, and the dotted line indicates the ideal clip line. When doing this the bird should be restrained under one arm, leaving the other hand free for clipping. It's even easier if another person helps. The head must be held firmly and the beak clipped carefully until it resembles what's shown in Fig. 2. Always keep an eye out for excessive beak growth. Your birds will be much happier if you never allow it to become a problem.

Unfortunately, some birds will suffer with beak deformities serious enough to warrant culling. The worst of these is where the lower beak develops much shorter than the upper beak (Fig. 3), causing severe eating and drinking problems. This is a deformity

that is inherited, so again, these birds should not be kept. A breeding target would be to find the lines that carry this deformity, and to breed it out. Bantam Leghorns often have this problem.

Another deformity to watch for is 'twisted beak' (Fig. 4), where the beak veers to one side or the other instead of running straight. Once again, this hampers feeding and so birds showing this problem are best culled. Some breeds also have problems with a so-called 'open beak' (Fig. 5), where there's a gap between upper and lower beaks. This can also impede feeding ability. Ex-battery birds will often have the top beak clipped to half its length, to prevent feather pulling in their stressful environment (Fig. 6).

Beaks vary across the poultry classes. A duck bill is highly sensitive and fairly pliable to allow probing and dabbling – dabbling ducks also

have a feathery fringe to the bill to allow filtering of their food. There are no teeth either, so the chewing of the food is impossible. What's more, birds don't swallow as we do, having no soft palate, and a less mobile tongue. All they've got is an immovable hard palate and swallowing is achieved by the bird throwing its head back to move the food into the oesophagus.

Poultry saliva contains no enzymes; it's purely there to provide lubrication. The oesophagus (or gullet) is designed to be able to take large pieces of food; it has longitudinal folds that can stretch out and take wide mouthfuls easily. Anybody who's watched a duck swallow a whole snail will understand this!

CROP GATHERING

The crop is a large pouch situated at the base of the neck, on the left-hand side, and is easy to see and feel when full. The food is held in here to be

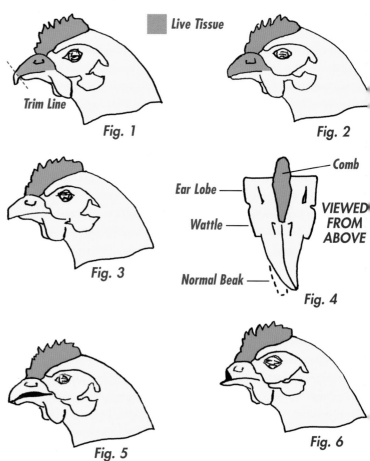

Live Tissue

Trim Line

Fig. 1

Fig. 2

Fig. 3

Ear Lobe — Comb

Wattle —

Normal Beak —

VIEWED FROM ABOVE

Fig. 4

Fig. 5

Fig. 6

"Food can move both forwards and backwards between the two parts of the stomach."

softened; dry food takes up water and swells. The crop is a good guide to whether a bird is eating or not.

Once softened, the food is then moved to the stomach, by waves of contractions along the oesophagus. A chicken's stomach consists of two parts, and the first of these that the food reaches is called the proventriculus. This is the glandular section, where acid and the digestive enzyme pepsin (used to break down protein) are produced. Part two of the process occurs in the gizzard, which is very muscular and has strong, rough, ridges over its surface to break down the food by mechanical action. Grit is used as an abrasive agent here against whole grains and seeds etc., which is why grit is such an essential dietary requirement. Birds kept on a free-range basis will find enough grit from the soil, but housed birds must be given a supplement.

Food can move both forwards and backwards between the two parts of the stomach, ensuring good protein digestion and a small food particle size to aid ultimate digestion. Once the food has been adequately digested, it's moved out of the gizzard and into the duodenum, which we'll look at in more detail next month. For now, though, I'm going to concentrate on beak and oral cavity-related problems.

FOWL POX
This condition can often cause lesions inside the mouth (they'll have a thick white coating), and there are normally other scab-like lesions over the featherless parts of the bird's head. Fowl pox is not common in the UK, but when seen, culling of affected birds is advised as it's a viral disease and there's no treatment available.

THRUSH
The yeast Candida albicans is a common inhabitant of the upper gastrointestinal tract of poultry. Thrush (crop mycosis, or candidiasis) usually only results if the immune status of the bird is low; if it's stressed (environmentally or nutritionally), diseased or following a long course of antibiotics. Antibiotics do not only reduce bacteria that are harmful to the bird, but they also wipe out those

bacteria that form a protective layer over the skin and mucosal surfaces – the lining of the mouth, oesophagus, crop etc. This allows opportunistic bacteria, fungi or yeasts (such as Candida albicans) to multiply unchecked, and cause various types of disease.

The lining at the site of infection becomes thickened, and ulcerated areas with thick white cheesy matter over the top will develop. This is more common in younger birds. Treatment is by copper sulphate in the drinking water. Temporary control is gained with the anti-fungal agent nystatin, which has effects on yeasts, especially C. albicans, and is administered by giving drops into the mouth. Gentian violet may also have some short-term effect.

Control is governed by reducing any stresses on the bird. Ensure a clean environment, a static grouping so pecking order is not disturbed and correct feeding etc. Also, avoid the long-term use of antibiotics if possible.

CROP IMPACTION
This problem is often seen with free range poultry. No chewing means that grass blades that are several inches long cannot be broken down in the mouth, and so go through the gut still at this length. While sitting in the crop, these blades (or other materials such as plastic and string) become wound together into a plug that cannot go on down through the oesophagus. Anything else that the bird then eats just sits on top of that plug until the crop becomes distended, and feels hard to the touch.

Emptying the crop is achieved by running some warm water down the chicken's throat (giving it time to breathe), massaging the crop and then tipping the bird upside-down, and continuing to massage until the crop contents are expelled through the mouth. The 'upside-down' part needs to be done quite quickly to ensure that the bird isn't too long without a breath, and doesn't breathe in any of the fluid. There is a knack to this, so it's worth joining your local poultry group where people will be only too willing to help and teach such techniques.

Controlling crop impaction involves

keeping birds on grass that's cut short. Avoid areas of uncut ground with tough, fibrous grasses. If a large number of birds are having this problem, a mixture of Epsom salts, molasses and vegetable oil apparently can help. I haven't tried this so can't speak from experience, but it does remind me of a 'gravy' that a farmer friend used to give ailing lambs, so there may be something in it!

GIZZARD IMPACTION
If the crop keeps refilling, even if the bird is on short, soft grass or indoors, the problem may well be a gizzard impaction. Here, the grass or other foreign matter that's got through the crop can form a rope that blocks the top of the intestinal tract where it joins the gizzard. Gizzard impaction is a much more serious condition and so I would advise culling.

Although any age of bird can be affected, young birds out on their first grass are especially susceptible as their gizzard will not have developed enough to cope with grass. This is also seen in birds that are on grass but are getting insufficient grit – if the soil has no stones in it, then additional grit should be provided. Other things to do are to mow regularly, and to remove clippings if they are long.

Now, once past the crop on our journey through the digestive system, there's less chance of bacterial or viral infection until we reach the other side of the stomach – but more of this next time. However, trauma is a risk anywhere really, though the oesophagus, after the crop, and the stomach are fairly well protected inside the skeleton.

ENDOPARASITES
There are many different types of worm that infect poultry of all sorts. Lots of them, such as Chilospirura, Dispharynx and Gongylonema are generally agreed to be non-pathogenic – not able to cause disease. There are two, however, that do deserve a mention.

Capillaria contorta and C. annulata are both hair-like worms found in the oesophagus and crop (C. contorta also found in the mouth), and are too small to be easily seen with the naked eye. They are found in chickens, ▶

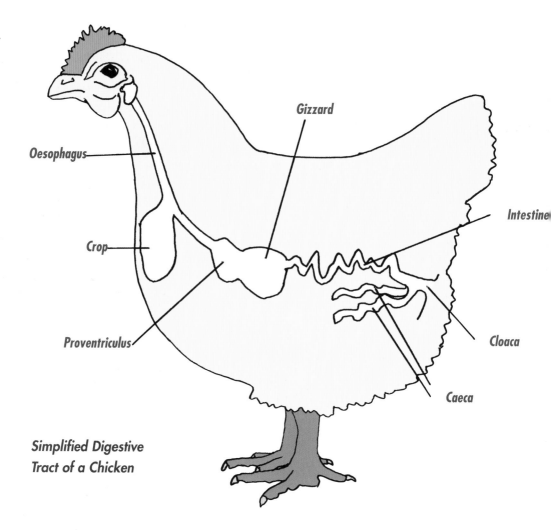

Oesophagus

Gizzard

Intestine

Crop

Proventriculus

Cloaca

Caeca

Simplified Digestive Tract of a Chicken

"These worms bury their heads into the lining of the mouth."

ducks, turkeys and wild birds, and the larvae develop inside earthworms before becoming infectious to birds. So if your outside birds are free-range, or live in a wire-topped run that wild birds sit on, and also have access to soil, then Capillaria is a risk. These worms bury their heads into the lining of the mouth, crop and/or oesophagus, causing inflammation and a diphtheric membrane (a thick layer of dead and dying cells) that reduces the normal contractions of that part of the gut, causing loss of appetite and rapid weight loss.

Worm burdens can be very high if ground conditions are right for the earthworms – wet ground around drinkers; feeding birds from the floor; high contact of wild birds or infected

poultry with the soil in which the earthworms live.

Tetrameres can also occur in free range poultry (fowl, waterfowl and pigeons) with the larvae developing in grasshoppers, beetles and crustaceans. They infect the proventriculus, and the female worms are bloodsuckers, so can cause anaemia if there are enough of them. Again, these worms bury their heads in the lining, but of the proventriculus this time, so local damage and infection are also seen. Young birds are most likely to succumb to this particular worm, although it's usually only present in moderate numbers and so no signs are seen in adults.

Treatment is with wormer, and the only one licensed for poultry is Flubendazole – only licensed for use

against roundworms and gapeworms, not against the two worms described. For accurate diagnosis and treatment details, contact your nearest poultry vet. Control and management are much more important. Controlling the intermediate host (earthworms, beetles, grasshoppers etc.) is impossible and impractical, so breaking the cycle of bird-to-intermediate-host-to-bird is more realistic. This can be done by resting the ground between flocks, or never putting birds on the same ground for two years running.

Small arks are the best solution for small flocks or groups of birds. With large flocks, the field system of a central house surrounded by four paddocks may be more practical. Wet patches of earth should be avoided if possible, so move outside drinkers around. Also position feed troughs away from the house pop holes, so that the ground around the doorway doesn't 'poach'. There are many different control measures that can be taken, but I'll go further down that wormy road next time!

The finely ground, almost liquid food leaves the gizzard and enters the small intestine, where it's mixed with bile and digestive enzymes. The bile neutralises acids from the stomach, and breaks down larger fat molecules. The digestive enzymes continue to work on the proteins, sugars and smaller fat molecules. Most of the absorption of these breakdown products takes place here; the large intestine is chiefly involved in the re-absorption of water.

Chickens also have a pair of long, blind-ending caecae, that correspond to our appendix. These contain a soup of micro-organisms that help to digest the cellulose from the plants that the birds eat – were it not for this, this extra nutritional source would be voided and lost.

Food is moved through the gut by peristalsis – waves of muscular contraction which propel the food along the intestines, towards the cloaca. The cloaca is the single opening through which all faecal products, urine and eggs/sperm are passed. A normal chicken dropping should have two distinct parts – a fairly firm greenish or brown part that is the faeces, and a white, pasty part that's the urine. Birds in a normal state of health will produce anything from 25 to 50 droppings a day, hence the need for regular mucking-out.

A colour change in the faecal part of the dropping may indicate a change of diet, or be a sign of disease; many infections produce different coloured faeces. Diarrhoea is indicated when the coloured part becomes runny, even though the white part will normally remain unchanged. A problem with the urogenital tract will change the consistency and/or colour of the white part of the dropping, while the faeces stays the same. A systemic disease, affecting more than one body system (both digestive tract and urogenital tract), will alter both parts of the dropping.

As with the upper part of the digestive tract, there are many infections, parasites and conditions that will affect the intestines and caecae. Starting with infectious causes of digestive upset, there are some that have additional consequences for humans, be it by direct contact, indirect contact or from the consumption of eggs, meat or meat products.

SALMONELLA

Salmonella has species that are either host-specific or non-host-specific. The host-specific Salmonella pullorum of chickens and turkeys is the cause of Pullorum disease. This has been eradicated from the UK poultry flock because of its production costs: it reduces egg numbers, reduces fertility and increases mortality and decreases growth in young birds. Salmonella gallinarum, which is again host-specific for chickens and occasionally turkeys, is uncommon in the UK, causing fowl typhoid. Signs are seen more often in growers and adult birds, especially outdoor flocks where the management is poor.

Some roundworms are also thought to be involved in the disease process. Affected birds show decreased production of eggs, reduced appetite, increased thirst, a yellow, jelly-like (mucoid) diarrhoea, depression and respiratory problems. Voluntary slaughter of affected flocks is suggested, but it's stated that owners can be reluctant to cull if exhibition birds are involved, leading to a reservoir of infection in the pure-breed exhibition flocks in this country. Wild birds are also listed as a potential reservoir for this infection, especially those feeding around outdoor pure-breed flocks.

The non-host-specific species of Salmonella cause relatively few disease signs in poultry, but lead to many cases of disease in humans. Found in chickens, turkeys and ducks among others, the bacteria tend to be carried in the gut (with their numbers kept low by the normal gut bacteria). When the eggs, meat or meat products are incorrectly stored or cooked and then eaten by humans, disease results. Salmonella enteridis and Salmonella typhimurium are the most commonly seen types.

The birds become infected through rodent contamination of the food or its constituents, by vertical transmission through the egg (both through bacteria on the shell and also in the contents), and/or if the birds are under environmental stress. The infection passes through the flock as birds eat food contaminated with the droppings, or by picking through litter contaminated in the same way. Chicks of under six weeks old are more likely to show signs of depression (huddling with fluffed feathers, not moving, not reacting to noises or movement around them), and will be more prone to diarrhoea and death, with slow growth seen in the survivors.

If Salmonella is suspected, post-mortem tests on the intestinal contents are used for diagnosis, with any positive results being reported to the State Veterinary Service. If S. enteridis or S. typhimurium are found, then the flock parenting the chicks will be slaughtered. Treatment is a hotly-debated subject – it's been shown that the use of antibiotics can increase the length of the time that a bird is a carrier (ie the bird does not show any signs itself, but sheds Salmonella bacteria in its droppings, remaining an infective risk to other birds and people coming into contact with it and its droppings). There are also many strains that are resistant to several different antibiotics, so bacterial culture and sensitivity tests should always be done before a course of antibiotics is started. Hence the usual advice to slaughter rather than treat. If treatment is viewed to be a valid alternative by the attending vet, high standards of hygiene, isolation and other biosecurity methods must be implemented. When eating eggs and meat from your own birds, it should be remembered that poor kitchen hygiene provides the greatest risk factor.

E. COLI

Esherichia (E) coli infection is a naturally occurring bacteria in the intestinal tract of poultry (as it is in many domesticated animals). Most of the strains do not cause disease, but there are a few that lead to diarrhoea, septicaemia (blood ▶

poisoning), enteritis and egg peritonitis, among others. The range of E. coli disease is very large and is more likely to occur if there are predisposing conditions, such as respiratory disease, vent injury or egg impaction in layers. Those strains that cause digestive signs tend to produce a toxin (enterotoxigenic E. coli) or be invasive (enteroinvasive E. coli). Infection of the eggs (caused by faecal contamination) is one of the main factors in transmission, so it's very important that nest boxes should be supplied and kept clean.

The main route of entry for disease into adult birds is via the respiratory tract – if the housing is kept well ventilated, regularly cleaned out to prevent build-up of droppings (and hence increased levels of E. coli in those droppings) and dry, this route can be controlled. As already stated, there have to be predisposing factors for this infection to cause disease. The main age group affected is from four to 12 weeks old. Mortality is usually no more than about 5%, but recovered birds will never do as well as a normal healthy bird.

E. coli is called a 'production disease' because it causes losses in carcass quality, lower food conversion rates and longer time before target weight is reached. Once the strain of E. coli has been determined by the vet, medication may be administered if the strain is sensitive to the antibiotics available. Again, many strains are resistant to many antibiotics. The checking and correction of any management and husbandry methods, is a far more valuable step to take in response to this infection to help with future prevention.

CAMPYLOBACTER
Another infection that's more of a worry to us than to the birds is Campylobacter, many species of which are normally found in the intestines of poultry. Again, Campylobacter species are often carried in the guts of birds with no signs of disease. Campylobacter jejuni is an important cause of diarrhoea with fever, stomach cramps and vomiting in humans, yet shows no signs in the birds. A carrier bird will shed bacteria with its faeces, so any contact with bird or droppings, or contamination of foods with bacteria through poor hygiene, may trigger human illness (or in domesticated animals).

Where predisposing factors are found (stressed birds in a poor environment, or another illness, say), birds can develop avian infectious hepatitis, which is a chronic illness, with few deaths and many sick birds for an extended period of time. Tracing the course of human illness will often find the source of the infection, but treatment is not an option as most birds carry this infection anyway, with no ill-effects. Preventing further outbreaks is again down to cleaning up the passage of food, or improving the hygiene and management of the birds and their keepers.

CLOSTRIDIAL DISEASES
These are often seen in litter-reared chickens and turkeys. Birds between two and 10 weeks old are affected, with the gut either breaking down or ulcerating; death follows illness and diarrhoea. The use of penicillins can control these necrotic and ulcerative enteritis problems. Clostridia are a

difficult, if not impossible, bacteria to eradicate, so hygiene and good management are the only means of prevention. If a very infectious strain is identified, it may be necessary to slaughter and move the site.

Botulism has different signs of paralysis (floppy, not rigid) and limberneck before death. The botulism can go on to cause deaths in cattle feeding on ground that has been spread with chicken litter – carcasses of the birds that hold the botulinum toxin are eaten by the cattle that then develop ascending paralysis and die. This has recently been a large problem in Northern Ireland, where some dairy herds have been wiped out. The bacteria themselves are not a problem, but the toxin that they manufacture is what does the damage. Once the paralysis is seen, there is no treatment for the condition apart from euthanasia.

Hygiene is a factor here – as long as all chicken carcasses are removed before litter is spread, there is less chance of an outbreak. The same holds true for smaller set-ups; all carcasses should be disposed of responsibly, especially if the bird died from an illness or was found dead with no apparent reason.

YERSINIOSIS
Now for just a quick word about Yersiniosis here. This infection is carried by wild birds, but only affects poultry in cases of poor environmental conditions and high infectious challenge. Children can develop signs similar to appendicitis, but again treatment is not used because improvements in hygiene and husbandry levels are more important, especially removing contact with wild birds.

VIRUSES
Viral infections can also affect the intestines of poultry. Duck Virus Enteritis is sometimes seen, and has resulted in large losses across Europe and Asia. Also called Duck Plague, it's caused by a Herpes virus and leads to photophobia (fear of light), loss of appetite with increased thirst and death, with or without watery diarrhoea. Mortality can be very high and the problem is usually linked to migratory wild waterfowl. Diagnosis is by postmortem, and positive results lead to quarantine and slaughter.

Coronavirus enteritis of turkeys, or Bluecomb disease, is a widespread condition that causes loss of appetite, thirst and diarrhoea. Some birds develop a dark head, and the death rate (mortality) can reach 100%. Diagnosis is from faeces and/or postmortem. Treatment is isolation and good management, with antibiotics only used to prevent secondary bacterial infection. Antibiotics have no effect on the virus itself – only the bird can fight that off – but we can help to prevent other bacteria from making matters worse.

PEMS
Poult Enteritis Mortality Syndrome, or PEMS, is a relatively new condition in

the UK, but has caused major losses in the USA turkey business. PEMS seems to be due to a combined infection of Coronavirus and Astrovirus (although nothing in this life is certain). It leads to depression (huddling, fluffed, non-responsive), loss of appetite and wet droppings. Young poults have a higher mortality, but any age of turkey can be affected. Recovery can take a few weeks, so even survivors take longer to mature to the required size, and profit margins are lost. Good basic husbandry and cleanliness seem pivotal to the incidence of this infection.

Other viral infections include Reovirus (causes yellow-tan coloured diarrhoea in young turkeys, malabsorption in chickens), Rotavirus (can occasionally cause diarrhoea in chickens and turkeys, often carried with no signs of disease in these and pheasants), and Aviadenovirus which causes Haemorrhagic Enteritis of Turkeys. This affects young turkeys with variable mortality, causing bloody diarrhoea and depression before death.

There's quite a range of worms and beasties that can take up residence in all species of poultry, and we'll start by considering the roundworm. Ascaridia galli and Ascaridia dissimilis are stout, thick, white worms. They are the largest worm found in poultry, with females reaching up to 12cm long. Infection is by eating an infective egg from faecally-contaminated food, soil or grass. The time it takes between eating the worm egg and the worm itself maturing sufficiently to start laying its own eggs, is six weeks in young birds and eight weeks in adults.

The eggs in the droppings on soil may be taken up and carried by earthworms, so birds with soil access may be at greater risk. The number of worm eggs in the soil of a run can rise very quickly, due to the short length of time from infection of a bird to egg production in its faeces. If the run is not moved, or the droppings not collected and removed, the number of infective eggs available to, and eaten by, the birds continually rises as the birds carry more and more.

The signs of roundworm presence can include weight loss, diarrhoea, huddling, feather fluffing and even death if a bird is heavily infected. Moderately infected birds may just be 'poor-doers', showing slow weight gain, and not being as alert or quick as the other birds. A large number of worms can cause a blockage of the intestine, leading to death. This is also a risk if worming a bird with a large worm burden – when a large number of worms die off at the same time as the wormer takes effect, they can knot together and cause an obstruction.

There is an increasing age-resistance to roundworm. As the bird gets older the intestinal environment changes, becoming less favourable for the worms' survival. Once birds pass the three-month mark the effects and size of a worm burden will reduce. Poor environmental conditions are once again a factor in worm numbers. Wet areas around drinkers, or boggy ground, can increase the numbers of infective eggs surviving in

"Moderately infected birds may just be 'poor-doers', showing slow weight gain."

the ground or bedding, thus increasing the chance of the birds becoming heavily infected. Soil-floored runs and cages allow access to earthworms that carry the worm egg safely inside them until the earthworm is eaten by a chicken – earthworms, of course, are present in large numbers in wet soil. Also bear in mind that an imbalanced diet may give birds less resistance to the worms, and so the worms have a more severe effect. A deficiency of vitamin A is thought to be a factor here.

The basic ground-rules of prevention are: 1. To feed a good balanced ration suitable for the bird that is eating it; 2. To keep runs and cages clean and not to allow droppings to mount up; 3. To feed from a feeder or trough, not from the floor; 4. To move soil-based runs regularly on to fresh ground; 5. To worm 'at risk' birds regularly with Flubenvet (one tsp per 9kg of food, daily for a week – there is no need for egg withdrawal). Worm the whole flock together. If moving runs on to completely fresh ground, or moving stock indoors, worm for five days before moving and for a couple of days after, then

the new ground or cage should be worm-free.

The second important roundworm is Heterakis gallinarum. At only 1-2cm long, thick and white, this worm does not worry the birds (chickens and turkeys) in its own right. It owes its importance to the fact that it carries another parasite – Histomonas meleagridis, which causes blackhead. Heterakis is more often found in outdoor and free-range birds. As in Ascaridia, the eggs can be carried by earthworms, or just in the soil or food that has been contaminated by droppings from an infected bird. After being eaten the worms take about 27 days to reach egg-laying maturity, but usually cause no sign of disease. The same methods of prevention outlined earlier apply in this case too.

BLACKHEAD

Blackhead, or Histomoniasis, is an important condition in turkeys that are housed outdoors. Histomonas meleagridis is a protozoan (a single-cell organism) that infects the liver of the bird that has swallowed it. The bird will have either unwittingly eaten an infective egg of Heterakis, or an earthworm that's carrying Heterakis eggs.

Histomonas can survive inside a Heterakis egg in an earthworm for as long as the earthworm lives, so infective organisms are in the soil for several years. Signs of Blackhead can be seen 14 days after infection, and include loss of appetite, yellow droppings and depression.

Mortality in turkeys can be up to 90% if the condition isn't treated. Survivors will have chronic damage to the liver and caecum. The liver becomes marked with circular yellow sunken areas, that are unmistakable. Chickens and game birds can also be affected, although to a much lesser degree. Chickens are often a link to turkey infection, as they carry Heterakis and Histomonas with little or no signs, and turkey infection can often be traced to ground shared with, or formerly used by, chickens. Sitting hens if used to hatch turkey eggs, may infect the young poults very early in life.

There are only two drugs licensed for the prevention of Histomoniasis in this country. Emtryl pre-mix contains dimetridazole and is licensed for use ▶

in game birds, either in water or in feed. There is a seven-day withdrawal for meat, and it should not be used with laying birds. Salfuride 50 contains nitrofursol, and is used as a pre-mix for feed. There is a five-day meat withdrawal. Prevention by means of reducing Heterakis infection is another option – this should be used alongside management steps such as not mixing turkeys and chickens, and not putting turkeys on to ground or litter used by chickens within the previous two years.

This may mean moving the turkeys indoors on to fresh litter, or on to raised or wire floors to prevent Heterakis infection. All birds should be treated together (whether signs are seen or not), and preventative drugs continued in any risk situations to prevent recurrence. Both of these drugs must be incorporated into the feed by the supplier (who has to be a Grade A manufacturer); local feed merchants will be able to point you in the right direction, but a prescription from a vet who has seen your birds may well be necessary.

TAPEWORM
A very large number of tapeworms are found in poultry, although many of these rarely cause a problem. An adult tapeworm buries its head in the lining of the bird's intestine. The body of the worm is usually made up of segments that mature as the creature grows; the tail segments are full of eggs and are shed, being passed to the outside with the droppings. The eggs mature in the environment, are ingested by an insect or snail (among others) and then infect the bird when it eats this insect or snail. The worm then develops in the intestine of the bird.

Davainea proglottina is often seen in poultry. It's only 0.5cm long and is carried by snails. The worms take between 10 and 15 days to mature in the bird. Just a few may be sufficient to cause weight loss, loss of condition of plumage, weakness and slow growth. A heavy burden can lead to bloody diarrhoea.

Raillietina tapeworms are longer (12-25cm, according to species) and some species are much more likely to cause disease. Raillietina cesticullus is found in beetles that the bird then eats, so becoming infected. Other species can be found in ants. Infection with a heavy load of Raillietina

tapeworms can cause marked weight loss, but there appears to be an age-related immunity to these worms (chicks over 10 weeks old are more resistant to infection). Prevention of all tapeworm infection centres around separating the birds from beetles, snails and ants – not an easy task. Treatment is very difficult as there are no licensed tape-wormers for poultry. Your local vet should get in touch with the drug companies manufacturing poultry roundworm products for advice. I will explain the rules of licensing and prescribing drugs in a later edition.

Trematodes, or flukes, are a waterfowl problem – birds become infected as they eat snails and molluscs that are carrying the fluke eggs. These cause fewer problems than tapeworms, and wildfowl can carry large numbers of these with no ill-effects. If there is a problem, separation of birds from molluscs and from wild waterfowl areas is a good start. I have been unable to find much

"The tail segments are full of eggs and are shed, being passed to the outside with the droppings."

information about these, so can assume they are of little importance healthwise.

OTHER PROBLEMS
Another infection that's more of a worry to us than to the birds is Campylobacter, many species of which are normally found in the intestines of poultry. Again, Campylobacter species are often carried in the guts of birds with no signs of disease. Campylobacter jejuni is an important cause of diarrhoea with fever, stomach cramps and vomiting in humans, yet shows no signs in the birds. A carrier bird will shed bacteria with its faeces, so any contact with birds or droppings, or contamination of foods with bacteria through poor hygiene, may trigger human illness (or in domesticated animals).

Where predisposing factors are found (stressed birds in a poor environment, or another illness, say), birds can develop avian infectious hepatitis, which is a chronic illness, with few deaths and many sick birds for an extended period of time. Tracing the course of human illness

will often find the source of the infection, but treatment is not an option as most birds carry this infection anyway, with no ill-effects. Preventing further outbreaks is again down to cleaning-up the passage of food, or improving the hygiene and management of the birds and their keepers.

CLOSTRIDIAL DISEASES
There are various other problems caused by trouble in a bird's intestine or caecae. Grass impaction can affect the first part of the small intestine – covered fully in Part 1 of this series. Trauma can happen anywhere: damage to the oviduct during egg impaction can result in peritonitis; feather pecking can cause damage to the vent that may scar and cause difficulties with egg laying; Marek's disease can affect the gizzard nerve, causing damage and loss of movement of the gizzard and small intestines, leading to death. The list is endless. The main means of prevention of all of these problems is observation. Keepers must learn to spot and correct the typical management mistakes – wet litter around drinkers, birds on grass that's too long, stale ground, dirty drinking water, poor house ventilation, lower pecking order birds not being allowed to eat, feather pecking, etc. Good management is having a gut instinct for when something is not quite right, then being able to work out and correct the problem to the best of your ability. Being able to spot birds that are a bit slow coming forward for feed, looking a bit fluffed, to know when a dropping is normal, to notice when some food is being left or when water intake goes up are all good ways to catch a problem early and hopefully nip things in the bud.

Never forget that a bird is a prey animal and, as such, its instinct is never to look sick or it gets eaten. So, by the time a bird start showing visible signs of sickness, you can be certain that it's very ill indeed. Watching your birds closely for a decent length of time each day, so that you learn what they normally do and how they behave, is a worthy way to spend your time. It's interesting as well as useful as the experience you gain will enable you to spot potential problems as soon as possible. ❧

Internal Parasites

Endo-parasites are found inside a bird's body, and are often referred to as Helminths; a general term covering a range of parasitic worms that live on animals. Bob Cross explains more.

The most important group of endo-parasites, from a poultry-keeping point of view, is the Nematodes; round worms that primarily inhabit the bird's digestive tract. Included in this group are: large roundworm; Capillaria species; caecal worm; gizzard worm; gape worm. There are others, too, known as Cestodes; more commonly referred to as tapeworms.

LARGE ROUNDWORM (ASCARIDIA GALLI)

These worms follow a direct life-cycle, although it can't be completed inside the bird. Infection is caused when the chicken eats embryonated eggs, found in the litter or on the land (it takes 10-12 days for an egg to become infective once it's been passed out of a bird).

The eggs hatch in the proventriculus, from where the larvae move on to the lumen (internal cavity) of the intestine. They remain there for 8-9 days, then penetrate the mucosa – the innermost of the four coats of intestinal lining. It's here, at this stage, that the greatest amount of damage is done to the host.

By day 17 or 18, the larvae return to the lumen, maturing by day 28-30 and starting to lay eggs to repeat the cycle. The life cycle tends to be shorter in younger birds. Worm eggs can be introduced to a site on dirty footwear and equipment, but are equally likely to arrive on infected stock. Problems are also more likely to occur where the management practices leave a lot to be desired, in other words, where birds are overstocked, in bad deep-litter conditions or in runs that have been in constant use for many years and are 'fowl sick'.

Symptoms: Depressed appearance, poor weight gains, lower egg production and pale yolk colour, are the primary signs of Ascaridia. In heavy infestations there may be some mortality. It's also associated with younger stock, although birds over three months old are much more resistant to infection. However, where the right conditions prevail they are still vulnerable. Any internal damage that is caused during the growing stage will quite possibly impact on a bird's performance later on in life.

Internal signs: Mature roundworms are usually between five and 7.5cm long, and will be found in the middle part of the small intestine. Often they will be present here in large numbers, spilling out when the intestine is slit open. The intestine lining will be damaged, and there may be signs of enteritis and anaemia.

Ascaridia dissimilis is a large roundworm which affects turkeys, and it can cause serious losses. While the intestine often contains only a few adult worms, there may be many in the larval form causing severe enteritis in the mid-part of the small intestine, often with bacterial complications. Typically the result will be poor growth and increased mortality level.

CAPILLARIA WORMS

These are also referred to as 'hair worms', and there are several species: Capillaria obsignata; C. caudinflata; C.

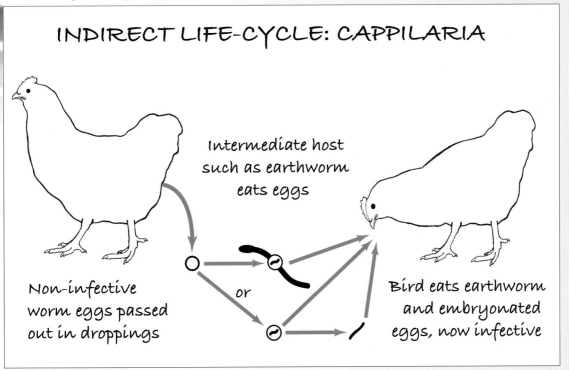

INDIRECT LIFE-CYCLE: CAPPILARIA

Non-infective worm eggs passed out in droppings

Intermediate host such as earthworm eats eggs

or

Bird eats earthworm and embryonated eggs, now infective

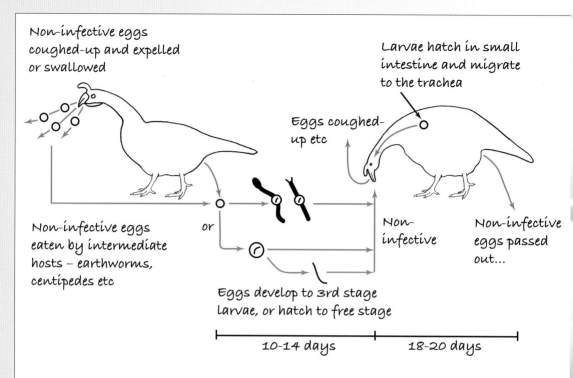

Non-infective eggs coughed-up and expelled or swallowed

Larvae hatch in small intestine and migrate to the trachea

Eggs coughed-up etc

Non-infective eggs eaten by intermediate hosts – earthworms, centipedes etc

or

Non-infective

Non-infective eggs passed out...

Eggs develop to 3rd stage larvae, or hatch to free stage

10-14 days   18-20 days

INDIRECT LIFE-CYCLE OF THE GAPEWORM (TURKEYS)

contorta are three examples.

They are found in the upper part of the digestive tract (crop, oesophagus, proventriculus, intestine) and, as you might imagine, are very thin – measuring 1-1.5cm in length. Some follow a direct life-cycle, while others use the common earthworm as an intermediate host (an indirect life-cycle).

Symptoms: The general signs of Capillaria infestation are droopiness, poor performance, pale yolks, wasting, anaemia and diarrhoea. Deaths may be seen in heavy outbreaks.

These worms can be difficult to see because they are so small; washing the

WORM LIFE-CYCLE TIMINGS

Large roundworm (Ascaridia galli)
Growing birds   35-42 days
Adult birds   49-56 days

Hair worms
Capillaria obsignata   20-26 days
Capillaria contorta   30-60 days

Caecal worm (Heterakis gallinarum)
          24-30 days

Gizzard worm (Amidostomum anseris)
          14-22 days

Tapeworms (Davainea species)
          14-21 days

contents of the gut through a fine sieve may help find them. Inflamed and thickened intestines (the lining of which may slough away), enteritis and anaemic carcasses are all additional signs of infection.

CAECAL WORMS

Heterakis gallinae is commonly known as the 'caecal worm' and inhabits the caeca. The worms themselves do little damage, but are important because of the role their eggs play in the transmission of blackhead – especially relevant if you're keeping turkeys. The life-cycle is direct, and it's in the eggs that the blackhead organism Histomonas meleagridis can survive for many months, enabling it to be carried over from season to season in apparently rested runs.

Symptoms: It's likely that the majority of birds in domestic flocks are infested with caecal worms, even though they don't display any outward signs or suffer from obvious ill-effects. The worms are 1-1.5cm long, shaped like an 'S' and greyish-white in colour.

GIZZARD WORM

This is Amidostomum anseris, and

is known for affecting geese.

The life cycle is direct, and infestation follows ingestion of infective larvae from pasture. It's probably the commonest cause of disease in young geese, although older birds are more resistant. Outbreaks are most likely to occur where goslings are reared on land that's continually stocked with geese.

Symptoms: Growing goslings stop ▶

Good house and run management play vital parts in the control of endo-parasites

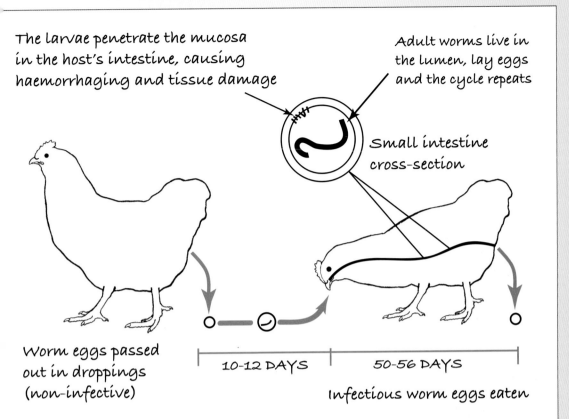

The larvae penetrate the mucosa in the host's intestine, causing haemorrhaging and tissue damage

Adult worms live in the lumen, lay eggs and the cycle repeats

Small intestine cross-section

Worm eggs passed out in droppings (non-infective)

10-12 DAYS

50-56 DAYS

Infectious worm eggs eaten

ASCARIDIA GALLI WORM DIRECT LIFE-CYCLE

growing, quickly losing weight and condition. In a short period of time they become emaciated and weak, then death follows.

Where death has occurred, the carcasses will be thin and wasted. The worm will be found in the gizzard, under the horny lining. You'll be able to see the lining coming away from the muscular gizzard body, being separated from it by blood-stained mucous. Worms will be found but, as they are small (less than 2cm long) and fine, they are

WORM FACTS

Worm eggs cannot develop:
– in very dry atmospheres
– in temperatures below 10°C or above 35°C
– where there is no oxygen

The eggs are destroyed by:
– continued drought
– direct sunlight
– very high temperatures
– prolonged frozen conditions

The eggs can survive:
– most disinfectants
– for many months in litter or soil
– in an intermediate host

difficult to detect. However, swilling the gizzard in a jar of clean water then holding it up to the light will reveal their presence and confirm infection.

GAPEWORM

Syngamus trachea is the gapeworm which affects poultry (gamebirds, turkeys and chickens). Young stock – up to six weeks old – is especially susceptible. Wild birds can also be infected, and these will act as carriers of the parasite. The life cycle may be direct; the worms in the trachea lay eggs, which are coughed-up and are then expelled or swallowed – either way, they end up in the grass.

After a period of 10-14 days, the worm egg is infective, containing a 'third stage' larva. This, or a free larva that has hatched out already, is picked-up by a bird. Then, once inside the bird, the larvae migrate from the bowel to the lungs, then on to the trachea.

Alternatively, infestation may be brought about by the bird eating one of a number of intermediate hosts of the worm – earthworms, snails, centipedes,

flies etc. After ingestion the cycle follows the same route as if it had been 'direct'. The intermediate hosts collect, transport and protect the larvae, enabling it to survive from year to year.

Symptoms: Gasping for breath, death from suffocation in heavy infestation, especially in the case of turkeys and gamebirds.

Gapeworms will be found in the trachea, bronchi and lungs, not only confirming their presence but also eliminating other possible respiratory troubles. Adult gapeworms are 'Y'-shaped and bright red in colour when found in the trachea. The females are about 2cm long, the males slightly smaller, and are permanently joined.

TAPEWORMS

Another worm group worthy of mention here is the Cestodes; tapeworms that come in several species which affect poultry. Most are rarely seen but one – Davainea proglottina – may give cause for concern where large numbers build-up in the intestine of chickens.

D. proglottina follows an indirect life

cycle, with the intermediate hosts including slugs and snails. The chicken becomes infected through eating these creatures, containing the partially-developed parasite known at this stage as a cysticeroid. Many of them may be present in each slug or snail. Tapeworms tend to be found only in extensively managed flocks, as the intermediate host is absent where birds are kept indoors.

Symptoms: The signs of tapeworm infestation include diarrhoea and wasting in birds with access to range.

Tapeworms will be difficult to see present as they are only grow to about 4mm in length. Other signs include thickening of the intestine, the lining of which contains much mucous, which may be haemorrhagic.

WORM DAMAGE

Worms cause harm by damaging the part of the bird where they live which, in turn, can lead to haemorrhaging and anaemia. Heavy infestations in the gut can result in blockages and, at the same time, they are taking nutrients out of the feed and poisoning the host with their waste.

The end result is impaired performance in terms of growth and egg numbers, as already mentioned. In breeding birds, poor hatchability may be noted, with chicks showing signs of nutrient deficiency. Occasionally, in ascaridia infestations, it's possible for a worm to find its way up the oviduct and end up inside an egg, which, on discovery will do little for egg sales!

Remember that there will always be the potential for a parasitic worm challenge, regardless of the system under which poultry are kept; even birds in cages can become infested. However, there are things that can be done to reduce the likelihood of problems and, where they arise, their severity – refer to the 'Anti-worm Precautions' table. Most of the points detailed there are self-explanatory but, I think that the last one

ANTI-WORM PRECAUTIONS

- Avoid using land that may be contaminated, if possible
- Preferably rear on fresh ground
- Rest land at the end of the season
- Keep grass cut short so direct sunlight can get to the worm eggs
- Maintain litter in a dry friable condition
- Avoid scratch feeds on the litter, especially if it's contaminated with a lot of droppings

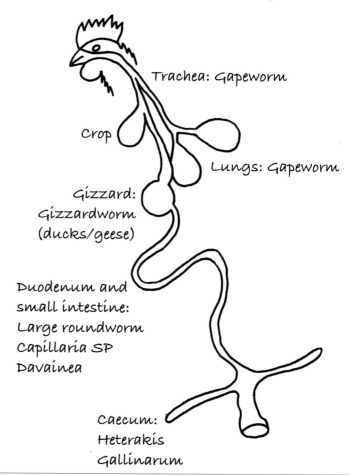

Ingestion sites of internal parasites

Trachea: Gapeworm

Crop

Lungs: Gapeworm

Gizzard: Gizzardworm (ducks/geese)

Duodenum and small intestine: Large roundworm Capillaria SP Davainea

Caecum: Heterakis Gallinarum

requires further explanation.

To be successful, the worming of poultry needs a reasoned approach. There is little point in a one-off treatment; it may kill all the worms in the bird, but it won't touch the eggs in the litter or elsewhere on the land. To be effective, treatment must be repeated so that any worms which hatch after the first dose, are thoroughly mopped-up. Even then, it's unlikely to be 100% successful.

An ongoing programme of anti-worm treatments – killing worms before they are mature enough to lay eggs – will eventually, drastically reduce the worm egg numbers and, therefore, the worm challenge to the birds. But, to do this effectively, it's necessary to appreciate the life-cycle timings (between egg and mature worm). Armed with the timings detailed in the table here, it should be perfectly possible for you to administer the treatments at the most effective times.

It's probably reasonable to assume that most domestic flocks in this country are suffering the affects of worm-related challenge, although they may not always show it. As with other disease, prevention is always better than cure and, for this reason, a poultry vet should be consulted if you're at all suspicious. A worm egg count, made from fresh droppings submitted to a veterinary laboratory, will reveal the presence of the parasite, the seriousness of the situation and determine whether treatment is required.

There is, at present, only one wormer that's licensed for use with poultry (Flubenvet, manufactured by Janssen Animal Health). It's effective against the species described above, in most cases giving a 100% kill. However, where a problem arises, or the product is used in a prophylactic role, veterinary advice should be followed regarding timings, dosage and withdrawal periods. ☙

DRUG PROBLEMS

Lindsay Sissons, asks: "Why go to the vet when your farmer friend has a bottle of sheep stuff you can use?"

The idea of this article is to explain how drugs are made available, the restrictions placed on both vets and clients, and why we should all be responsible about the drugs used on our poultry.

There's been much debate about the use of licensed or unlicensed drugs – it's a complicated issue with many sides, some ethical, some financial and others plain old common sense. The topic of drug prescription and administration is a complicated one, so I'll deal with that first.

Vets are tightly bound by legislation when it comes to prescribing any prescription-only drugs, as they should be. The vet is only allowed to prescribe medication to a bird that can be said to be 'under his care'. This means that the owner of that bird must be a client of that vet, and that the bird must have been seen either just before medication was prescribed, or that the flock must have been seen recently or regularly enough for the vet to have a good knowledge of the flock health situation. The vet has to have made notes on the bird or flock in question. He also has to know enough from the history of the bird's condition, and from a physical examination, to be able to make a good diagnosis and so prescribe the correct drugs. In certain cases, further tests or post-mortems may be necessary to provide a more accurate diagnosis.

A diagnosis should be obtained, as far as is possible, in all cases. But many conditions have several different contributing factors; take a respiratory infection for example. The initial predisposition (weakening of the immune system, if you like) can be caused by poor housing or other environmental stress; primary infection can be a respiratory virus, with secondary infection from Mycoplasma and various bacteria. Just throwing a bucket of first-line, broad-spectrum antibiotic at it will help, but it won't solve the problem.

Antibiotics are available in several types. Some are effective against a wide range of bacteria (broad spectrum), while others are useful only against a limited

number of specific bacteria. All antibiotics are supplied with a data sheet detailing the bacteria against which they can be used. In an ideal world, the vet would diagnose the causing bacteria, and match a narrow-range antibiotic to that specific infection. In the case of multiple infections, picking a broad-spectrum antibiotic that's active against most of the causative organisms is a good option. Of course, the vet's job isn't simply to provide the drugs. It's also to advise on the contributing factors, to suggest ways of reducing stresses, maybe discuss vaccination where appropriate, and to generally reduce the degree of illness in the flock as a whole.

"Of course, the vet's job isn't simply to provide the drugs."

But the business of choosing the drug is where things start to get a little more complicated. The Guide of Professional Conduct states that the drug selected must be licensed in the UK for that species, for the condition being treated, and that it must be used at the dosage recommended by the manufacturer. If there is no such drug licensed – as is often the way with poultry – then the vet has to follow a code called the 'Cascade'. This covers the options for the vet selecting the next best drug.

The first step is to find a product that can be used against the same condition in a different species. For example, using Ivermectin off-licence for parasites in poultry, when it's licensed for cattle and sheep. Another option is the treatment of a different condition in the same species (using Flubenvet off-licence against tapeworm in poultry, when it's licensed for roundworm). If there is nothing suitable in this group (and the vet must have a good reason for needing to look further afield), then the next step is to select a medicine licensed for use in humans in the UK. The final step would be to prescribe a medicine concocted by the vet himself. However, the last two steps mentioned here would rarely be used in poultry.

Where any drug is used off-licence, the vet should explain that this is happening, and should also clearly outline all possible side-effects (after consultation with the manufacturer if necessary – most manufacturers have an anecdotal database of information relating to off-licence use for each drug). In addition, the owner should sign a letter stating that he/she understands the implications of off-licence drug use.

Meat and egg withdrawal periods (not eating eggs or slaughtering for meat until the time period stated has elapsed), are one of the important areas that should be stressed by the vet when discussing off-licence drug use; appropriate withdrawal periods should be stated on the data sheet. When using drugs off-licence, the BVA (British Veterinary Association) suggests a MINIMUM of seven days egg withdrawal from the last treatment, and 28 days meat withdrawal from the last treatment. The vet must study the data sheets for both the drug he is using, and related drugs, to find a suitable withdrawal period. In some cases, withdrawal can be a lot longer than the minimum recommended by the BVA.

> *"We should never use medication as a substitute for good husbandry."*

Withdrawal is designed to prevent residues of the drug used being present in the eggs or meat, and thus entering the human food chain. For those people on organic systems, the rules are much more stringent, with withdrawal periods on licensed drugs being twice the normal recommended length. If an unlicensed drug is prescribed then, again, the vet decides the normal withdrawal period for that drug, and the owner should then double or treble it according to the advice the vet gives.

So, why are some drugs licensed and others not? Licensing a new drug is a very complicated and expensive business. The profit gained from a drug licensed for poultry would be relatively small considering all the investment necessary for testing etc. The manufacturer would have to be guaranteed a decent profit to licence a given drug and, unfortunately, poultry doesn't represent a big enough slice of the veterinary drug market to guarantee this. Many drugs are also not licensed for food-producing animals to keep them available for the future (for humans and animals/birds), in case of widespread resistance.

Ten years ago, Ivermectin was meant to be a last line of defence against parasites that were resistant to everything else. In the poultry world, many people seized on it as a cure-all, and used it as a first-line treatment without veterinary guidance. Now, as a result, we have mites that are Ivermectin-resistant. Ironically, the first-line products, such as the Cypermethrins (although now off-licence in chickens too), remain largely effective. Now, of course, the poultry world is searching for harder-hitting versions of Ivermectin, instead of taking stock and responsibly using the products on offer.

To leave ourselves some leeway for these resistant strains of parasites, bacteria and Mycoplasma, we need to carefully choose an effective drug from those available – and to use the older, more basic, ('less strong' if you like) drugs that are effective against each condition instead of the new 'all singing, all dancing' products that appear on the market. The latter should be reserved for those cases where tests reveal resistant organisms.

So, we've gone full circle and are back with the vet and his diagnosis. Once the product to be used has been selected, the vet has more legislation to follow concerning its supply to the client. Dispensing rules are very strict about labelling information and container types etc. The client should be instructed in both administration of the product and its correct storage. The disposal of the container (and any remaining product) should also be discussed. The client must be warned of all possible side-effects, and a data sheet may be offered for food-producing animals.

Hopefully, you're now starting to appreciate that prescribing drugs is not just a case of: "Try some of this, it might work!" Instead, a complete picture of the birds' situation needs to be built up to help get the best possible diagnosis and allow the accurate prescription of an effective drug to remedy the situation. What worries me is the fact that, nowadays, so many people are willing to try goodness knows what just because it's been recommended by the bloke down the road. Giving medication to our stock represents a huge responsibility – there are significant consequences for the birds' health and future well-being, plus our health too. Their well-being is our first priority; keeping them healthy with a combination of good husbandry, quality feed, suitable housing and medical treatment only when necessary.

We should never use medication as a substitute for good husbandry. Treating a bird with long-term antibiotics for respiratory infections, instead of tackling the inadequate ventilation in its house, is certainly not a sensible option. The overall well-being of a poultry flock always relies on the owner looking at the whole picture, not simply treating one or two birds on an individual basis.

Our health covers all areas of our contact with the birds. Show judges have been questioning for a while whether they should be wearing latex gloves while judging. It stands to reason that at least a few of the birds handled at any event will have been on medication, and judges are increasingly concerned about the cocktail of drugs that they may be absorbing through their hands.

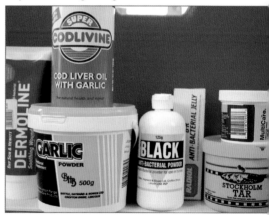

As far as meat consumption is concerned, many people often say that the meat from their own birds is better because they know exactly what's gone into it, but do they? Drugs 'borrowed' from the poultry keeper in the next village are invariably off-licence, and often come with no dosage instructions (neither dilution rate or treatment period guidance). Plus, users of such products rarely understand the likely side-effects or the full extent of withdrawal periods.

All the legislation that the vet must adhere to exists to protect the bird, the owner and the vet. Always remember that, by keeping the bird in a healthy environment, the risk of disease and the need for medication can be reduced. But when treatment is needed, it's the responsibility of the owner to ensure that the best and safest medication for that condition is used. ❦

RESPIRATION

Bob Cross concentrates on poultry diseases, with an explanatory look at respiratory problems

All of us who keep livestock of any kind want it to be fit and healthy and enjoy life; poultry, of course, is no exception. There's little reward to be had – either monetary or in terms of satisfaction – from looking after poultry that are always poorly. So what can we do to prevent disease and maintain a healthy flock, and how big a problem is it?

Let me start by trying to allay a few common fears. Read the disease section in almost any poultry book and you're virtually bound to come away fearing the worst; there are just so many possible problems! But what you've all got to remember is that there's no reason to assume that your birds will get everything going. In fact, with a bit of

care and attention, most of these nasties can be avoided.

PROFESSIONAL HELP

To help with the identification of chicken problems, it's useful to understand a little bit about poultry health and disease then, if the worst comes to the worst, you'll be in a position to make an informed decision about calling in a professional. Consulting a vet may seem a little excessive but don't forget that they are the ones with the knowledge and, more importantly, the ability to prescribe an effective treatment. Failure to get help can prolong the illness, causing more suffering and potentially greater losses. Also, my general advice is to be very wary of 'traditional' and

'folklore'-type remedies and treatments. These are less likely to be truly effective and can, in some cases actually be cruel or even illegal.

So, to begin with, what do we actually mean by 'disease'? As far as I'm concerned, it's represented by any departure from normal health, and thus includes anything which compromises that status. It can be caused by an organism such as a virus, bacteria, mould, yeast or fungus, protozoa, parasite etc. But nutritional deficiencies, organ or body failure, cannibalism and physical damage can cause health problems too. Finally, there's poisoning and even genetic problems to be considered as other possible triggers.

But it's worth emphasising again, before we go any further, that if a bird's health is causing you concern, then you shouldn't think twice about calling in a vet (preferably one with practical poultry experience). What follows is intended to provide a layman's guide, giving a general insight into some of the most common poultry ailments and their prognosis. I'm not setting out to offer precise diagnosis and, in all but a few cases, certainly will not be recommending specific treatments.

Regardless of the cause, there will always be tell-tale signs of disease; the more serious the problem, the more marked the symptoms. It's always important to detect problems early so that steps can be taken to reduce the severity, and provide an early cure. Of course, recognising the signs of trouble is

Healthy, happy birds; that's what we all want. With reasonable amounts of care and attention, you can ensure they stay that way.

almost second nature to a seasoned stock-person but, to those with less experience, these sorts of early signals can be a good deal less obvious.

The health and welfare of poultry must be checked at least once a day, and it's usual to do so more often. When carrying out these checks,

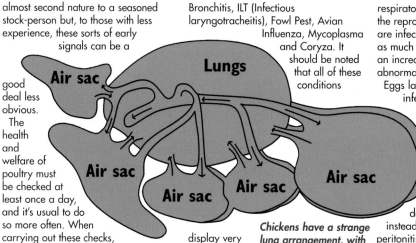

Lungs

Air sac

Air sac

Air sac

Air sac

Air sac

Chickens have a strange lung arrangement, with air sacs and no diaphragm to control their breathing.

HOW BIRDS BREATH

Avian respiration differs from ours in a number of ways. For a start, birds have no diaphragm; they rely on bone and muscle movements to work the lungs. Secondly, the air passes through the lungs and into air sacs and on into bones. The reverse then happens, and the air is expelled, so it actually passes through the lungs twice. On each occasion gaseous exchange takes place, doubling the efficiency of the system. Filled with air, the air sacs, and the bones, provide an essential aid to buoyancy in waterfowl and confer lightness, which is a necessity in any that fly.

it's important to take time to get to know the birds, and to recognise their normal behaviour patterns – any deviation from the norm can then be regarded with suspicion. Where disease is suspected, there are a number of things you can do while you are waiting for help. Isolating the affected flock/bird(s), preventing visitors, making the birds more comfortable, stimulating food and water consumption and making sure the house and all its equipment and fittings are clean, will all help the situation.

One of the most common causes of health problems among domestic poultry flocks is respiratory infection. This includes such diseases as Infectious

SIGNS OF GOOD HEALTH
• Bright eyes and tight feathering
• Red comb and wattles
• Clean nostrils
• Normal food and water consumption
• Normal growth and/or egg production
• Keen active birds

Bronchitis, ILT (Infectious laryngotracheitis), Fowl Pest, Avian Influenza, Mycoplasma and Coryza. It should be noted that all of these conditions display very similar symptoms, and so professional help will be needed for a conclusive diagnosis and effective treatment.

INFECTIOUS BRONCHITIS
The causal agent for this disease is a Corona-virus, of which there are several serotypes. It affects only chickens. The virus can be airborne, or passed, bird-to-bird, via discharges. What's more, recovered birds may transmit the virus to susceptible birds for a few weeks after recovery, but are themselves immune and after that don't remain carriers.

For your information, a serotype is an individual identified by the antigens that it produces. An antigen is a substance which triggers the production of antibodies that are able to neutralise antigens, or render them susceptible to destruction by the body.

Symptoms: As the name implies, the respiratory tract becomes inflamed with this disease, making it difficult for the bird to breath. Consequently, sneezing and coughing may result. If a bird is held close to the ear, a 'tracheal rattle' can be heard. In chicks there may be nasal discharge, and the eyes may be watery – less so in adults.

Mortality will tend to be higher in young stock than in older birds, indeed there may be none in adults.

Upon internal examination, it may be found that the trachea and the bronchi are reddened and contain mucus and 'cheesy' matter, while further down the respiratory system the air sacs in older chickens may contain froth.

Effects: As well as causing

respiratory problems, this virus damages the reproductive tract. When laying hens are infected an egg production drop of as much as 50% can occur, followed by an increase in the production of abnormal eggs.

Eggs laid by birds that have been infected at or after sexual maturity, may be misshapen, have poor or no shells, and suffer internal faults such as watery whites. Some birds may become what's known as 'internal layers', which means that the yolk can't enter the oviduct and is deposited in the body cavity instead. Here it putrefies, causing peritonitis and then death.

The level of damage will depend on the severity of the virus strain, and the degree of protection the bird has from vaccination or naturally acquired immunity.

Treatment: Because the clinical signs of infectious bronchitis are similar to other respiratory diseases, diagnosing the condition will require samples to be sent to a veterinary laboratory. This may involve live and/or dead birds, or blood samples taken as the birds are recovering.

Unfortunately, there is no treatment for for this disease. What's more, as a result of the 'challenge' it causes, the birds may succumb to a secondary infection by bacteria. Those suffering in this way will need treatment with prescription-only antibiotics. These will give the birds every chance of recovery from the virus, although some of the damage done to the reproductive tract may take much longer to return to normal.

Vaccination is the best method of preventing infectious bronchitis, and usually involves a course of 'live doses' administered via the drinking water during the rearing period, followed by a 'dead' vaccine given by intra-muscular injection at point of lay. The latter gives protection for a year, after which the bird will need a booster.

NEWCASTLE DISEASE
This disease, together with Fowl Plague (which is a form of Avian Influenza), was known as 'Fowl Pest'. The term was adopted for legislative purposes to include both diseases under the Fowl Pest Orders of 1936 and later amendments to them. These required the prompt notification of the existence (or suspected existence) of the condition, either by the owner or a veterinary ▶

SIGNS OF TROUBLE

- Dull eyes and ruffled or loose feathering
- Pale, discoloured, swollen or scabby head points
- Poor stance – neck tucked in, tail down, drooping wings, lame etc
- Sneezing, coughing, gasping
- Drop in production – either growth or egg output
- Mis-shapen eggs, poor shell quality
- Drop in food consumption
- Changes in water consumption
- Watery or green droppings
- Mortality

surgeon, to the nearest police constable. Further orders covered movement restrictions and prohibitions, slaughter and compensation. This legislation is still in force; it remains a notifiable disease and must be reported. Nowadays though, a vet would certainly be a more appropriate recipient of the news than the nearest police constable. Also, don't get excited at the prospect of financial compensation as this is unlikely to make

you rich!

The causal agent for this disease is paramyxovirus, and there are mild to virulent strains which manifest themselves accordingly. The virus can be transmitted from bird to bird via respiratory discharge (passed by sneezing or through communal drinkers) or droppings. The disease can also be carried between farms by personnel, on vehicles, equipment, wild birds, dust particles and on the air.

The incubation period is 3-6 days. and the virus can survive in a viable state for quite a time on dirty crates and equipment, but is killed if exposed to bright sunlight for 30 minutes.

All types of poultry are susceptible to Newcastle Disease under natural conditions, and other avian species may play a role in the spread of the disease. There's also evidence that man may become infected through handling diseased birds or carcasses and, in doing so, suffer conjunctivitis and other types of mild illness.

Symptoms: In chicks and young growers, respiratory symptoms are often seen – gasping and coughing, plus the 'voice' changes in tone, and may be lost altogether. The birds are uncomfortable, huddle together and appear depressed. Loss of appetite and thirst are also signs and, later on and in recovered birds, there may be nervous symptoms such as lack of balance, varying degrees of paralysis, walking in circles and twisted necks.

In laying birds, the appearance of the disease and its spread is often rapid. Respiratory symptoms may be anything from mild to severe, including loss of appetite together with signs of depression. Egg numbers can fall sharply, possibly to zero, as an early indicator.

In some instances, it may be that a drop in egg production is all that's seen. Many of the eggs that are laid will be misshapen, or have abnormal shells – porous or depigmented. If the disease is caused by one of the less pathogenic strains, then it's likely that the mortality rate will tend to be low.

The pattern with the 'peracute' (*acute* = sharp, *per* = extremely so) form is very rapid, and will affect most of the birds exposed to the infection. After an initial dull appearance, which rapidly turns to depression, they lose their appetite but will retain their thirst – this may actually increase.

Egg production ceases, and the droppings change; becoming a yellowish-green, watery diarrhoea with very little solid matter. Severe respiratory stress will be noted. Birds will stretch their necks and open their beaks in an attempt to draw breath, and their breathing will be noisy with much gurgling, rattling and coughing. There may be a discharge of mucous from the eyes and nostrils, and some signs of dribbling from the mouth. If you care to take the temperature, this is likely to be 0.5-1.5°C above normal (41.3°C). Mortality in this situation can run at 80-90%, and

Avian Influenza presents few obvious signs, apart from a bluing of the comb (cyanosis).

Respiratory problems are a common cause of trouble among chickens

those birds that survive may develop the nervous symptoms. A few birds may make a full recovery. In turkeys the symptoms are less pronounced and the nervous signs are rare.

Effects: The signs of Newcastle Disease include inflamed and congested tracheas, pneumonia with the air sacs appearing frothy and cloudy and cyanosis of the comb (a blueness caused by lack of oxygen).

The proventriculus (the glandular stomach attached to the gizzard) and intestines may show pinpoint haemorrhaging. In laying stock, there may be yolk material in the abdominal cavity and this can, in turn, cause peritonitis.

The symptoms are similar to other respiratory diseases, so the virus must be identified, which involves isolating it using tracheal or cloacal swabs, and looking for high antibody levels in the blood.

Treatment: There is no treatment for Newcastle Disease. An outbreak (or suspected outbreak) must be reported and the flock slaughtered. However, it can be prevented by vaccination, usually involving a number of doses of 'live vaccine' to prime the system, followed by an injection of 'dead vaccine' at point-of-lay to provide prolonged protection.

AVIAN INFLUENZA

As with Newcastle Disease, this is a notifiable disease. It's caused by a myxovirus, and there are several serotypes. Most types of domestic poultry can be affected, and it's the HPAI (highly pathogenic avian influenza) strain identified as H5N1 that's currently causing concern, both for birds and humans.

There's some evidence that humans have contracted the disease already, and a number of deaths have been attributed to it. Airborne virus particles from the discharges of infected birds and their droppings are a source of transmission, as is clothing and equipment that's become contaminated. Wild birds can have the disease, possibly without showing any ill effect, and so can spread it further afield. The virus can survive in frozen carcasses for many months.

Symptoms: Infections caused by a mild strain of AI may show few symptoms; in growing birds possibly signs of dullness and inactivity, along with a few extra dead birds. In laying stock this can be accompanied by a slight dip in egg production and quality. Secondary infections may well follow, which will add to the losses. Infections with the highly pathogenic strains can prove rapidly fatal, with the first signs being many deaths in a very short time. Other symptoms that may be seen include; ruffled feathers, depression and droopiness, loss of appetite, respiratory distress, cyanosis, swelling of the head,

neck, eyes, comb and hocks, a blood-tinged discharge from the nostrils, diarrhoea, a sudden drop in egg production and soft-shelled eggs.

Effects: Post mortem examination may show the following. If the skin is removed it will show a straw-coloured liquid in those tissues underneath it. Haemorrhaging may be apparent in the intestine, proventriculus and gizzard, and the lining of the latter is easily removed. It will also be seen in the trachea. Blood vessels appear engorged the muscle on the breastbone is swollen, together with that of internal organs and, here again, haemorrhaging is a feature. Young broilers show dehydration, but other signs are less pronounced or absent.

The symptoms of the disease are similar to other respiratory diseases and, as such, require laboratory diagnosis to establish the identity of the virus and eliminate other possible causes.

Treatment: There is no treatment for avian influenza and, at the present time, vaccination is not permitted in this country. It's not certain that the immunity produced by the current vaccines is effective against all strains of the virus, and there are concerns that it may also mask the symptoms making it more difficult to identify outbreaks and control the spread of the disease. A dual policy of slaughter and containment is adopted to prevent the spread of the disease and cause its eradication.

INFECTIOUS LARYNGOTRACHEITIS (ILT)

ILT is caused by a herpes virus; only one serotype is known. The virus may be airborne, or carried on contaminated materials and equipment such as crates and egg packing. It can also be transferred by people, on their clothing or footwear.

Birds that have recovered from the disease may remain carriers of it, and can infect new stock arriving on 'multi-age' sites. It affects chickens and pheasants, and has an incubation period of between four and 12 days.

Symptoms: Severe respiratory distress is seen due to the presence of bloody, catarrhal and gaseous exudate (fluid-like discharge) in the trachea and larynx. When a plug of this material forms, and blocks off the airway, the affected chicken has extreme difficulty in drawing in air, and may die of suffocation. In an attempt to breathe, birds will extend their necks and open their mouths, gasping for air, returning to the normal position on exhalation. Inhalation may cause a high-pitched noise and, while doing so, some birds may be seen to be lying down in an attempt to conserve energy. Sneezing and coughing are also signs.

Occasionally the bird will manage to dislodge a plug of blood or blood-stained mucus, which will be coughed up, expelled and may be seen splashed on the walls, floor or posts about the house. The eyes may become watery, with this developing into conjunctivitis. Occasionally, but less often, nasal discharge is apparent. Indeed, these may be the only signs where one of the less virulent strains is responsible.

As with any disease, appetite will be reduced and there will be signs of depression and malaise. Mortality in a typical ILT outbreak runs at around 1% a day, however, there will be less, or possibly none, with the milder forms of the disease. There are no nervous signs, thus ruling out a misdiagnosis of Newcastle disease.

Effects: Severe inflammation of the larynx and

Commercially-reared birds, like these Speckledy hybrids, will have been vaccinated against most common diseases. The same can't be said for most pure-bred stock.

haemorrhaging in the trachea, the presence of bloody mucus and cheesy exudate (material that oozes out which looks like soft cheese) in these organs. Confirmation of infection is by histological (study of tissues) examination of the trachea, and by isolation of the virus; both of which are jobs for the veterinary laboratory.

Treatment: ILT infection can be controlled by the use of a mild vaccine, which is usually administered via an eye drop. Even in the event of an outbreak it's advisable to vaccinate to prevent the disease spreading further.

CHRONIC RESPIRATORY DISEASE (CRD)

This condition is also known as Air Sac Disease and Airsaculitis, and the organism that plays a major part in it is a Mycoplasma, and specifically Mycoplasma gallisepticum. It's likely that the majority of domestic, pure-bred poultry flocks carry this organism without showing any signs, or causing any noticeable problems. The condition becomes apparent when respiratory viruses and a secondary infection (usually E. coli) enter the equation. Stress caused by vaccination, beak trimming, moving or by unfavourable conditions in the house, such as poor ventilation and sudden temperature changes, may be responsible for its manifestation. Mycoplama can be passed from bird to bird, or carried on dust or droplets through the air.

More worryingly, it can be transmitted through the egg, from parents that

Happy hens tend, by and large, to be healthy hens. Make sure housing is suited to their needs.

appear healthy but are in fact carrying it. Chickens and turkeys are the species affected. When the latter are infected, the organism is referred to as M. meleagridis.

Symptoms: Young stock show signs of respiratory distress. One of the first signs may be a dampening of the nostrils, noted by dust and food particles adhering to them. Sniffling, sneezing coughing and congestion follow later. The disease spreads slowly through the flock, unlike other respiratory infections such as Newcastle disease, Infectious bronchitis, ILT, or coryza.

Appetite is depressed and growth rates are reduced. In laying and breeding birds, egg production drops of 30-50% may be seen, and hatchability will also suffer. As time goes by some birds, especially turkeys, will develop swollen faces, as a result of exudate in the sinuses. Some birds appear to recover, and then fresh cases arise. The disease does not result in a large number of deaths.

Internal signs will vary according to the severity of the infection, and that of secondary infections. In uncomplicated cases they may be no more than those associated with a common cold, with some mucus in the trachea and froth in the air sacs. But where secondary infections are involved, the trachea may be inflamed and red, and the air sacs may contain cheesy exudate.

Confirmation of infection involves isolating the organism from samples submitted to a veterinary laboratory. This will also eliminate other potential causes such as ND, IB and ILT.

Treatment: There are a number of drugs for treating this condition; all require veterinary prescriptions and guidance for use. To a certain extent the disease can be kept in check by

eliminating stress, and by reducing the presence of the bugs responsible for the secondary infections; in other words, by ensuring good management practices and standards of hygiene. Similarly, vaccination against the common respiratory diseases will help eliminate the role that these play in mycoplasmosis. Regard all new stock with suspicion until such a time that it can be deemed safe; isolate them before introducing to the rest of the flock. The same applies to birds that have visited shows.

All commercial poultry (in this country, but not necessarily across the water) originate from stock that's been subject to blood tests to identify and eliminate carriers. But this is an expensive process, so is unlikely to be an option for the small flock keeper.

INFECTIOUS CORYZA

This disease is caused by the bacterium Haemophilus gallinarum. It spreads rapidly from bird to bird by contact, through the drinking water and on dust particles. It may also be passed on via handlers who fail to observe simple hygiene measures. The disease can be of a chronic or acute nature, and tends to affect older birds. Chickens appear to be the only species that suffer with it.

Symptoms: Depending on the severity of the infection, the first symptoms will be sneezing and coughing, plus a slight watery discharge from the nostrils. This becomes thickened and foul-smelling. The birds find it difficult to breathe, shaking their heads in an ▶

Poultry welfare – including the regular supply of fresh feed and water – is a vital issue. Always seek advice from an experienced expert if you're not sure

attempt to remove the mucus, some of which may be found on the wing feathers where they have wiped it from their beaks.

The facial tissues may become swollen, causing the eyes to become partly closed, and conjunctivitis may be noted. Food and water intake may be depressed, which in turn leads to weight loss and/or a reduction in egg output. In mild infections the bird may appear otherwise healthy but, where other infections complicate matters, they may become lethargic and adopt a 'droopy' posture. Mortality, in most cases, is low.

The internal signs are similar to those of CRD. Confirmation involves the services of a veterinary laboratory to isolate the organism from samples taken from the sinuses and air sacs, and to prescribe a course of treatment. However, this will only take away the symptoms and the birds will remain carriers. So to aid birds in their recovery, steps should be taken to improve bird comfort and hygiene, and stimulate their appetite. Preventative measures include correct ventilation, and encouraging birds to use the perches at night where they will breathe clean air.

It would be nice to think that Chronic Respiratory Disease was a thing of the past; it should be. In the 1960s and '70s it caused major problems for the commercial poultry industry. In those days most commercial birds were 'positive' for mycoplasma, and viral respiratory diseases presented a constant threat because there were no reliable vaccines. The situation wasn't helped by the fact that standards of welfare and hygiene on poultry farms left much to be desired. Nowadays, though, all commercial stock in this country is free from mycoplasma when it leaves the hatchery. We have vaccines to prevent the viral challenge, and the hygiene and welfare standards have improved thus reducing E. coli incidences. In small flocks, however, this is not the case and the problem still exists. But by addressing one or two of the aforementioned factors, it could be reduced.

ASPERGILLOSIS

This disease is also known as 'brooder pneumonia' or 'fungal pneumonia', and is caused by the fungus, Aspergillus fumigatus. It's widely distributed throughout nature, and is found on hay, straw, grain, leaves etc. If conditions become damp, the aspergilli grow and form spores, which are then inhaled and, in turn, become moulds growing on the tissues of the respiratory system and air sacs, causing the disease.

Transmission is, therefore, from mouldy litter or from contaminated food. Where nest litter is mouldy, the spores can be carried on the egg shell to infect other eggs in the incubator, and the chicks as they hatch.

Aspergillosis affects chickens, turkeys, game birds, ducks and geese. Young stock are more susceptible than older birds, and there are chronic and acute infections. We're also at risk; the human form being known as 'Farmers Lung'.

Symptoms: Birds affected with the acute form show signs of respiratory distress, characterised by rapid, 'croupy' breathing, sneezing, coughing, gasping and struggling to breathe at all towards the end. Food consumption goes down, but thirst increases. As the disease progresses, appetite is lost altogether. Many birds look dejected and stand around with ruffled feathers appearing totally disinterested in life. They become weaker and many die within a few days.

Mortality rates can run as high as

Keep an eye on egg production; uncharacteristic fall-offs can be a sign of trouble.

90%, but the figure is usually much lower. Some birds will survive but take a long time to recover condition and catch up. The chronic form is more of a 'wasting' disease, with respiratory symptoms and sporadic deaths.

The main areas of infection are the lungs and air sacs. Acute infections show small, (pinhead to small pea) yellowish-white nodules in the lungs, yellow plaque-like lesions in the air sacs, and small nodules in other organs. Where the infection is of a chronic nature, lesions are found in the lungs, and may appear as solid cheesy lumps. In the air sacs, the lesions may join to form a thick coating which becomes greenish-grey in colour due to the sporing heads of the A fumigatus. Lesions have also been found in other internal organs, and in the eyes of chicks.

Where infection has occurred in the incubator, there will be a greater than normal number of 'dead-in-shell' cases. On breaking these open, Aspergillus growth will be seen as a bottle-green to purple-grey sporing colony on the inner shell membrane of the air space of the egg.

The presence of aspergillus can be seen with the naked eye, but laboratory examination is required to confirm identification and eliminate IB, ND, ILT and Salmonella pullorum.

Treatment: There is no treatment for Aspergillosis; infected flocks should be culled, especially where the disease is of the chronic form and infection is protracted. Any dead or culled birds must be removed and destroyed.

Preventative measures would include careful choice of litter, avoiding any that smells mouldy or damp, likewise with foodstuffs. Maintain it in a dry state by correct drinker and ventilation management. Hatching eggs become infected in the nest box especially where hay is used; it is better to use white wood shavings, treated straw or even fresh cat litter.

ESCHERICHIA COLI

Commonly referred to as 'E.coli', Escherichia coli is a bacterium. It lives in the intestines of all warm-blooded animals and, in the normal, healthy state, the body keeps numbers under control. E. coli is an opportunist, and takes advantage of the body's lowered resistance as a result of a disease challenge, or some other form of stress. Numbers rapidly multiply, invading body tissues and adding to the bird's

Staying on top of the rodent situation is an important factor in controlling poultry disease.

problems and, as such, it's regarded as a secondary infection.

It can be transmitted through drinking water and litter, with the latter source posing a greater threat. When litter becomes wet and capped, not only do the numbers of the organism escalate, but these conditions also compromise bird comfort and welfare, leaving them even more vulnerable to infection. Birds reared intensively, in overcrowded, unsanitary conditions, are most likely to be affected.

Hatching eggs with dirty shells may be responsible for transmitting the organism to the chick; on hatching it enters the body via the navel, and causes yolk sac infection. This can cause serious losses in the first two weeks of a chick's life.

Symptoms: E. coli often follows closely on the heels of a viral infection. Where the intestinal tract is involved, the appetite is reduced and production, be it weight gain or egg output, suffers. Affected birds appear 'droopy', with ruffled feathers and they lose colour. Mortality rates run at anything between five and 50%, (the lower figure is more likely if treated promptly), and will vary depending on the severity and cause of the infection.

If the air sacs are infected, the symptoms are similar to those of CRD; there is severe depression and respiratory noises such as rattling, coughing and gurgling, and the comb becomes darkened.

Internally, the upper half of the intestine may be inflamed and, with

chronic infections, the toxins produced by the E. coli destroy the lining. The membrane around the heart, which is normally crystal-clear, becomes cloudy and contains liquid and exudate. Occasionally, the liver becomes enlarged and darkened in colour, often appearing green. The air sacs may be inflamed and contain yellowish-white, cheesy material. The colour of the flesh and skin takes on a darker hue.

Carcasses need to be submitted to a veterinary laboratory to identify E.coli, and differentiate it from a number of other organisms that display similar signs and conditions.

Treatment: E. coli infections are treatable with antibiotics. Your vet will prescribe and advise the best course of action. As it's often a secondary infection, it's as well to act in a proactive manner and seek advice when the primary infection occurs. In this way an infection may be prevented rather than cured. As has already been intimated, this problem is often associated with dirty conditions plus poor husbandry and management practices.

In the long term, the most effective and cheapest way of prevention is by: maintaining high standards of house and run hygiene, providing clean fresh drinking water, attention to correct ventilation, and vaccination against the common viral diseases to prevent primary infections. All these will help reduce the extent or frequency of occurrence. ❧

SHAKE, RATTLE AND...SNEEZE!

*e your birds suffering with respiratory problems?
ll, house ventilation could be at the root of the
blem, advises Lindsay Sissons*

piratory signs in birds can be due to several different and
rying-sounding causes. These include: viruses – infectious
nchitis virus, pneumovirus, infectious laryngotracheitis virus;
teria – Pasteurella, mycoplasma; fungi – aspergillus; contact
ants – disinfectants, lime used to clean pens, dusty sawdust.
order to produce these signs, the agent involved must be
aled. The respiratory system of birds means that inhaled air
es into the caudal air sac, then through the small lung, into the
cranial air sac, then out.

> *Birds produce ammonia (from their droppings), eat and water vapour.*

Rattling birds – that rattle when held and shaken gently – often have a build-up of matter from the infection or irritant in the sacs. Sneezing birds have nasal and upper respiratory tract ns with or without sinus enlargement and discharges, gasping ds may have a mucus or fungal plug in the trachea. Coughing ds have tracheal irritation.

HALING TROUBLE

ny of these conditions are predisposed to by environmental
rtfalls – especially the quality of the air inhaled and what it
ntains. Ventilation is one of the most important issues to
nsider when building, buying or inspecting existing poultry
using. Birds produce ammonia (from their droppings), heat
d water vapour, while the bedding will produce dusts, fungal
ores and bacterial spores.
mmonia is a strong respiratory irritant predisposing to
condary infection. All of these will build up in an improperly
ntilated house and will be carried into the air sacs and lungs

able to work in the house or put his head in it, without smelling
ammonia, getting a dusty irritation in his nose, without sneezing
or coughing and without getting too hot.

At the other extreme, of course, is too much ventilation, where the birds are found huddling in a corner and the beds are wet from incoming rain. The stress from cold draughts and the wet will lower the

> *"Multi-pen houses can have problems with individual pen ventilation."*

birds' resistance to any opportunist infectious agents. Ideally, air
should be able to enter the house from a low level, through a
small grill perhaps, well wired and with a rounded partial cover
to prevent direct draughts. This air then passes over the bedding,
collecting ammonia, dusts and spores as it goes, while also
warming and collecting water vapour and rising to exit the house
through an outlet at the top of the wall or in the roof. This outlet
should be capped appropriately to prevent rain and direct winds
entering.

ADEQUATE AIRFLOW?

Small houses generally have adequate air inflow through the
gaps round pop-holes and doorways, and outlets below the roof.
Larger multi-pen houses can be tested with smoking damp straw
in a metal bucket, say, to see how the air is flowing and to
enable problems to be corrected. Ideally, the keeper should be
able to sense a very gentle air flow about himself without feeling
a real draught. Multi-pen houses can have problems with
individual pen ventilation and may need additional wired areas
placing to encourage good air flow – again, the keeper needs to
put his head into each pen to check this.

So, improving ventilation in the house reduces the levels of
predisposing and infectious agents in the inhaled air and thus
reduces the levels of respiratory signs in the birds.

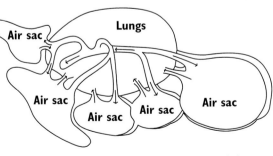

gram to show the small lungs with multiple air sacs (8 in a chicken)
he air sacs act as bellows to move air through the lungs

en inhaled. The prime aim of ventilation is to maintain a flow
fresh air through the house that will draw ammonia, moisture,
at and infective agents out of the shed. The keeper should be

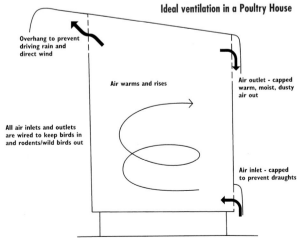

Ideal ventilation in a Poultry House

Overhang to prevent driving rain and direct wind

Air warms and rises

Air outlet - capped warm, moist, dusty air out

All air inlets and outlets are wired to keep birds in and rodents/wild birds out

Air inlet - capped to prevent draughts

HEALTHY HENS?

Bob Cross continues his overview of potential poultry problems with a look at four more nasties.

MAREK'S DISEASE

Marek's disease is caused by a Herpes virus, and it affects only domestic fowl (chickens and bantams). The virus is found on infected premises, and can live for many months in dead skin and feather fluff cells from infected birds. Infection takes place at an early age, with day-old chicks either ingesting or inhaling the virus. These cells will constitute a major part of chicken shed dust, can be carried on clothing and equipment, and also spread to adjacent pens by wind. Susceptibility decreases rapidly with age; the virus needs to gain entry to the body in the first few days of life. The risk of infection through the egg is low, or non-existent.

Symptoms: The birds show signs of paralysis. The condition that was referred to in the past as either 'Fowl Paralysis' or 'Range Paralysis' is now one of the forms in which Marek's disease manifests itself. Where this occurs the first signs are limping, but this soon progresses to the classical form of paralysis where the bird lies on its side with one leg stretched forward, and the other one backward. If the nerve to the eye is involved, this results in either pin-point pupils or split irises. Other signs include droopiness due to partial paralysis of parts of the body. Birds may show some difficulty in breathing, and others may not hold their wings tight to the body, or adopt an

Never hesitate to call in a vet if you're in any doubt about the health of your birds. Time wasted by indecision can be a big factor in the ultimate effects of a poultry disease.

abnormal posture.

Weight loss will follow if birds cannot reach food and water, or if the viscera are involved, and where this is a protracted affair the feathers around the vent will become soiled and smelly. Mortality in unvaccinated flocks may be between five and 50%, but isn't usually seen before 10 or after 30 weeks of age. But there are exceptions; it often occurs at point-of-lay, triggered by the stresses in the birds' life at this time. Some breeds or strains within these breeds seem very susceptible to the disease, and where this is the case and small numbers are involved, the entire flock may be lost.

Effects: There may be tumours in various organs around the body, including the liver, spleen, kidneys, ovary, testes, proventriculus, and also in the skeletal muscles. Varying in size from (pinhead to a marble) they are clearly visible, and may be present in such numbers to make the affected organ enlarged and distorted.

Where paralysis is a factor, there will be tumour-like lesions on the nerves, especially those of the legs and wings. These are found under the muscle on the inside of the thigh, and at the base of the wing or under the kidney respectively. To the untrained eye they can be quite difficult to detect. In the ocular form, the iris will appear broken, or the pupil will be paralysed. In the latter case, if the bird is still alive, this can be demonstrated by exposing the eye to changing light intensities and noting the lack of response.

Birds affected with Marek's Disease are often very thin and dehydrated, either as a result of their internal problems, or simply because they have been unable to reach food and water. The skin can become involved, and tumours may form around the feather follicles.

Where Marek's is suspected, sick and dead birds should be sent for examination by a specialist poultry vet, to eliminate other diseases such as Lymphoid Leucosis which displays some very similar symptoms.

Treatment: There's no cure for Marek's Disease; affected birds should be culled. It can be controlled by vaccination at day-old – preferably before the chicks leave the hatchery. Where small numbers of chicks are involved, this is usually administered via an injection into the thigh muscle. Vaccination should be regarded as a method of preventing the development of the tumours and paralysis, but not for preventing infection. High standards of hygiene must be maintained, with particular attention to clean-out and restocking with day-olds. Where the disease is a problem, and vaccination isn't an option, chicks can be reared on a clean site to the age of four weeks or more before placing them where the disease is known to prevail. The use of resistant strains of chickens also has potential.

LYMPHOID LEUCOSIS

Lymphoid Leucosis (also known as 'Big Liver Disease' and 'Visceral Leucosis'), is caused by a Retrovirus, and while it bears many similarities to, and may be confused with, Marek's as tumours are a feature, it must be regarded as a totally different disease.

The virus is transmitted through the egg, and from bird to bird at a young age, possibly through saliva and droppings. While the virus is ubiquitous in poultry flocks, its survival without a host is limited to hours, which effectively limits its spread. It affects mainly domestic fowl.

Symptoms: The disease is usually associated with losses in laying and breeding flocks aged between 16 and 40 weeks. Within the flock there are continually a few sickly-looking birds, appearing weak and listless; appetite is reduced along with egg production. Handling the infected birds will reveal emaciation and perhaps some with enlarged abdomens. Loose droppings and soiled vent feathers may be noted in some birds. Unlike Marek's Disease, there are no nervous signs, such as paralysis.

Effects: The virus transforms cells into neoplasms (literally 'new growth' – tumours) and, upon post-mortem examination, these feature prominently. Tumours will be seen in the liver, spleen, kidneys, ovaries and the bursa of Fabricius. The liver is often enlarged to

Maintaining a healthy flock is all about being aware of the behaviour of your birds. Knowing their habits, and recognising when routines are altered, can give you a valuable head start when dealing with disease.

become many times its normal size.

Leucosis also appears less frequently in other forms: Osteopetrosis causes thickening of the bones of the wings and legs; the bones becoming abnormally shaped, bowed and hard to break. Erythroid is characterised as leukaemia. Together with enlargement of the liver, spleen and other internal organs, the skin may take on a pale or yellowish colour, and the bone marrow will be seen to be semi-liquid and bright red. Myeloid leucosis shows similar signs in the liver, spleen, kidneys and ovary to those already mentioned; the bone marrow becomes pale pink and homogenous, and anaemia may be a feature.

Confirmation of the disease requires the services of the veterinary laboratory. Live birds and/or carcasses should be submitted to identify the organism, and eliminate other possible causes.

Treatment: There is no cure, and vaccines aren't available. Infected birds should be culled as they are noticed. Preventative measures include identifying infected breeders and eliminating them from the flock, plus using strains that are resistant to the disease. Good standards of husbandry and attention to hygiene and sanitation may lessen the effect of the disease, while a short break when the site is depopulated may help re-establish a virus-free environment.

INFECTIOUS BURSAL DISEASE (IBD)

This disease is also known as 'Gumboro' disease – named after the town in America where the first outbreak occurred. It's caused by a Birna virus, the strains of which can be subdivided into classical and variant. It's a highly infectious virus, and can be transmitted from bird to bird by handlers (on clothes), droppings, contaminated equipment and transport.

It's quite possible that a major outbreak in the UK during the 1980s was brought into the country in frozen chicken carcasses. The disease, apart from causing mortality, reduces the birds' ability to develop immunity and, consequently, survivors may be subject to other infections later in their lives. The disease affects young chickens.

Symptoms: IBD tends to manifest itself in chickens between two and eight weeks old, however, it's occasionally seen right up to 20 weeks. Chicks infected at under two weeks old may not show any signs at the time – it only becomes apparent later on, either by blood test or as a result of subsequent associated infections.

The disease has a sudden onset, and the outward signs are short-lived. The mortality – which is often 5-15% (but can be much higher, cases of 90% have been known where highly pathogenic strains of the virus have been involved) – is spread over five or six days, peaking in the middle period, and then returning to normal. Other symptoms include depression and inactivity, a reduced food intake, high temperatures, prostration, huddling, lack of co-ordination and a wobbly gait.

One of the main signs of the disease is seen in the Bursa of Fabricius, hence its name. The bursa is located inside the body, above the vent and below the tail, and is involved with the development of immunity. In acute cases the bursa becomes enlarged (up to twice its size), often becoming gelatinous, and changing from a creamy colour to being reddened with blood. After a few days it atrophies – the timing depending on the strain involved – and, in chronic cases, it

may remain small and waste away without the enlargement stage. Carcasses may be dehydrated and the kidneys pale. In some cases haemorrhaging is seen on the legs and thighs.

Blood tests may reveal a lack of white blood cells, and isolation of the virus will confirm infection and rule out other health issues with similar symptoms.

Treatment: There is no cure for the disease, but subsequent infections on the same site are less severe. Vaccines are available to help prevent infection, and can be administered to both parent stock and offspring. In the former they give immunity through the egg to prevent disease during the chicks' first days while, in the latter, they give continued protection. The use and timing of vaccines requires veterinary guidance. Although once on a site it's unlikely to be eradicated, special attention to cleaning and disinfection may pay dividends. General hygiene measures, such as isolating infected birds and a change of clothing when visiting different flocks, may help reduce the spread of the disease.

FOWL CHOLERA

Fowl cholera is caused by a bacterium, Pasteurella multocida. The disease is passed from bird to bird through food and water contaminated with oral, nasal or bowel discharges. Rats and mice appear to play some part in the contamination of feed and water supplies, and in the continuance of the organism.

Chickens, turkeys, waterfowl, pigeons, game, and wild birds are all susceptible to infection.

Symptoms: In the 'peracute' (very severe) form, the first indication of a problem will be mortality.

Young chicks can be affected by Infectious Bursal Disease (IBD), that's also known as 'Gumboro' disease.

In acute cases the presence of internal haemorrhaging is apparent throughout the carcass, especially under the skin, surrounding the heart, in the lungs, gizzard, intestines, and in fatty tissue. The liver is usually enlarged and infiltrated with small (pinhead) white spots of necrotic material. Where the wattles are swollen, there will be cheesy material separating the layers of skin. Swollen joints will contain either a thick opaque fluid or a yellow cheesy material surrounding the tendons or filling the cavity. In birds that have taken some days to die, the flesh has a fevered, reddish appearance, and there may be pneumonia of the lungs and mucus in the windpipe.

In peracute forms there may be few internal signs; diagnosis is only possible by isolating the organism and identifying it from samples submitted to a veterinary laboratory.

Treatment: Affected flocks can be treated with antibiotics and other drugs for which a prescription will be required. This will remove the symptoms and restore production. It may not produce a total cure as some birds can remain chronic carriers, re-infecting the flock. Where this happens, the treatment must be repeated. Vaccines are also available, and professional advice should be taken if this option is chosen.

The bacteria are fairly easily killed by good farm disinfectants, used as per the maker's recommendations. They are also killed by hot water, instantly at 100°C, or within five minutes at 60°C. What's more, lifespan without a host is short – probably as little as 14 days. Using this information, a number of strategies can be devised in the wake of an outbreak. Rat and mouse control is vital to prevent recontamination of clean premises.

Good husbandry – keeping houses and runs clean and rodent-free – is vital to the health of your birds.

This may account for 90% of the flock and, indeed, there may be no other pointers to the disease. Where acute serotypes are involved it'll be less, while in chronic infections, although there will be an increase in the number of deaths, the mortality will not be high.

Other symptoms associated with the acute and chronic types include depression and a reduction in food intake, bodyweight and egg production. The degree will be in proportion to the severity of the outbreak; if there's an almost complete loss of appetite, then it follows that egg output will be seriously affected and birds will rapidly lose condition. Affected individuals may stand apart from the rest of the flock. Greenish-yellow diarrhoea, swollen joints and lameness, difficulty in breathing and increased thirst (due to a high fever) are all signs. The comb and wattles may be blue or swollen, and other facial parts may appear similar to those associated with coryza infections.

Egg yields are a good indicator of poultry health. Reductions should be investigated.

SALMONELLA AND COCCIDIOSIS

Bob Cross focuses on another two nasty poultry-related diseases.

SALMONELLA INFECTION

Salmonella is a bacteria and over 2,000 different species have been identified, of which more than 700 are known to cause food poisoning in humans. Many of these will go undetected, and their presence is only revealed as a result of laboratory testing. There are other species however, which cause problems for the poultryman by way of disease in his stock.

Bacillary White Diarrhoea (BWD) and Fowl Typhoid: These two diseases are both caused by Salmonella, the former by S. pullorum and the latter by S. gallinarum.

BWD is usually seen in young chicks, although typhoid is a disease more associated with adult stock. Transmission of pullorum is through the egg, from infected hens which may appear outwardly healthy, but which are 'carriers' of the organism. Chicks which hatch from these eggs will be infected, and can also infect other chicks, either in the incubator or in the brooder pen, via droppings.

Fowl typhoid is transmitted through infected droppings, nasal and oral discharges, carcasses and by handlers; on their clothing, shoes and the equipment they are using. Chickens, turkeys, pheasants, ducks, geese and guinea fowl are also susceptible, and can carry the infection.

Symptoms: Pullorum chicks appear chilled and huddle together, often making distressed chirping sounds and producing a white foamy, sticky diarrhoea, causing pasting around the vent. Appetite is severely checked, the breathing laboured, with many chicks dying suddenly. Mortality may be in excess of 60% and, where infection has taken place at the hatchery, the chicks die in the first week. Those infected on the farm will succumb between weeks one and three.

Gallinarum symptoms include listlessness, loss of appetite, increased thirst, and diarrhoea (which may be sulphur-yellow in colour). The comb and wattles become pale and shrivelled as birds suffer, and egg production falls.

Mortality runs at around 50%, but can be much higher if no treatment is given. In adults it's likely that there will be no outward signs, although internally the ovary may contain abnormal yolks, either misshapen or appearing brown or greenish in colour.

Chicks which are infected may show unabsorbed yolk sacs, and survivors in the post-brooding stage may have greyish nodules surrounding many of the internal organs. The caeca contain a cheesy core. Confirmation of infection is by bacteriological examination.

Effects: Gallinarum: internal signs include swelling of the liver, spleen, kidneys; the liver may be bronze-green in colour, with tiny white spots of dead tissue on the surface. Often, on handling, it breaks up easily. The intestines can become inflamed, filling with mucous and the ovary displays signs similar to those of pullorum. Again definitive diagnosis requires the services of the veterinary laboratory.

Treatment: There is no satisfactory cure for these diseases. Treatment with drugs may alleviate the symptoms and reduce losses, but those birds that recover may be carriers and perpetuate the infection to the next generation. Cleaning and disinfection of contaminated premises and equipment will help check the cycle of disease transmission, and blood testing of breeding birds to eliminate carriers should stop it at source.

Carcasses of infected birds, and those identified as carriers, should be disposed of promptly using an effective method such as incineration. Rats, mice and other vermin (including wild birds), should be excluded from the site as these may act as vectors and also harbour the infection. Care should also be taken when introducing new stock from dubious sources; quarantine and isolation would be wise precautions. Waterfowl should be housed separately to other types of poultry to help prevent contamination via the water route.

COCCIDIOSIS

This disease is caused by a Protozoa, which is a small unicellular parasite. There are nine species that affect chickens, eight that concern turkeys, several which involve waterfowl and others to which game birds are susceptible. Non-avian livestock can also become infected. The causal organism is host-specific, in other words those that affect chickens will not harm other types of stock, and vice versa.

The genus of protozoa responsible for coccidiosis in the chicken is Eimeria, and the nine species are; E. ascervulina, E. necatrix, E tenella, E. maxima, E. brunetti, E. hagani, E. praecox, E.mitis and E. mivati. The first five in the list are the most important.

Their life cycle involves time both inside and outside the body. The first stage occurs when an oocyst is released from the host. This is a seed-like body, which is non-infective and can be re-ingested by the bird causing it no harm. While on the ground, given the right temperature and moisture conditions, it undergoes development and maturation. This process is called 'sporulation' and takes 24-48 hours. The chicken eats the sprouted oocysts which then hatch in the intestine, releasing their contents. These are known as sporozoites, and they enter the lining of the intestine. While here they undergo further developmental generations, forming merozoites which, in turn, produce the gametes that form the next generation of oocysts, which pass out in the faeces, thus repeating the cycle. The clinical symptoms of coccidiosis will be seen in 4-6 days after infection.

Symptoms: The chickens look dull and listless, adopting a hunched posture. The feathers are often ruffled, the combs pale, wings dropped and eyes closed. Appetite is depressed, weight loss follows and, in laying flocks, egg production will be adversely affected. The faeces may be

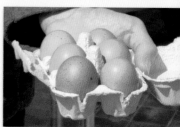

Eggs often associated with Salmonella, but it can seriously affect stock too.

blood-stained and, in some cases, blood alone may be passed; diarrhoea is often a feature.

Mortality will vary but often can be in excess of 50%, with the species of the disease, housing conditions, the existence of an anti-coccidial supplement in the feed or its efficacy, and the immune status of the bird all having an influence on this figure.

Where the birds are receiving no treatment in the feed, the onset will be rapid and the losses are likely to be high, so diagnosis and treatment must follow without delay. Coccidiosis can affect birds of any age, but tends to be a disease seen at the growing phase. During this time the birds develop immunity which, as long as they receive a constant low-level challenge, will be maintained throughout their lives. Certain other diseases may adversely affect the birds' ability to develop immunity to coccidiosis. Warm, damp conditions are especially conducive for the development of the oocysts, so it's important to be vigilant under these circumstances.

Effects: Caecal coccidosis: Mainly caused by E. tenella and usually seen in chickens up to 12 weeks old. The caecal wall will be severely haemorrhaged and, in older infections, the caecum will contain a tough core. Pure blood may be voided. The other four important species result in intestinal coccidiosis.

E. ascervulina: Can affect birds of any age; the upper half of the small intestine shows haemorrhagic lesions and greyish-white streaks on the gut wall.

E. necatrix: Usually affects birds between six and 16 weeks, but can be much earlier and be responsible for big losses. Infection is found in the middle of the small intestine. The gut is enlarged to possibly twice its size, the unopened intestine is covered with white spots interspersed with either dull or bright red areas haemorrhaging to the inside.

E maxima: Birds of any age are susceptible, less pathogenic than most resulting in low mortality. Affects the lower end of the small intestine. The gut becomes filled with pinkish mucous or a greyish-brown exudate. The gut wall becomes thickened and the intestine dilated.

E. brunetti: Affects birds of any age and may be responsible for high mortality. The lower half of the intestine and rectum are affected, the gut wall is swollen and the lining may slough away; a white cheese-like material may be found within. The caeca and cloaca are inflamed.

Treatment: When coccidiosis is suspected veterinary assistance should be sought without delay, and dead birds and faecal samples should be submitted to confirm the presence of the organism and to rule out other possible causes with similar symptoms.

There is a range of drugs available for the successful treatment of the disease. These require a prescription and should be used as per veterinary advice to prevent contraindications, and to achieve maximum efficacy. Survivors of an outbreak should show few outward signs, although their gut will be scarred and they may not be quite such efficient converters of feed. Where the caeca has been involved it may have reduced their ability to absorb water from the faecal matter as it approaches this end of the gut, resulting in rather wet droppings. Once infected with one species of Eimeria, birds will acquire immunity to it but will still be susceptible to the others.

There are a number of preventative measures that should be adopted. Medicated feed can be used throughout most of the rearing period, reverting to plain feed just before the onset of lay or slaughter, observing withdrawal periods. In recent years vaccination has become an option, although probably not for owners of small flocks. From a management and husbandry angle, it's important to maintain the litter in a dry friable state to hinder the development of the oocysts. This may be achieved by, among other things, correct stocking densities, ventilation rates and drinker adjustment. Care should be taken when making any changes such as those involving feed or movement, to ensure they are achieved causing the minimum of stress to the birds.

Before restocking, the house must be clean – oocysts can remain viable for many months and one gram of litter can contain tens of thousands. All old litter must be taken away and the house washed and disinfected. The oocysts are quite resistant to many disinfectants but one called 'Oocide', produced by Antec, has been developed for this purpose. Ammonia may prove useful but there are risks involved with using it.

With regard to the provision of feed and water, it's important to prevent infection via this route; feeders and drinkers should be sited and adjusted so as not to become contaminated, and receive daily attention to maintain cleanliness. If birds are reared outside in runs on grass, these should be moved daily thus breaking the cycle and preventing the birds ingesting the organism in its infective stage. ❦

SALMONELLA TESTING

Although most poultry flocks are now free of the above salmonella, this has not always been the case. It comes as the result of a long and continuing effort. While the importance of good hygiene cannot be over-stressed, much more has been achieved by identifying the carrier birds and eliminating them.

The causal organism was first identified by Rettger in 1900. By 1910 he and his associates had a much better understanding of the organism's ability to survive in the ovary of recovered birds, and the transmission of infection via the egg to the next generation of chicks. From these discoveries it became clear that, if the carriers could be identified in a breeding flock, the cycle of infection would be broken and one major source of transmission eliminated.

The 'agglutination test' was adopted in 1913. The test involves mixing a sample of blood with a drop of antigen to detect the presence of antibodies in the sample. If the blood be positive, 'clumping' occurs and the mixed sample appears granular. This indicates that the bird is a reactor, and it's destroyed. The antigen is dead BWD cells and the antibodies would be the protective substances that the bird's body produced to defend itself from attack. In a negative sample, the mixed fluid remains cloudy.

Initially, testing was by the 'tube method', which required a sample of blood to be collected in a tube. The bird's identity was then written on the tube and it was sent off to a laboratory for the serum to be tested. This was obviously very time consuming, and was superseded by the 'rapid plate' test. This involves taking a spot of blood from either the wing vein or the comb, and mixing it with a drop of the antigen on a glass or enamel plate. The results become apparent in a couple of minutes.

The plate is marked-off, usually into 24 squares, with each one representing one bird. By the time the second half of the plate is being used, the results of the first half can be read. The testing procedure was adopted by the Ministry of Agriculture as part of its Poultry Health Scheme, and continued into the 1980s when it was relaxed. It was reintroduced to breeding flocks a decade or so later, as part of the Salmonella prevention measures.

When testing first started there were many reactors, and the birds were individually crated until their results were known. Latterly whole flocks were tested without finding a single reactor; such was the success of the project. It's unlikely that the disease will be found in commercial stock, but it may well still be found in the real backyard flocks, and those living in a semi-feral state in farmyard environments.

Other salmonella of importance include S. typhimurium and S. enteritidis. These are both important as they can cause food poisoning in humans. There may be no symptoms to indicate infection, and they only come to light as a result of other testing. Should these or any other Salmonella species be found, they must be reported through your vet to Defra, who will advise on subsequent action. Some protection against these can be provided with vaccines, although other routes of entry must be blocked, including contaminated feed, litter, wild birds and, probably worst of all, personnel.

Delving into Droppings

Terry Beebe gets down and dirty to discover just what poultry droppings can tell you about the overall health of a chicken.

They say that the eyes are the window of a person's soul. Well, in a similar, albeit slightly less romantic way, a chicken's droppings can be regarded as a spyglass to its general state of health. While some may find the idea of diagnosing droppings distasteful, for the poultry owner who wishes to keep on top of their birds' condition, the state of their droppings can provide an extremely valuable pointer.

Vets appreciate the full value of detailed droppings diagnosis, which is why samples are so often requested during the early stages of a bird's treatment. However, while a veterinary laboratory will carry out a full, clinical analysis of a faecal sample, there are plenty of useful clues to be gained by the non-professional simply from the appearance of droppings.

It's not infallible, of course, and what you conclude from what you see should only ever be taken as a guide. As always, for the definitive answer, I'd advise you to consult and experienced poultry vet. Another potential snag is that, although some usefully practical pointers can be gained about general health conditions, and some specific diseases, what can't be ascertained from a visual diagnosis like this is the precise cause of the problem. For that it's likely that you'll have to involve a professional laboratory, via your vet.

What's normal?

To begin with, it's probably worth spending a few moments describing exactly how to recognise just what a healthy chicken's droppings should look like.

If all's well, then what you should expect to find is a fairly firm, rounded dropping with two distinct sections. The larger portion should be darkly-coloured (black/brown/grey), and the smaller bit should be almost pure white, usually forming a sort of cap or crown at one end. The dark portion is the solid waste, while the white part is the urine.

Under normal circumstances, the whole dropping should be quite firm and well-formed. If you find this from your birds, then it's likely that they are all in a pretty good state of health.

Yellow peril!

If you discover that your birds are producing yellow-coloured, loose droppings then this can point to a number of potential problems. While this can be triggered by nothing more involved than a diet rich in corn/split maize or green stuffs, there are other more worrying possibilities. For a start, this custard-like appearance is known by many experienced breeders as a classic sign that the birds have a worm problem. In addition,

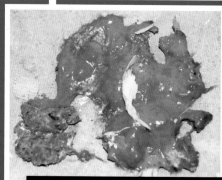

Yellow-coloured, loose droppings can point to a number of potential problems, including dietary defects, worms and even respiratory troubles.

such droppings can also point towards respiratory infection; this is a problem which will need to be treated by a vet, but it's normally easily cured by the use of correct medication.

'Worming' poultry regularly should be an important part of every keeper's good husbandry regime, however, don't write-off the possibility of worm infestation simply because you have carried out a preventative treatment. Worms can be picked-up at any time, so you should always be on your guard.

Try to keep a close watch on the birds and, if the symptom persists and a fresh worming treatment doesn't control the problem, then put the matter in the hands of your vet. The liquid, yellow droppings are certainly easy enough to spot, and further investigation will often reveal small worms in the fluid – some still visibly wriggling. Egg production can also suffer as a consequence.

I recommend that a good quality wormer is used at least twice a year and, although these are prescription-only products, they're easily obtained from a poultry vet. My choice is one called Panacur, which is mixed with the birds' drinking water and works over a 4-5-day period; very easy and economical to use.

There are quite a few other treatments on the market, in either tablet, powder or liquid form. Consult your local

Green-coloured droppings like this can reflect a dietary imbalance, but they can also be an indicator of serious internal infection. Treat them with suspicion.

poultry supply specialist for further information.

Coccidiosis

This is probably one of the most dangerous of all the problems which can be easily identified by an experienced keeper from the appearance of droppings. The disease is caused by an internal parasite, and is always more common in young birds that have yet to reach full, sexual maturity – it typically strikes chickens aged between six and 12 weeks.

The signs are usually very plain to see but, in most cases, a cure is relatively straightforward assuming the disease has been caught at an early enough stage. To begin with, the birds themselves become lethargic, with wings drooped and heads held low; they look very sorry for themselves. As far as the droppings are concerned, check those found under the birds' roosting perches, and look for the presence of redness. If further investigation reveals the presence of small, blood-red coloured, jelly-like worms, then coccidiosis is likely

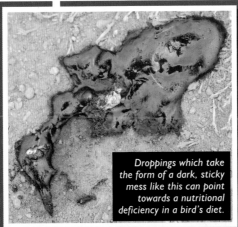

Droppings which take the form of a dark, sticky mess like this can point towards a nutritional deficiency in a bird's diet.

to be the cause. This discolouration in the droppings always stands out well against clean litter, and is easy to spot.

Unfortunately, if the infestation has already reached this stage before you notice it, then the parasites are generally well established, and you're likely to suffer fatalities I'm afraid. Discovering this also means that you'll have to keep all the birds from the 'infected' house isolate so that they can be treated as a group. Don't, for any reason, mix them with other birds you may have from outside that particular house. The worms are easily and quickly transferred from bird to bird via contact with infested droppings. With this in mind, take care not to tread infected droppings from house to house on the soles of your shoes.

Treatment is by oral dosage of an anti-coccidiosis product such as Amprol, which has to be obtained on prescription from your vet. The birds should be treated as soon as possible, and it's necessary to dose every bird in the group both to clear up the problem, and minimise its spread. If this condition is ignored it'll kill your birds, so be warned.

Other possibilities

One of the worst things to find in

This is the sort of dropping to expect from a healthy hen, with distinct dark brown/grey and white parts.

poultry droppings is a green colour. While this can be fairly innocent – indicating a diet rich in green matter, or one containing too much protein – sometimes this sign has a rather more deep-rooted cause.

I've found from experience that once pale green fluid appears in droppings, it's a sign that the bird is suffering with a serious internal infection. Regrettably, problems of this sort normally result in the bird's death. I've had birds of my own with this problem checked professionally but, even though the results throw-up nothing significant, the chicken will usually go on to die.

Old poultry books recommend Epsom salts and various other concoctions, most of which are either unavailable or even illegal to use these days. So I tend to try and keep the affected birds isolated and as comfortable as possible, with a constant supply of fresh water containing a small dosage (10ml) of cider vinegar. I also worm them orally by syringe as a back-up. I've had some success with this approach but, to be honest, the results aren't that impressive.

What you've got to remember when keeping poultry, is that most parasite-related problems your birds are likely to experience will stem from ground-based infection, or from that passed on by other birds or, indeed, ourselves.

High levels of cleanliness in everything you do really is one of the keys to success. Make use of specialist disinfectants, clean fresh feed and, most importantly, good clean bedding that's changed on a regular basis. Top quality bird management always delivers the best results and can, in the long run, save you time and money. As I've said many times before, prevention is always better then cure.

PARASITE PATROL

Terry Beebe gets to grips with the most common types of parasitic pests that you're likely to find crawling around on your hens.

Chickens of all sorts are prone to parasite infestation, whether it's by those which live internally within the bird (endoparasites), or those which exist on the skin (ectoparasites). We'll be dealing with the latter group in this feature.

Dusting your birds against lice should form part of your regular, good-husbandry program.

Any sort of parasite can present a potentially serious threat to a hen's wellbeing, causing unnecessary stress and suffering, plus a reduction in laying performance. So it's vital that all forms of parasite are effectively controlled. Thankfully, this isn't a difficult or expensive process, but it does take time and effort. There are plenty of anti-parasite treatments available nowadays (both chemical and organic), so there really is no excuse for letting things get out of hand.

Unfortunately, the warmer weather we're all experiencing these days and, in particularly, the lack of a really cold winter, means that poultry parasites are becoming more and more of a year-round threat. Consequently, keeping your defences up against these potentially dangerous pests is now a constant requirement. You really should make

a 'parasite patrol' part of your routine maintenance program, as treatment needs to be at least once a week all through the year.

Common pests

While there are a fair number of ectoparasites that can affect poultry, the list can be whittled down to four, commonly-found types; lice, red mite, Northern mite and scaly leg mite. These pests can all pose a long-term problem and, under ideal conditions, are capable of surviving off the host bird for a very long time, which is why they can be so difficult to eradicate.

The louse is probably the most common of all the poultry-related parasites and, although not as potentially dangerous as the red mite, lice will certainly irritate the bird and cause it discomfort. This then has detrimental, knock-on effects on both egg laying and breeding potential.

To check for a lice infestation simply inspect the area of skin around the vent, parting the feathers and fluff in a search for small, buff-coloured, cigar-shaped creatures that move quickly. The females are larger than the males, but the male tends to look more lemon-shaped.

One of the most obvious general signs of lice are white, cotton wool-like balls at the base of the feathers. These are the egg cases, and are stuck securely in place by the female. You may also notice birds spending longer than normal preening, especially around the vent area. While this isn't always a sign of lice, it can provide a useful, practical pointer. Hatching times vary with temperature and the weather conditions, but normal incubation takes about 10 days.

An adult louse will live for several months on the bird (depending on conditions) but, once away from the

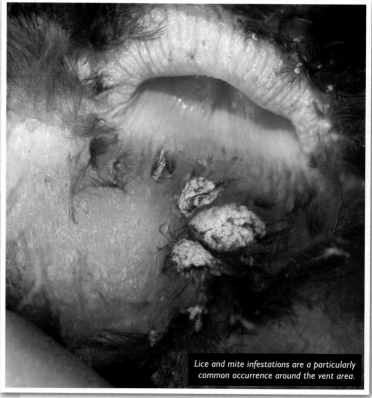

Lice and mite infestations are a particularly common occurrence around the vent area.

The activities of the tiny scaly leg mite can be unsightly for the owner and excruciating for the bird. Treat all cases as early as possible.

after feeding – which is another reason why they can be tricky to recognise.

Consequently, the big danger is that the presence of red mite is missed by the inexperienced keeper, which allows the infestation to become really established. This is very bad news as, despite their tiny size, these mites are perfectly capable of killing birds, especially broody hens and chicks which are most vulnerable. Unfortunately, in a lot of cases it's only when the birds start to look very ill, or die (due to loss of blood), that keepers first realise there's a problem.

Being on your guard at all times is the key to keeping red mite under control. Make regular and careful checks of the hen house interior; you're looking for the tell-tale grey dust which appears around the joints and knots in the shed timber. Check under perches and behind hinges and bolts too – in fact, anywhere where these creatures could possibly cluster. I've even known cases where they've been found inside light switch fittings! Sometimes these mites will breed so heavily that they'll be seen as a clump which, when squashed, will run red.

ost, lifespan is limited to about a week. As you might expect, lice breed at a frightening rate, and a single pair can produce literally thousands of offspring in a very short time. Reproduction is stimulated by high temperatures.

My approach, when dealing with the eggs, is to remove them by hand. In my experience the use of a basic louse powder is never completely effective against the eggs, so I prefer to remove them completely.

There are many specialist treatments on the market, such as Louse Powder from Barrier Health Care. These are very popular with most keepers and, being powders, they are both convenient and easy to use. To 'powder' a bird

successfully it's vital to get the product right down to the base of the feathers; don't simply sprinkle it generally on top. The key areas to target are under the bird's wings and around the vent and, to make sure of a proper application, part the feathers to reveal the skin then shake on the powder in each area.

For a more permanent control solution you'll need to approach your vet. As an alternative to the powders, you can opt for fluid-based treatments applied with a dropper. These work by entering the bird's bloodstream, ensuring that the treatment is consumed by any biting parasite, such as lice. You'll pay more for this sort of prescription-only product, and will have to consult your vet to get it, but the results are good.

Red mite

This creature is by far the most worrying poultry-related parasite you're likely to come across; it's a little vampire and its effects can be devastating. It doesn't live on the bird, and only strikes at night as its victims are roosting. During the day these pests tuck themselves away out of sight in crevices and cracks in the hen house walls and perch mountings, making them difficult to spot for the uninitiated. What's more, their normal colour is buff/grey – they only turn red

> **There are plenty of anti-parasite treatments available nowadays (both chemical and organic)**

Due to the red mite's nocturnal habit, the best time to check for it is in the evening, after you've locked-up your birds. One of the best ways of assessing the situation is simply to watch your roosting birds. If they appear disturbed and uncomfortable, their wattles and combs look unusually pale (anaemic), and you've also noticed a decline in egg production, then red mite could well be the problem. If the infestation is a bad one, you may even pick up some on you from being in the hen house. They don't live on humans, but you'll certainly be aware of an uncomfortable itching if they're on you.

In practical terms the truth about red mite is that it's virtually impossible to eradicate; the best that most of us can hope for is to keep it tightly in check. To do this regular spraying of the poultry house and birds is essential. I use a product called Poultry Shield, which is a type of liquid detergent that can be sprayed deep into all the nooks and crannies where you suspect red mite may be hiding. Unfortunately, it's unlikely that even the most enthusiastic spraying will ever penetrate deep enough to ▶

It may be tiny but when operating at infestation numbers, the red mite can be a deadly enemy to chicks and broody hens.

attack the unhatched eggs, which is why I recommend a re-treatment after 5-7 days, to catch the newly-hatched mites.

If you want to check the birds themselves, do so in the evening after they have been roosting for a while. Part the feathers and search the skin in all the warm areas (under the wings, around the vent, base of the tail). If you find any it's likely that they will live up to their name and will be red, due to the blood they've just feasted on.

Scaly leg mite

The condition produced by the scaly leg mite used to be popularly known as 'foot mange' or 'scabies', and it's a serious problem which can affect all poultry, pheasants and turkeys. Waterfowl however, very rarely suffer with it.

It's an aptly-named parasite that produces characteristic areas of crusty, raised scales on birds' legs, which gradually worsen if the condition goes untreated. The mite burrows under the scales and into the skin below. Doing this obviously causes pain and acute irritation for the bird, and it's the presence of the mites, plus the waste products they generate, which forces the scales to lift.

If not dealt with, the parasite will eventually force the scales right off the leg, leaving them bare and extremely sore. Treatment should always be administered before this stage is reached. In nearly all cases both a bird's legs will be affected and, although not a potentially deadly condition, the consequences of scaly leg mite can cripple a bird.

The female mite lays her eggs under the layer of crusty scabs, and the young hatch after 10 days. The youngsters remain here until they reach maturity, after which the breeding cycle is continued. These tiny white creatures are very hard to see with the naked eye, and can live off their host in the housing and floor litter. Consequently, it's easily transmitted from bird to bird, which is why it's always sensible to keep affected birds isolated.

The first thing to remember when dealing with the problem is never to pull off scales in an attempt to 'tidy-up' the affected area. This won't help the sufferer, and is also likely to release more mites into the environment, increasing the risk of the condition spreading.

Preventing scaly leg mite in the first place is very tricky because it's one of those conditions that's hard to detect in the early stages. Once the scale-lifting starts to become visible the mites will

Keeping on top of parasites is all about remaining vigilant, adopting good welfare practice and being sensible with your treatments.

be established. All you can do is check your birds' legs regularly, looking for the slightest sign of scale unevenness. Obviously you should avoid buying-in affected birds but, if you're in any doubt, a smear of Vaseline on their legs can be a useful precaution.

Fortunately, dealing with a scaly leg mite infestation is relatively simple. Most of the traditional treatments have now been outlawed under modern welfare legislation, although effective treatments

remain. One of the simplest is to paint on a coating of a product called Duramitex or your vet can supply license-only products. Both will work wonders and, once the coating has dried, the whole leg and foot should be covered with a layer of Vaseline. The rather grizzly but necessary reason for this is to suffocate any mites that the initial treatment has failed to kill. It also helps with the scales' healing process.

Johnson's make a special scaly leg dropper which is available from most good suppliers. It's cheap to buy but is only

Fortunately, dealing with a scaly leg mite infestation is relatively simple

supplied in a small bottle so, for treating many birds, the paint-on approach is probably favourable.

Treatment which involves painting the legs needs to be repeated every 4-5 days, until the condition starts to improve; the overall time needed will depend on the severity of the infestation. New scales will start to grow, first appearing very fresh and pink, but carry on with the treatment until they start to harden.

Finally, there's a very effective, insecticide-based treatment which is a drop-on liquid that works by entering the blood stream. However, this is a prescription-only product, so can only be supplied through your vet.

These grey deposits are a tell-tale sign of red mite. Treatments need to be sprayed carefully into all nooks and crannies to stand any chance of success.

Northern mite

The simplest way to identify the presence of Northern mite is by the discovery of clumps of grey or dark-coloured material (a bit like cigarette ash) on and around

Parasites are naturally attracted to the warm, damp areas of a bird's body so, when inspecting, always check under the wings, around the vent and at the base of the tail.

the base of the feathers. Typically these will be found around the vent area but, in particularly bad infestations, the signs can be more widespread. You may also find evidence of skin infections. Northern mite bite and break the skin, causing soreness and significant irritation to the bird.

Outwardly, though, all can appear normal, and herein lies the danger. It's not unless you take the trouble to part the feathers and look closely that you'll discover the truth. The deposits you find are clumps of the mites and their droppings. While not as potentially deadly as red mite, this type of parasite can cause serious damage if left unchecked. Crested breeds such as the Poland can suffer particularly badly. Northern mite infest the crest, then get into the eyes and ears, where they can cause blindness and deafness. Consequently, regular (weekly) checks are vital.

Prevention is very straightforward; simply keep the birds regularly treated with a good mite killer spray. If you discover that a bird is infested then it's best to bathe it (gently, to minimize the stress levels) in a mixture of warm water and insecticide shampoo – Dynamite do a very good lice shampoo which I can highly recommend. As the bird is being washed you'll see the water turn dirty, and a black sludge will appear in the bowl as the mites and droppings are removed.

Repeat the washing a couple of times and then leave the bird to dry in a warm place. Never wash and leave a bird wet in cold or draughty conditions. If you have a heat lamp sit the bird under that until it has dried out, and don't apply powder or spray until it's completely dry. Some mites will inevitably survive so the treatment should be repeated after a few days. 🐾

THE RED ARMY!

They're lurking in poultry sheds up and down the land, emerging at night to drink the blood of our birds. Terry Beebe declares war on the red mite.

The problem posed by red mite is nothing new; infestations have been breaking out in hen houses for as long as I can remember. But the past few years do seem to have been worse than usual. I'm sure that the banning of creosote, and related products, as an anti-pest treatment hasn't helped, nor

have the generally higher temperatures we've been experiencing recently. Winters certainly don't seem as severe as they used to be and, without that all important prolonged 'cold snap' to keep these sorts of pest in check, the situation simply gets progressively worse.

Whatever the reason, though, I'd certainly rather spend my time preventing an infestation, which I believe is a lot more useful than trying to find the cause.

AGAINST THE ODDS
Effective prevention of red mite is very

Infested houses must be treated thoroughly and regularly with an effective anti-parasite product if red mite is to be kept under control. It's a hard pest to beat completely.

difficult. These tiny, bloodsucking creatures seem to love new timber, so a brand new shed is always a target, even though it might be the last place that you'd expect to find the problem. So the only approach is to treat every poultry building you have during the winter period, when any red mite that may be lurking inside, are at their most dormant.

Red mite hide during the day (unless you've a major infestation in which case you will see them in daylight); sheltering in timber joints, between shed boarding, on the underside of perches, and in any other nooks and crannies that'll give

Anti-mite treatments, which are diluted by water and can be applied using a spray like this, are economical and effective to use.

them protection. They especially love to work their way up under the felt on a shed's roof, which creates a major problem. Dealing effectively with this sort of infestation means replacing the felt – quite a major job.

Soaking the shed in both a modern anti-mite product and a suitable disinfectant, really is the only way you'll stand any chance of keeping on top of the problem. What's more, the process will need to be repeated throughout the season. In days gone by, keepers had a variety of weapons in the armoury, including creosote, diesel and even old engine oil – my grandfather used the latter to dip the ends of his perches, and to work into the timber joints of his

poultry houses. This certainly worked well, but can't be recommended ▶

RED MITE LIFE CYCLE

1. **Adult females lay eggs 12-24 hours after their first blood meal.**
2. **Eggs hatch after 48-72 hours (depending on temp.).**
3. **Six-legged larvae moult after 24-48 hours, without feeding, to become 'first-stage' bloodsucking nymphs.**
4. **Another moult occurs after a further 24-48 hours, to produce 'second stage' nymphs.**
5. **Third moult occurs soon after, heralding the arrival of adulthood.**

Normally red mite appear grey in colour but, after a feed, they turn bright red like this colony.

nowadays due to environmental plus health and safety concerns.

But don't imagine that it's only the hen house that'll be affected; the runs can suffer too. I've known cases of the mites crawling three feet into the house at night to feed on the roosting birds, returning to the run again during the day to hide. So it's vitally important to include the run in your treatment programme as well.

If these precautions are taken from the start, then you'll have a good chance of keeping the red mite under control, and maybe even eradicating the problem altogether. But what you must bear in mind is that each treatment only kills the adult mites; the eggs already laid will live on to hatch another day, which is why the treatment must be repeated.

Another unfortunate fact is that red mites are very easily transmitted from bird to bird. So, exhibiting poultry, or buying stock from a sale or auction, can be classic ways of introducing the problem to your flock. These tiny pests can live for several weeks away from any host, and crawling from one bird to another in adjacent pens, is no problem

CHOOSE YOUR WEAPON!

Barrier Red Mite Concentrate: A well established UK-produced product that's completely organic, and available in 500ml and five-litre containers. The dilution rate is 20 parts water to one part concentrate, which makes this product very economical to use. What's more, it's safe to use both in the poultry house and on the birds.

Barrier Red Mite Powder: A specialist powder produced specifically for the red mite problem. Primarily intended for use on the birds themselves, and supplied in a handy shaker. Especially good for use on broody hens and their chicks, and also in the nest box bedding. Application is very similar to using talcum powder – sprinkled on as required. Approved by the Soil Association, and suitable for organic situations.

Microshield Poultry Shield: A well established product classified as a mite treatment and cleaner. It's easy to use and can be diluted at a water/product ratio of 10:1. It's available in 500ml, one-litre and five-litre containers and is supplied with full instructions.

Mite Kill: This aerosol spray works instantly, but isn't licensed for use directly in poultry so needs to be prescribed by a vet or licensed supplier. It's widely used by poultry and pigeon fanciers and certainly works effectively. However, being an aerosol it's not so economical.

Ardap: This is another anti-mite product which, like Mite Kill, isn't suitable for use on the birds, so its availability is similarly restricted. Being another aerosol-based product, it can be expensive to use and tricky to ensure good coverage. Also, the birds must be removed from the house if you choose this product.

Buzz Duster: Available in both aerosol and dusting powder forms, this product works extremely well. Once again, it's not licensed for use directly on poultry, but can be extremely effective at tackling infestation within a cleared house.

Grey deposits like this, found in a hen house, should be regarded with suspicion. It's probably a mixture of hungry red mite and their excreta.

at all. This ability to live off-host, means that you can inadvertently be a carrier yourself, transporting them into your environment on clothes, footwear or any equipment that you may have moved from one place to another. Keep this thought in mind also when visiting, or receiving as guests, other people with chickens or pigeons. It never hurts to be too vigilant!

EFFECTIVE MEASURES

If you're in the unfortunate position of

In really bad red mite infestation cases, the mites can actually live on the birds permanently. Whatever the level of problem, though, dusting the birds with an approved treatment is always a good idea.

being infested, then you need to take the following steps to deal with the problem. First of all, empty the shed completely and clean each corner, and all the joints in the timber, as thoroughly as you can. Next, soak the inside with a suitable anti-mite treatment/cleaner. There are a number available from specialist suppliers, but I've tried two – Poultry Shield and Barrier Red Mite treatment – and found them both to be effective, safe and easy to use, even in an organic situation.

Both products should be diluted with luke warm water, and used to soak the shed well, especially all the joints. It's no good just sprinkling a bit here and there; thorough coverage is essential, and the process must be repeated several times on a weekly basis. Missing out a repeat treatment will allow a fresh set of eggs to hatch, and your problems will be multiplied by many times.

As you will have gathered by now, the red mite is one of nature's better survivors. It can survive and remain undetected in empty sheds for months at a time, so don't be fooled into thinking that an unoccupied house is 'safe'. The simple act of introducing your stock will bring the mites into action almost immediately, and the effects can be quite devastating.

Recently I received a call from a distressed woman whose broody hen and chicks had just died on the nest. It was only when she moved the dead birds that she discovered that the area was absolutely crawling with red mite. Unfortunately, she simply hadn't noticed them, or taken any preventative measures beforehand. This sad example illustrates perfectly just how vital vigilance is.

If mites are uncontrolled, and allowed to repeatedly feed on the birds as they roost, a gradual weakening and eventual death will be the result. Chicks, obviously, are affected much more quickly. Egg production will suffer too. Essentially, red mite are little vampires. Before they feed they are buff/grey in colour but, after taking their fill (literally), they turn completely red, hence the name.

Effective control is made difficult by the red mite's growth rates – females become able to produce eggs after just 3-4 days, and are capable of laying clutches of seven after each feed. Although overall life span is relatively short (sometimes no more than a week), it's all about reproduction, and populations can grow alarmingly quickly. These creatures also have the ability to hibernate without food, and can survive in this way for as long as 34 weeks.

Unfortunately, there's no immediate answer to the red mite problem, and the reality is that it'll affect most of us at some time. The only way to deal with it is to remain constantly aware of the possibilities, and to be swift and effective with your action once trouble is discovered. Observe your birds carefully during your daily feeding and cleaning duties and, if they don't seem their normal selves, take a few minutes to check why. It's all part of good poultry husbandry and adopting this sort of routine will pay dividends in so many ways, both for you and your birds. ❦

SPOTTING THE SIGNS

Symptoms of red mite infestation include the following:

- Mild or severe irritation in the birds, and a loss of egg production
- An increase in the number of eggs laid on the floor, as the hens avoid an infested nest box
- An increase in vent pecking, cannibalism and general distress
- Anaemia (pale in face) leading to a 'dull' bird and possibly death
- Pale-coloured egg yolks
- Eggs covered with red staining/spotting and mite faeces
- Keeper suffering with itching or skin irritation (worst cases)

Three popular red mite treatments, widely available from poultry supply specialists.

AVIAN INFLUENZA

Lindsay Sissons, explains the basics of so-called 'chicken flu' and wonders if it'll cause the next human flu pandemic

In recent years the Press has delighted in telling us that Avian Influenza will cause the next great flu pandemic, but since the initial stories broke, the supply of information appears to have dried up. Many questions have been asked regarding the whys, wheres and hows, with no signs of any answers. This article provides a quick run-through the latest thoughts and theories.

First, the basics. Avian Influenza is caused by Type A influenza virus. There are many different strains of Type A virus, all of which vary in their ability to cause disease, and severity. The virus is spread by droplet infection. Infected birds shed minute droplets, containing the virus, from their respiratory systems and these are inhaled by other birds. Alternatively, spreading also occurs after contact with infected faeces, although this need not only be from direct contact. The virus may also be spread on clothing, housing, transport crates and other equipment.

Wild waterfowl (including migratory birds) are thought to be the main reservoir of infection, with sea birds also implicated – waterfowl have a degree of natural resistance to the influenza virus, and so usually show no signs at all. But in domestic poultry, natural resistance is lower and so turkeys (especially susceptible) and chickens will be more likely to show signs. It's thought that all birds have a degree of susceptibility to the avian influenza virus.

Clinical signs vary widely. There are two main types of Avian Influenza virus:

1) Low pathogenic virus – this means a virus that has a lesser ability to cause disease in an infected bird. Signs can be sub clinical (there are no outward signs to see, but there are mild signs of infection within the bird at post-mortem), or there can be mild to moderate signs including production losses (decreased egg production, say), mild depression, coughing and/or sneezing and sometimes sinusitis. These signs may be made worse by a secondary bacterial infection.

2) Highly pathogenic virus –

"Waterfowl have a degree of natural resistance to the influenza virus."

these strains of the virus are very likely to cause disease in the birds that are infected. Signs in these cases are more severe and include any or all of the following: coughing and gasping, swelling or oedema of the head and neck, cyanotic wattles and comb (deep purple in colour), diarrhoea, neurological signs and bloody beak and nasal discharges. Mortality (death) rates can be very high with birds dying 1-2 days after the onset of signs. Some birds may die without showing any signs at all. These outbreaks of more severe disease are also called 'fowl plague'.

Diagnosis of an outbreak is by a technique called 'virus isolation'. Samples from freshly dead birds (if vets are on site taking samples, killing a point-of-death bird and sampling straight away may give better results) are set in embryonated eggs and the resulting virus isolated and identified. Blood samples can also be used to see if birds have been exposed to the influenza virus at

some point in the past. Avian Influenza resembles many other complaints, so diagnosis must be obtained if there is any doubt. Differential diagnoses include Newcastle Disease, Fowl Pox, Mycoplasma, Staphylococcus infection and other respiratory and systemic infections.

There is no treatment for this virus and the isolation of an avian influenza viral strain will result in a quarantine and slaughter policy. It is a notifiable disease and so DEFRA should be informed of any suspicious clinical signs. The Avian Influenza and Newcastle Disease (England and Wales) Order 2003 was brought in during the outbreak in the Netherlands, before the wild waterfowl migratory season. It allows powers of entry, testing and sampling, followed by the slaughter of affected poultry (compensated). DEFRA is at the moment reviewing the contingency plan for Avian Influenza and Newcastle Disease, so details for managing an outbreak are not currently available. The last outbreak of Avian Influenza in Great Britain was in 1992.

The recent and continuing outbreaks in Asia and Holland (spreading to Belgium and Germany) with the death of humans as well as poultry, and the outbreaks in Canada and the United States, have led to many Governments stockpiling anti-viral drugs. They've also been preparing contingency plans to counter the next human flu pandemic (in 1918/19 between 40 and 50 million people died worldwide in a flu outbreak). Experts agree that flu pandemics tend to occur three or four times a century – the last one was in

1968/69, so another one is expected soon. But why should this bird flu be so great a risk?

The avian influenza virus is a member of the Orthomyxovidiae family of viruses. These viruses do not contain DNA as a complete source of genetic material, but they contain RNA. The job of RNA is to make copies of the genetic material and so allow the virus to replicate. The important fact here is that this virus cannot replicate itself without the use of a host cell and its genetic material. Now, most viruses have a 'proof-reading' mechanism, if you like, for checking that all replicated genetic material is correct, and no mistakes occur. The influenza virus does not have this ability to 'proof read' and so mutations occur frequently. A mutated virus will have different characteristics from the original virus. For example, low pathogenic viruses can mutate into high pathogenic viruses, and can suddenly start causing outbreaks of severe disease.

There are many, many strains of influenza virus that infect all different species. Pigs are thought to play an important role in the chances of mutations between viruses occurring, as they can become infected by both avian and mammalian influenza. A pig with a mammalian influenza in the same yard as a chicken with avian influenza, will have viruses from both strains of influenza in its cells at the same time. The theory is that as both these viruses use the host cell to replicate, and neither of them have the necessary proof-reader to make sure that mistakes don't occur, there's a chance that the genetic material could get mixed up and produce a mutant influenza virus that is different from both of the 'parent' viruses. This new, mutant could be a highly pathogenic strain that may cause a flu outbreak in populations that have no natural immunity. It is now thought that humans can act as a 'mixing-pot' as well as pigs, and several strains of avian influenza have

now gained the ability to infect humans from birds.

Several countries have succumbed to flu outbreaks recently, to various different strains of virus. In 2003 Hong Kong saw human illness from the H9N2 virus (the H9 is the sub-type of the virus and the N2 is the strain), while the Netherlands saw one death and 83 ill from the H7N7 strain. In 2004, Canada had human cases with H7N3 influenza. The US, China, Indonesia, Japan, Laos and Thailand have all recently had outbreaks of Avian Influenza.

But the strain that's causing the most worry is H5N1. In 1997, an outbreak in Hong Kong led to the death of six people and 18 other cases, and the Government immediately enforced the slaughter of all of the country's 1.5 million domestic birds. It has been stated by numerous sources that the cull prevented an influenza pandemic. The H5N1 strain represents a genuine fear for the next influenza pandemic, as it mutates rapidly and easily takes up parts of other viral genetic material. It's also the strain that affected Cambodia, with three deaths to date, and Vietnam, with 36 deaths so far. North Korea has also an ongoing recent outbreak with no human cases yet, and a hard cull going on at the moment.

The human risk from avian flu strains at the moment is from contact with infected birds, or their faeces, and becoming infected with one of these mutated strains that can cross from birds to humans. This can cause severe

country. So why the extreme reaction to cases of avian influenza in poultry? In Italy, for example, 10 turkey flocks have just (end of April, 2005) been diagnosed with a low pathogenic strain of avian flu with no risk to public health but, nevertheless, 180,000 birds are being slaughtered.

Now, if a man has human influenza and comes into contact with a chicken that has got avian influenza of a strain that is capable of infecting humans, there is every chance that the two different influenza strains can swap a bit of their genetic material, and produce a mutated influenza strain that is capable of passing from human to human. This is the step that hasn't happened yet, but that will cause the worldwide flu outbreak that we have been warned about. The mass slaughter of infected birds is undertaken to reduce the contact between humans and the virus responsible, and so minimise the risk of further mutations and the production of a new human-to-human flu virus, to which humans will have no immunity. There are no vaccines for H5N1 influenza yet, but they are being worked on. A vaccine for a new strain of virus will take at least four months to produce in useful quantities. Anti-virals are effective but expensive, and are limited in their supplies, so cannot be relied upon to fill the gap between the first infection and the mass use of the new vaccine. Worldwide travel provides an added problem – the spread of infection will be greatly increased by the air travel between continents.

All in all, if Avian Influenza does mutate to allow human-to-human infection, then the real risk of another influenza pandemic cannot be avoided. If, on the other hand, confirmed positive cases are dealt with swiftly and firmly, as seems to be happening now, that risk can continue to be waylaid until other more permanent ways are found to prevent it. ❧

> "The last outbreak of Avian Influenza in Great Britain was in 1992."

respiratory illness from which some will die. But the numbers of cases are very limited – in Vietnam in two years, 36 people have died; far, far less than many other causes of death in that

THE AI THREAT

David Spackman, NDP, BVSc, MRCVS, explains the origins of Avian Influenza, and assesses the risk posed by it for poultry keepers the UK.

The disease we now call Avian Influenza was first diagnosed in 1878, but was then called 'fowl plague'. Up until 1981 it was coupled, for all practicable purposes, with Newcastle Disease. However, the two diseases, although similar in many respects in their clinical appearance, are caused by viruses from different families; Paramyxo in the case of Newcastle Disease, and Orthomyxo with Avian Influenza (AI).

The causative agent for AI was shown to be a virus as long ago as 1901, but it wasn't until 1955 that it was proved to be closely related to the Influenza A virus of mammals, first isolated in the 1930s. The virus causing fowl plague, which resulted in high mortality, was then found to be indistinguishable from similar viruses which caused little or no mortality in birds. Thus, in 1981, it was decided to abandon the name 'fowl plague' and adopt instead the terms 'Highly Pathogenic Avian Influenza' (HPAI) for those serotypes causing high mortality, and 'Low Pathogenic Avian Influenza' (LPAI) for those which did not.

This terminology continues to this day,

General depression is one of the symptoms associated with AI, although it's a hard one to judge.

but disguises the fact that the two types are closely interrelated, share common antigens or surface features which determine their subtype, and that LPAI can mutate at any time and become HPAI, after which it is capable of causing high mortality in birds.

Perhaps we should expand on the term 'antigens'. These are protein projections on the surface of the virus particle, and are of two types – haemagglutinin (H antigen) and neurominidase (N antigen). Although in mammals, Influenza A, B and C types have been identified, to date, only Influenza A has been found in birds. The H and N antigens are important in protective immunity and show great variation.

There are currently 15 H antigens and 9 N antigens, and the virus can have any combination of these; 135 possible different types of virus, eg. H5 N1, H7 N7. In practice, it's principally the H5 and H7 types which cause the most damaging disease in birds. These have been shown to be coupled with N1, N2, N3, N7, N8 and N9 in disease outbreaks around the world, in poultry or wild birds.

The current situation in SE Asia is due to the H5N1 subtype, but this is no stranger to our shores, having been discovered in chickens in Scotland in 1959. But it was quickly contained then, as have all the other HPAI outbreaks which have appeared in the UK since. Most never extend beyond the farm where they are originally found, and this certainly should be the case in any future outbreak which may occur in the UK, because of the contingency plans already drawn-up.

In the 1950s, it became clear that vast pools of Influenza A virus existed in feral birds, especially waterfowl. Studies in Canada isolated 27 combinations of H and N, and over 25% of waterfowl examined yielded Influenza virus. Flocks of turkeys in Minnesota, USA, where they are reared on range, show an annual presence of low virulence strains, where mortality is low, but effects on growth rate cause severe economic

Birds suffering from Avian Influenza show a darkening of the comb and wattles (cyanosis), but this is just about the only visible sign that's easy to spot.

...sses; the turkey is the most susceptible ... the virus.

Commercial ducks have also been ...own to be infected, but rarely show ...ymptoms. For the most part they are ...esistant, even to strains which cause ...igh mortality in chickens and turkeys. ...ll other domestic poultry species are ...lso susceptible to challenge. It is ...enerally agreed that most outbreaks ...ave originated from migrating ...aterfowl passing on the infection to ...cal wild bird species which, in turn, ...ass it on to domestic poultry, especially ...ose kept outdoors. There have been no ...utbreaks in turkeys in Canada since ...ey've been reared indoors.

Remote as the possibility is, it's wise to ...e alert to initial signs in the birds. If ...fected by low virulence (LPAI), there ...ay be nothing to be seen that is ...emarkable enough to raise questions in ...e poultryman's mind. It should be ...emembered, however, that, as in the ...etherlands in 2004, LPAI strains can ...ddenly mutate into HPAI, resulting in ...igh mortality and risk of spread to other ...nits, principally by wild birds (but also ...y man, via egg trays, lorries, people, ...quipment, etc).

The spread from bird to bird within a ...ock is caused by faeces, saliva and ...xhaled moisture droplets containing ...rus particles. Any infection is made ...orse by poor environmental factors, ...uch as dust or ammonia, concurrent ...fection with other pathogens, such as ...ycoplasmas, E. coli and other ...espiratory viruses. The age of birds, the ...pecies and any nutritional deficiencies ...lso play a part.

Infection with HPAI may show a few clinical signs first, or may manifest as sudden high mortality with no earlier signs. Classically, clinical signs are rales (respiratory noises), excessive fluid leakage from the eyes and nostrils, swelling of the head and face, which may darken in colour due to subcutaneous haemorrhage (cyanosis), particularly the wattles, and diarrhoea. Mortality may be up to 70%.

There may be birds which, although they do not die, nevertheless show

"Keepers should always be alert to changes in the behaviour or appearance."

respiratory signs accompanied by diarrhoea and cease egg production. They may also give up eating and look severely depressed. Diagnosis can, however, only be made – with accuracy – by submission of live or dead birds to a laboratory suitably equipped with a security cabinet to carry out safe post-mortem work, followed by isolation of the virus from tissue submitted. Although there are some characteristic internal signs, these should not be looked for by the poultry keeper himself, as it may expose them to higher concentrations of virus, which might conceivably infect them.

Although much has been made of the possibility of crossover to humans, resulting in a pandemic, it should be borne in mind that, even in SE Asia where millions of poultry have been infected and slaughtered, only a handful

of people have died as a result of infection. What's more, these deaths have only occurred among those who live in very close proximity to their birds. This isn't a situation that's found in the UK, even among those who keep them in the domestic scene.

More likely, infection will result in conjunctivitis in humans, similar to the effects of being exposed to Newcastle Disease, or even some respiratory disease vaccines. In rare cases, slight respiratory involvement may be found as well. As I mentioned earlier, there are good contingency plans in place to confine and deal with any outbreak in commercial poultry.

However, it should be remembered that domestic collections, especially those which contain waterfowl or have conditions attractive to migrating waterfowl, are equally open to infection. So keepers should always be alert to changes in the behaviour or appearance of their birds, and report any suspect condition to the local Animal Health Office of DEFRA. Only by such action will the much advertised spread of AI in the UK be prevented.

A new approach adopted in Europe, including the UK, is to blood test a proportion of free-range poultry flocks as well as an increased number of wild birds, in order to detect antibodies to LPAI, which may have the ability to mutate to HPAI and cause severe problems. Any flocks discovered to be positive to LPAI, of the H5 or H7 serotypes, even though not causing current problems themselves will, nevertheless, be slaughtered out, and restrictions placed around the area where further investigations will be carried out.

There are special provisions, however, for rare and unique birds to be dealt with without slaughter, so fear of detection and loss of stock should not influence poultry keepers. This will reduce, almost to nil, the chance of an AI outbreak causing trouble in the EU, and certainly not allowing it to reach the proportions seen in SE Asia. It will also prevent the much talked of pandemic in humans so, if it's reported that a flock of birds has been slaughtered in the UK because of Avian Influenza, remember this is not a cause for panic, which the media will inevitably try to make it appear. Instead, it'll be a sign that the correct and sensible approach to a potential problem has been attempted.

Finally, it's also worth remembering that you won't get Avian Influenza from eating chicken eggs! 🦃

...irds can die suddenly from AI, after which a post mortem is the only way to ...onfirm the problem once and for all.

FIGHTING THE FLU

Neil Forbes, BVetMed, DipECAMS, FRCVS, RCVS and European Specialist in Bird Medicine, provides some practical pointers for those keepers concerned about the risks posed by the spread of Avian Influenza

On patrol! Unfortunately, it's waterfowl like these Runner ducks which are at greatest risk of infection of they are not prevented from mixing with wild and migrant bird populations.

So will it get here or not? It's the question on everyones' lips as Avian Influenza (AI) moves ever-closer to our shores. As we all know by now, this disease is spread predominantly by migrating waterfowl, many of which arrive here during the autumn from areas where AI outbreaks have already been recorded.

So, in reality, we're powerless to stop it arriving in the UK although, if we're lucky, it might not come this year. Nevertheless, as responsible poultry keepers, our main actions must be based around 'vigilance' and 'minimising the risk to our birds'.

WHY THE CONCERN?

There are 15 sub-types of the AI virus, but it's the H5N1 strain which we're currently battling against. This is the most pathogenic (causes the most disease), and also has the potential to 'mutate' faster than most other strains. Whenever it's active it has a greater potential than any other to mutate and spread further, which is why instant, comprehensive slaughter policies are essential.

Although the H5N1 strain can infect humans, the actual number of people who've caught it so far remains low –

about 120 between April 2003 and mid-October 2005 (more than half those infected have died). However, if the virus infects a human, pig or other animal, while that animal is infected with another flu virus, the two viruses can take part in 'gene swapping', to produce a new version of H5N1 with added human or other flu virus genes. The danger is that this new type may then be able to pass from human to human, causing a human flu pandemic. You may wonder why a vaccine has yet to be made.

"The vaccine manufacturers can't act until the 'mutant strain' arrives."

Well, the answer is simple; the vaccine manufacturers can't act until the 'mutant strain' arrives – only then will they know precisely what it is that they have to tackle. Unfortunately, though, even with this knowledge, it'll take the manufacturers at least five months to manufacture, test and distribute the vaccine, during which time significant numbers of people would die. But, to put this into perspective, thousands already die of normal flu every winter here in the UK.

"Outbreaks occurred where poultry were allowed to graze on the banks of lakes and waterways."

So what about our birds? Well, all birds are considered to be susceptible, with most becoming very sick and dying within 24-48 hours. Waterfowl are the exception. Certainly vigilance is the key. Everyone should be

PRACTICAL MEASURES

1. Prevent contact between wild birds and your birds – cover over or, better still, bring any free range or outside birds inside.

2. Prevent wild bird and rodent access to your inside birds, and their food.

3. Stop all visitors entering your site, and don't go visiting any other birds or areas where wild birds congregate yourself.

4. If visitors have to come, provide them with clothing which remains on site, and provide power washers, disinfectant and brushes for clothes, boots and vehicles.

5. If you see any dead or dying birds do not handle them, but contact the DEFRA helpline (tel: 08459 335577) immediately.

6. Try to avoid buying new stock. Bring in new blood lines or breeds as eggs. Any new birds which do join the flock must come from apparently disease-free stock, and be maintained in quarantine for at least 35 days after arrival. Your local vet may advise you about health screening which can be carried out during this period.

keeping a careful eye open for sick, dying or dead birds; groups of affected birds could be of particular concern. Sick birds can be reported by calling the DEFRA helpline on 08459 335577.

WHAT CAN I DO?

In planning to protect your flock you should, if at all possible, prevent contact between wild birds (especially waterfowl) and your birds. You should also prevent your birds having access ▶

For the greatest peace of mind, runs need to be completely secured from wild bird access, with wire sides and top.

BIRDS AT RISK

- Is your holding near a lake, pond or stream, in particular one which is frequented by wild birds (especially waterfowl)?
- Do your birds have access to outdoor areas?
- Do wild birds have access to the outdoor areas where your birds are?
- Do you feed and/or water your birds outside?
- Are there other animals on the holding with which your birds have contact?
- Do you share contractors, suppliers or employees with other poultry keepers?
- Do you attend bird fairs or shows?
- Do you farm birds on more than one site?
- Do you move birds to sites shared with other poultry keepers?
- Do you, your family or your contractors travel to areas currently experiencing avian influenza?

If you answer 'yes' to any of these questions, then a risk exists for your birds. For further support you should contact your local bird vet.

to areas where wild waterfowl may have been recently. It's interesting to note that in Romania and Turkey, outbreaks occurred where poultry were allowed to

by waterfowl.

Remember wild birds, other animals, staff and contractors can all physically transmit infection. So it's very important

cannot access your birds' food or water Maintain a record of all people who come onto and leave the premises. While it may be uncomfortable, prevent all non-essential visitors to your site. Anyone visiting should clean themselves before arrival and again as they leave, using a DEFRA-approved disinfectant.

Wire mesh size is an important practical consideration. The 'chicken wire' at the top here is not completely secure against all wild birds, whereas the square-mesh type below is

Ideally, if they really have to visit, provide overcoats and Wellington boots for their use on-site.

In the awful event that your flock becomes infected, it's vital that you recognise the problem immediately, You must inform DEFRA straight away and minimise the risk of the infection being

Food spillage like this must be cleared away. If left it'll provide a needless attraction for wild birds and rodents, increasing the risk to your flock.

graze on the banks of lakes and waterways, which had been frequented

to minimise all possible contact situations – ensure that other birds and mammals

Larger runs can be cost-effectively enclosed with plastic netting like this. But weight from above can cause tears or break fixings, so check it regularly.

Re-double your fight against the rodent population as these creatures are great spreaders of disease. This is an anti-squirrel poison box; note the damage to the feed bin beside it

AI is most likely to be brought here by migratory birds. If you keep waterfowl, then you'll need to be particularly vigilant.

Don't leave sources of feed out in the open for longer than necessary. If AI arrives, the last thing you want is to be attracting extra guests for dinner!

hoppers and feeding equipment must be regularly cleaned and disinfected. Damaged eggs, dead birds, litter and manure should be promptly and safely disposed of. All accommodation, crates and containers should be thoroughly and regularly cleaned. Any clothing, tools, equipment and medical instruments must be thoroughly cleaned between houses, if it's being moved from house to house or, worse still, farm to farm.

Pathogens (eg bacteria, parasites and viruses), will remain in the premises long after the birds have left. Remember, no disinfectant works unless the surface it is applied to has been previously cleaned. So, at the end of any cycle, it's vital that the whole premises is cleaned really effectively, prior to the liberal application of suitable safe and effective (DEFRA-approved) disinfectant.

Infection is commonly spread by wild birds and pest species. Effective rodent and pest control must be employed. Wild birds and rodents should not be attracted to your site by easy access to food, or spillage of cereals.

While these biosecuirty principles may be obvious to you, it's always worth checking that they are equally obvious to the rest of your family, or any staff, who handle or have access to the birds. The adequate training of all personnel is one final, vital issue. 🐦

passed on to other birds, wildlife or humans. Avian influenza is a notifiable disease. The law says you must tell the Divisional Veterinary Manager (DVM), at the local Animal Health Divisional Office, immediately if you suspect disease.

Unfortunately, there are few clinical signs in birds, apart from wattles and combs turning blueish and group death. The clinical signs in humans include: sore throat, cough and fever, potentially leading to complicated pneumonia. The big problem, of course, is that these symptoms are very difficult to distinguish from those presented by normal human flu, without complex laboratory tests.

BIOSECURITY

Basic good hygiene will minimise the risk of this or other infections effecting your flock. Moreover, if these preventive measures are employed, the risk of infection will be reduced. The following list details standard biosecurity measures which all poultry keepers should apply at all times.

Supply clean, fresh drinking water to your birds, and ensure that drinkers and water lines are clean. Your feed bins,

AVIAN INFLUENZA Q&As

Q. *Can we vaccinate our birds to protect them?*
A. First of all, there is no vaccine available which is wholly protective against AI. Secondly, in most European countries (including the UK), it's currently illegal to use any AI vaccine. The only likelihood of this changing would be if DEFRA advised the Government that vaccine should be used to 'ring-fence' an area of infection.

Q. *If my birds are ill and found to be suffering from AI, can DEFRA insist they are all destroyed?*
A. Yes, certainly they can.

Q. *If a nearby farm is found to be effected by AI, could DEFRA insist that my birds were killed?*
A. Yes, certainly.

Q. *If my birds get infected with AI, what are the chances I will get it?*
A. While the current virus form can infect humans, it's rarely done so and is not highly infectious to us. As long as you don't handle the sick, dying or dead birds, the chances of you catching AI are extremely low.

Q. *I keep free range poultry on land adjoining a wetland/water area. In view of the increased risks, should I have my birds culled?*
A. For the moment, this would be pre-emptive. If infection does occur in the UK, especially in an area close to you, culling may be prudent. But let's hope it never gets to that stage. In the meantime, the sensible action is to keep your birds caged or, better still, under cover.

Neil Forbes works at Swindon-based Great Western Referrals.
For more information visit: www.gwreferrals.co.uk

GETTING THE NEEDLE

Lindsay Sissons, outlines everything you ever wanted to know about vaccinations.

The prime role of vaccination is to protect a bird from an illness. Many of the illnesses that have a vaccine prepared against them have severe symptoms and high mortality, but some do not have a high death rate as a symptom. Vaccination is often used in these cases of 'production diseases' – diseases that do not kill many of the birds that catch it, but cause virtually all of the flock to become sick, causing weight loss, egg production drops, reduced fertility and so on for a period of time. This leads to reduced production from the birds and can cause enormous losses for the commercial poultry keeper.

Vaccination against a problem disease can prevent a bird from developing that disease and so reduce the need for drug interventions (antibiotics, say) as treatment. Birds that develop an illness generally shed the causative agent of that disease (this increases the disease challenge for the rest of the flock), so reducing the number of birds becoming ill by vaccinating will reduce the infective challenge to the flock as a whole.

Vaccination is also a mainstay of procedure when trying to eradicate a disease from the population. There's also no hazard to consumers from a vaccinated bird, as the vaccine merely stimulates activity in the immune system of the bird and is then eliminated.

STIMULATING STUFF

The vaccine works by using a little of the infective organism, or a little of a related but non-disease-causing organism, to stimulate the bird's immune system to produce antibodies. Once these antibodies have been produced, the body has, if you like, a memory of that organism, and can mount a rapid challenge when the disease is encountered for real, usually preventing the infection turning into the disease and keeping the bird healthy. Immunity can be 'whole-body' if the vaccine is injected or ingested, or 'local'. If the vaccine is inhaled or nose-dropped, only the upper respiratory tract will develop this 'local' immunity – good for respiratory viruses where the main route of infection is via the upper airways.

Vaccines are presented in two forms – 'live' and 'killed'. In the live version, the infective organism is developed so that it will stimulate antibody production without causing the disease. Usually with viruses and protozoans, the infective organisms are either treated with gentle heat or sub-lethal chemicals, or they are allowed to infect cell lines of other host cells in the laboratory, until they become unable to cause disease while still being infectious (attenuated). Live vaccine organisms still multiply and spread through the body of the bird that is vaccinated, and will spread to other birds in the flock, or even from flock to flock, in some cases. A live vaccine will stimulate a strong antibody response and, generally, a long-lasting immunity.

With the killed variety, the organism (viruses and bacteria) are either whole and have been treated to render them unable to cause disease, or the vaccine is made up from a specific part of the infective organism (a wall protein, say) that is known to trigger an immune response in the bird which is vaccinated. Two doses of a killed vaccine are generally needed, as the stimulus on the immune system is not as strong as with a live virus, and so the immunity gained is generally not so long lasting. A killed vaccine will not replicate within the bird that has been vaccinated. To increase the stimulus to the immune system, the vaccine is combined with an adjuvant – a substance such as aluminium hydroxide or liquid paraffin, for example. These vaccines are used to protect both the bird and its future offspring, by being given before point-of-lay (POL) is reached.

TIGHT REGULATION

The control of vaccines, their licensing and production, are very strictly regulated, with high standards set for all aspects of quality, safety in the food chain and efficacy in the field. Rules governing research and testing of vaccines are set in European law, with licensing regulations also enforced in this country.

The form the vaccine takes, and the route by which it is administered, varies depending on whether the vaccine is live or killed (inactivated). Live vaccines are generally supplied as a freeze-dried pellet in a vial, with a few available as a suspension in liquid. Killed vaccines are generally supplied as an adjuvanted solution in a vial.

Vaccines can be given by spray, in the drinking water, as intranasal or intraocular drops, or by injection. The reconstitution of the vaccine must always be undertaken carefully and the manufacturer's instructions should be followed precisely.

Spraying the vaccine is a route suggested for chicks of under seven days old, that are not drinking enough to guarantee the uptake of the correct amount of vaccine. Reconstituting the vials for bird spraying involves calculating the correct volume of water needed from the manufacturer's guidelines, then opening the vials under the water's surface.

The spray needs to be of coarse droplets applied from a distance of 30-40cm away from the birds, and is best administered when the birds are sitting quietly in dim light. The water source for a vaccine reconstitution needs to be free from any disinfectant, antibiotic or other contaminant that may affect vaccine efficacy. The person spraying should be wearing protective goggles and a mask of a specified standard (hayfever-like signs can result if adequate precautions aren't taken). House ventilation should be switched off until the spray has settled. The immunity gained from spraying very young birds can be limited, and generally revaccination is advised. Spraying the feed is a method used when vaccinating against coccidiosis

DRINKING IT DOWN

Vaccination via the drinking water is commonly used. Again, care in reconstituting the vaccine must be taken – will not be effective if it's too dilute, or contaminated. The water used should be non-chlorinated in most cases and any medications/sanitisers should not be used for 24 hours before and after the vaccine has been supplied. Two-thirds of the birds to be vaccinated should be able to drink at the same time, ensuring that lack of access to water does not mean that some go unvaccinated.

There should also be a period of water withdrawal (minimum of 30 minutes, maximum of two hours, but the birds will have withdrawn themselves overnight if vaccination is going to take place at dawn before the vaccine-containing water is presented. No other water source should be available to the birds while the vaccine containing water is being offered. The suggested routine for achieving maximum uptake of the vaccine is to dim the lights (or administer early in the morning before it gets too light), then remove other water sources. The vaccinated water should be reconstituted into the correct volume of water for the number of birds to be vaccinated, and both feed and the vaccine containing water placed in the house.

Skimmed milk is often added to prolong the life of the vaccine in the water. The reconstituted vaccine only lasts for a couple of hours, depending on the vaccine being given, so it's no good setting up the drinkers the night before, as the vaccine